Monninger Center
for Learning and Research

Gift to the Library Collection

Rama Madhavarao

Fairleigh Dickinson University
College at Florham
Madison, NJ 07940

Linear Algebra

Charles W. Curtis

PROFESSOR OF MATHEMATICS
UNIVERSITY OF OREGON

SECOND EDITION

Linear Algebra

AN INTRODUCTORY APPROACH

ALLYN AND BACON, INC.   BOSTON

Library of Congress Catalog Card Number: 68-21562

PRINTED IN THE UNITED STATES OF AMERICA

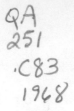

SECOND EDITION

To Timothy, Daniel, and Robert

PREFACE

Linear algebra is the branch of mathematics that has grown out of a theoretical study of the problem of solving systems of linear equations. This problem is one of the oldest questions in mathematics, and is still of fundamental importance for an understanding of the elementary parts of most of the other, larger, branches of mathematics and for applications to science and engineering. The abstract ideas of vector space and linear transformation, which are suggested by the study of linear equations, are today of far greater importance than their parent, and have become an essential part of every science student's early mathematical training.

One of the major changes from the first edition is that this book has been reorganized to introduce these important ideas in their full generality early in the book. The purpose of the first edition, to give an impression of the evolution of these ideas, is accomplished by giving attention to computations with systems of linear equations and matrices as illustrations and applications of the general concepts. Examples of linear transformations from calculus and geometry, and a chapter on vector spaces with an inner product and orthogonal transformations, also appear near the beginning.

Another purpose of the new edition has been to make the first part of the book somewhat more elementary. Following suggestions from instructors who used the first edition, this has involved adding illustrative material, a large number of new computational exercises, and proofs and discussions of some results left as exercises in the first edition.

This book is intended to be a first introduction to higher algebra. It presupposes only a standard analytic geometry and calculus course, and is intended to precede courses for mathematics majors in modern algebra and advanced calculus.

The concepts of rings, fields, groups, and polynomials and unique factorization, are all introduced naturally, in connection with the study of vector spaces and linear transformations. This material provides motivation for a later course on the axiomatic systems of modern algebra.

Examples from calculus, and a section on vector differential equations and the exponential of a matrix, and the interpretation of determinants as volume functions, all show the relevance of linear algebra to calculus. They should prepare students for courses on differential equations, and advanced calculus of functions of several variables, where linear transformations are used to approximate differentiable functions from one Euclidean space to another.

Physics, chemistry, and engineering students, who will be concerned with theoretical questions in their work, will profit from the applications to symmetry groups in two and three dimensions, the discussion of inner product spaces and vector differential equations, and the numerical procedures included as examples and applications of the theorems throughout the book.

The subject is presented from the beginning as a strict deductive science, and for many students will be the first course in which proofs of theorems are emphasized, as well as techniques for solving problems. The exercises form an integral part of the course, containing theoretical material as well as numerical problems. Answers to many numerical problems, and outlines of the solutions of most of the theoretical exercises, are given.

A text in linear algebra, designed to be understood by students in a short course, cannot include all the desirable advanced topics in the subject. In the theory of linear transformations there are stressed the theory of the minimal polynomial, conditions for a linear transformation to have a diagonal matrix with respect to some basis, the primary decomposition of a vector space relative to a linear transformation, and applications of these results. Not included are the important topics of factor spaces, duality, and elementary divisors and invariant factors, all of which, I believe, are properly treated from the more advanced standpoint of modules over rings, and can be studied advantageously in a later course.

A one-quarter or one-semester course can be based on Chapters 1–4 and part of Chapter 5, omitting if necessary some of the proofs and the optional sections 10 and 14. The material omitted can be used as projects for interested students. The entire book can be made the basis of a two-quarter course, or can be supplemented with material from modern algebra or geometric algebra to make a one-year course.

My chief acknowledgment is to the students who have studied linear algebra with me at Wisconsin and Oregon. Their contributions are implicit on every page, and the project could not have been carried out without their encouragement. My scientific indebtedness encompasses many sources and individuals, and especially the books and authors listed in the Bibliography. It is a pleasure to acknowledge the many helpful and constructive suggestions I have received from users of the book, and which have led to most of the changes in the new edition. Finally, I owe a great deal to the interest and encouragement my family has shown at every stage of the work.

Charles W. Curtis

EUGENE, OREGON

CONTENTS

1 THE REAL NUMBER SYSTEM *1*

    1. INTRODUCTION
    2. REAL NUMBERS
    3. SETS, INTEGERS, AND THE PRINCIPLE OF
       MATHEMATICAL INDUCTION

2 VECTOR SPACES AND SYSTEMS OF *18*
LINEAR EQUATIONS

    4. FIELDS
    5. VECTOR SPACES
    6. LINEAR DEPENDENCE
    7. THE CONCEPTS OF BASIS AND DIMENSION
    8. SYSTEMS OF LINEAR EQUATIONS
    9. SYSTEMS OF HOMOGENEOUS EQUATIONS
    10. LINEAR MANIFOLDS

3 LINEAR TRANSFORMATIONS AND MATRICES *64*

    11. LINEAR TRANSFORMATIONS
    12. ADDITION AND MULTIPLICATION OF MATRICES
    13. LINEAR TRANSFORMATIONS AND MATRICES

4 VECTOR SPACES WITH AN INNER PRODUCT *94*

    14. THE CONCEPT OF SYMMETRY
    15. INNER PRODUCTS

xi

5   **DETERMINANTS**   *114*

    16. DEFINITION OF DETERMINANTS
    17. EXISTENCE AND UNIQUENESS OF DETERMINANTS
    18. THE MULTIPLICATION THEOREM FOR DETERMINANTS
    19. FURTHER PROPERTIES OF DETERMINANTS

6   **POLYNOMIALS AND COMPLEX NUMBERS**   *141*

    20. POLYNOMIALS
    21. COMPLEX NUMBERS

7   **THEORY OF A SINGLE LINEAR TRANSFORMATION**   *162*

    22. THE MINIMAL POLYNOMIAL
    23. INVARIANT SUBSPACES
    24. THE TRIANGULAR FORM THEOREM
    25. AN EXAMPLE
    26. APPLICATION TO DIFFERENTIAL EQUATIONS
    27. THE JORDAN NORMAL FORM

8   **ORTHOGONAL, UNITARY, AND SYMMETRIC TRANSFORMATIONS**   *198*

    28. THE STRUCTURE OF ORTHOGONAL TRANSFORMATIONS
    29. THE PRINCIPAL-AXIS THEOREM
    30. FINITE SYMMETRY GROUPS IN THREE DIMENSIONS

SOLUTIONS OF SELECTED EXERCISES   *221*

SYMBOLS (Including Greek Letters)   *243*

BIBLIOGRAPHY   *245*

INDEX   *247*

Linear Algebra

CHAPTER 1

THE REAL
NUMBER SYSTEM

1. INTRODUCTION

This book is devoted to the theory of vector spaces, or linear algebra, as it is sometimes called. The special problems which led to the concept of an abstract vector space come from the theory of linear equations, matrices, and analytic geometry. In order to give an impression of the evolution of the subject, these problems will be discussed early in the book. It would be inefficient and a waste of time, however, to develop matrices and linear equations, for example, in exactly the way they were studied in the nineteenth century. We have made free use of modern developments in vector space theory to present the old material in an economical and efficient way, and to prepare the way for the abstract approach.

As we shall see, linear algebra is a rich subject, full of unexpected twists and turns. It would be a mistake, even in a first course, not to see on the one hand the powerful influence linear algebra has had on mathematical research and on the other the adaptability of linear algebra to computational procedures and its usefulness in numerical

1

work and analysis. Thus, we have included in this book some problems on applications and numerical computation, and also optional sections which take up special problems, sometimes of an advanced nature, but which require only the tools developed in the course. The optional sections may be used for outside reading or special projects for interested students.

2.   REAL NUMBERS

In this book much attention will be paid to presenting mathematics as a strict deductive science. In other words, we shall try to convince the reader that all our theorems can be proved by the methods of logical reasoning from certain clearly stated assumptions made in advance. As a matter of fact, the student and reader of this book will be asked to supply many of these arguments himself.

If we have any hope of putting the subject on a sound logical basis, we must have a clearly defined starting point. As the primitive concept of our subject we shall adopt the system of real numbers, which should already be familiar to the student from his earlier mathematical work. To remove any doubts, we shall list exactly those properties of the real numbers which we wish to use. We shall use this chapter also to introduce the reader to methods of proof in algebra, and shall give a somewhat more detailed exposition of the subject than may seem necessary at this point, in order to develop a number of concepts which will be needed later in the course. Some readers may wish to skip most of this section and the next one, and begin with Section 4 or Section 5, coming back to Sections 2 and 3 if they need them.

Before starting, we make a remark on the terminology. *Real number* is a technical term, and the real numbers are described exactly by the properties we assume concerning them. The fact that there are also complex or imaginary numbers should not lead the reader to believe that one sort of number is any more or less mysterious or more or less down to earth than the other.

Everyone is familiar with at least one intuitive description of the real numbers. For example, the real numbers may be described as the collection of rational numbers a/b, where a, b are integers and $b \neq 0$, together with all "numbers" which can be approximated arbitrarily closely by rational numbers. They may be described also as all numbers represented by writing finitely many digits (preceded by a plus or minus sign), then a decimal point, and then an unending sequence of digits. Still again they may be described as labels for the points on a line. This is not the place to explore the connections among all these ideas; we seek a precise and usable description of the real numbers. To accomplish this we shall give a set of axioms for the real numbers.

The axioms for the real numbers will be given in three groups: first the *algebraic axioms,* which can be summarized in the assertion that the real numbers form a *field,* then the *order axioms,* which introduce the concepts of positive and negative real numbers, and finally the *completeness axiom,* which guarantees that enough real numbers exist for us to do business.

Let us first make a general remark about sets* and the notion of equality. The real number system is a set of objects, and these objects are represented by symbols $\{a, b, c, \cdots; 0, 1, \cdots\}$. The symbol representing an object may be thought of as the *name* of the object. We shall assume that with any set of objects we are given a means of distinguishing whether two objects are different or not. In other words, given an object with name a and an object with name a', we assume that exactly one of two possibilities holds: either the objects are really the same, in which case we write $a = a'$ (read "a equals a'" or "a is equal to a'"), or the objects are not the same, in which case we write $a \neq a'$ (read "a is not equal to a'"). Thus, if we happen to have assigned the same object the different names a and a', we indicate this fact by writing $a = a'$.

We assume that the "equals" relation has the following properties:

(1) $a = a$ (in other words, we cannot use the same symbol in a given context to stand for different objects).
(2) If $a = b$, then $b = a$.
(3) If $a = b$ and $b = c$, then $a = c$ (this is a precise statement of the notion that things equal to the same thing are equal to each other).

If, as in the case of the real number system, we have certain operations defined on the elements of the set, then by using these connectives we can form expressions such as

$$\left(\frac{a - b}{2 + x}\right) + \left(\frac{3 + ab}{2}\right).$$

---

* A fuller discussion of sets is given in Section 3.

Such an expression, provided that it satisfies the grammatical rules governing the use of the connectives $-$, $+$, etc., represents a real number and is called a *formula*. As a further property of the relation of equality we assume the following:

(2.1) Substitution Principle.   *Let F be a formula representing a real number in which the symbol a occurs. If $a' = a$, then a may be replaced by a' in the formula F, and the new formula F' will represent the same real number as F; in other words, $F = F'$.*

Now we are ready for our definition of the real numbers. The algebra axioms, order axioms, etc., referred to in the definition are stated later in the section.

(2.2) Definition.   The *real number system* is a set $R = \{a, b, c, \cdots ; 0, 1, \cdots\}$ together with two operations, called addition and multiplication, which assign to each pair of real numbers (a, b) unique elements $a + b$ and ab of R, called the *sum* and *product*, respectively, of a and b. This system is assumed to satisfy the *algebra axioms*. We assume also that in R there is a subset P, called the set of positive real numbers, which satisfies the *order axioms*. Finally, the system is assumed to satisfy the *completeness axiom*. A system satisfying the algebra axioms alone is called a *field;* a field satisfying the order axioms is called an *ordered field*. Thus the real numbers may be described as a complete ordered field.

ALGEBRA AXIOMS.   For all a, b, c in R, we have the following:

(A-1) $a + (b + c) = (a + b) + c$ and $(ab)c = a(bc)$ (associative laws).

(A-2) $a + b = b + a$ and $ab = ba$ (commutative laws).

(A-3)   There exists an element 0 such that $a + 0 = a$ for all a in R, and an element $1 \neq 0$ such that $a \cdot 1 = a$ for all a in R.

(A-4)   For each a in R, there exists an element $-a$ (read "minus a") in R such that $a + (-a) = 0$.

(A-5)   For each $a \neq 0$ in R, there exists an element a^{-1} (read "a inverse") such that $a \cdot a^{-1} = 1$.

(A-6)   For all a, b, c in R, $a(b + c) = ab + ac$ (distributive law).

ORDER AXIOMS

(O-1) For each a in R, one and only one of the following possibilities holds:

$$a \text{ is in } P, \qquad a = 0, \qquad -a \text{ is in } P.$$

(O-2) If a and b are in P, then $a + b$ and ab are in P.

Before stating the completeness axiom, we shall derive some consequences of the algebra and order axioms. The statements appearing with starred numbers [for example, $(2.7)\star$] are not proved in the text, and the proofs should be worked out by the reader.

(2.3) *If* $a + b = a + c$, *then* $b = c$ *(cancellation law for addition).*

Proof. We should like to say "add $-a$ to both sides." We accomplish this by using the substitution principle (2.1) as follows. From (2.1) and the assumption that $a + b = a + c$, we have

$$(-a) + (a + b) = (-a) + (a + c).$$

On the one hand, we have by the algebra axioms (Which ones?),

$$(-a) + (a + b) = [(-a) + a] + b = 0 + b = b.*$$

Similarly,

$$(-a) + (a + c) = c.$$

From properties 2 and 3 of the equals relation, we have $b = c$, and the result is established.

An argument like this cannot be read like a newspaper article; the reader will find that he must have paper and pencil handy, and write out the steps, checking the references to the axioms, until he sees exactly what has been done.

(2.4) *For arbitrary* a *and* b *in* R, *the equation* $a + x = b$ *has a unique solution.*

Proof. This result is two theorems in one. We are asked to show, first, that there exists at least one real number x which satisfies the equation and, second, that there is at most one solution. Both

---

* A statement of the form $a = b = c = d$ is really shorthand for the separate statements $a = b$, $b = c$, $c = d$. The properties of the equals relation imply that from the separate statements we can conclude that all the objects a, b, c, and d are equal to each other, and this is the meaning of the abbreviated statement $a = b = c = d$.

statements are easy, however. First, from (A-1), (A-2), and (A-4) we have

$$a + [(-a) + b] = [a + (-a)] + b = 0 + b = b,$$

and we have shown that there is at least one solution, namely, $x = (-a) + b$.

Now let c and c' be solutions of the equation. Then we have $a + c = b$, $a + c' = b$, and hence $a + c = a + c'$ (Why?). By the cancellation law (2.3) we have $c = c'$, and we have proved that if c is one solution of the equation then any other solution is equal to c.

(2.5) Definition. We write $b - a$ to denote the unique solution of the equation $a + x = b$. We have $b - a = b + (-a)$, and we call $b - a$ the result of subtracting a from b. (The reader should observe that there is no question of "proving" a statement like the last. A careful inspection of the algebra axioms shows that no meaning has been attached to the formula $b - a$; the matter has to be taken care of by a definition.)

(2.6) $-(-a) = a.$

Proof. The result comes from examining the equation $a + (-a) = 0$ from a different point of view. For we have also $-(-a) + (-a) = 0$; by the cancellation law we obtain $-(-a) = a$.

Now we come to the properties of multiplication, which are exactly parallel to the properties of addition. We remind the reader that he must supply the proofs of the starred statements.

(2.7)★   *If $a \neq 0$ and $ab = ac$, then $b = c$.*

(2.8)★   *The equation $ax = b$, where $a \neq 0$, has a unique solution.*

(2.9) Definition. We denote by $\dfrac{b}{a}$ (or b/a) the unique solution of the equation $ax = b$, and will speak of $\dfrac{b}{a}$ as the result of *division* of b by a. Thus $\dfrac{1}{a} = a^{-1}$, because of Axiom (A-5).

(2.10)★ $(a^{-1})^{-1} = a,$ if $a \neq 0.$

Thus far we haven't used the distributive law. In a way, this is the most powerful axiom and most of the more exotic theorems in elementary algebra, such as $(-1)(-1) = 1$, follow from the distributive law.

(2.11) *For all a in R,* $a \cdot 0 = 0$.

Proof. We have $0 + 0 = 0$. By the distributive law (A-6) we have $a \cdot 0 + a \cdot 0 = a \cdot 0$. But $a \cdot 0 = a \cdot 0 + 0$ by (A-3), and by the cancellation law we have $a \cdot 0 = 0$.

(2.12) $(-a)b = -(ab)$, *for all a and b.*

Proof. From $a + (-a) = 0$ we have, by the substitution principle, $[a + (-a)]b = 0 \cdot b$. From the distributive law and (2.11) this implies that
$$ab + (-a)b = 0.$$
Since $ab + [-(ab)] = 0$, the cancellation law gives us $(-a)b = -(ab)$, as we wished to prove.

(2.13) $(-a)(-b) = ab$, *for all a, b in R.*

Proof. We have, by two applications of (2.12) and by the use of the commutative law for multiplication,
$$(-a)(-b) = -[a(-b)] = -[-(ab)].$$
Finally, $-[-(ab)] = ab$ by (2.6).

As a consequence of (2.13) we have

(2.14) $(-1)(-1) = 1$. (It is interesting to construct a direct proof from the original axioms.)

We come now to some consequences of the order axioms. First of all, we introduce the notion of inequality, "$a < b$."

(2.15) **Definition.** For all a and b in R, $a < b$ (read "a is less than b") means that $b - a$ is in P. We write $a > b$ (read "a is greater than b") as equivalent to $b < a$. We write $a \leq b$ to denote the statement that either $a < b$ or $a = b$. We define $a \geq b$ similarly.

We note in particular that a is in P if and only if $a > 0$. Note also that $a < 0$ means $-a > 0$.

(2.16)⋆ *For any two real numbers a, b, exactly one of the following possibilities holds:* $a < b$, $a = b$, $b < a$.

(2.17)⋆   *If $a < b$ and $b < c$, then $a < c$.*

(2.18)⋆   *If $a < b$, then $a + c < b + c$ for all c in R.*

(2.19)⋆   *If $a < b$ and $c > 0$, then $ac < bc$.*

(2.20)⋆   *If $a < b$ and $c < 0$, then $ac > bc$.*

(2.21)   *If $a \neq 0$, then $a^2 > 0$. (Here, of course, a^2 means $a \cdot a$.) In particular, $1 > 0$ since $1 = 1^2$.*

   Proof.   By (O-1) we have either $a > 0$ or $-a > 0$. If $a > 0$, then $a^2 > 0$ by (O-2). If $-a > 0$, then by (2.13) and (O-2) we have

$$a^2 = (-a)^2 > 0.$$

(2.22)⋆   *If $a \neq 0$, then $a > 0$ if and only if $a^{-1} > 0$.*

We conclude this section with a statement of the completeness property of the real numbers.

(2.23)   Definition.   A set S of real numbers is said to be *bounded above* if there exists a real number M such that $s \leq M$ for all s in S. The number M is then called an *upper bound* of the set S. The set S is said to possess a *least upper bound* L if L is an upper bound of S and if, for any other upper bound M of S, $L \leq M$.

(2.24)   Completeness Axiom.   If S is a nonempty set of real numbers which is bounded above, then S has a least upper bound.

EXERCISES

1. Prove that if a, b, c, d are real numbers, where b, $d \neq 0$, then:

   a. $\dfrac{a}{b} + \dfrac{c}{d} = \dfrac{ad + bc}{bd}.$

   b. $\left(\dfrac{a}{b}\right)\left(\dfrac{c}{d}\right) = \dfrac{ac}{bd}.$

   c. $\left(\dfrac{a}{b}\right)\Big/\left(\dfrac{c}{d}\right) = \dfrac{ad}{bc},$ if $c/d \neq 0.$

2. For each real number a, we define the *absolute value* of a by

$$|a| = \begin{cases} a & \text{if } a \geq 0 \\ -a & \text{if } a < 0. \end{cases}$$

Prove the following statements for arbitrary real numbers a and b.

a. $|a| \geq 0$.

b. $|a| = 0$ if and only if $a = 0$.

c. $|ab| = |a| \cdot |b|$.

d. $-|a| \leq a \leq |a|$. (This statement means $-|a| \leq a$ and $a \leq |a|$.)

e. $|a| \leq b$ if and only if $b \geq 0$ and $-b \leq a \leq b$.

f. $|a + b| \leq |a| + |b|$.

3. Prove that if $a < b$ then a real number x satisfies the inequality $a \leq x \leq b$ if and only if there is a real number λ, with $0 \leq \lambda \leq 1$, such that $x = \lambda a + (1 - \lambda)b$. For example, we have $a \leq \frac{1}{2}(a + b) \leq b$ where $\lambda = \frac{1}{2}$.

4. Prove that if $a \geq 0$, $b \geq 0$, and $a^2 \leq b^2$, then $a \leq b$.

3. SETS, INTEGERS, AND THE PRINCIPLE OF MATHEMATICAL INDUCTION

A knowledge of the principles of set theory is essential to an understanding of higher mathematics. While it is true that much of it can and must be learned by experience, it will be convenient to collect in one place explicit statements of some of the concepts and facts that will be needed later in the course. The most important of these is the principle of mathematical induction, on which the proofs of almost all the main results in this book are based.

We begin with the concept of a *set* of objects. We use the word *set* as synonymous with "collection," or "family," but from a mathematical point of view *set*, like *real number*, is a technical term which takes its meaning from the properties we assume sets possess.

Let X be a set of objects. For a given object x, either x belongs to the set X or it does not. If x belongs to X we write $x \in X$ (read "x is an element of X" or "x is a member of X"); if x does not belong to X we write $x \notin X$.

A set Y is called a *subset* of a set X if, for all objects y, $y \in Y$ implies $y \in X$. In other words, every element of Y is also an element of X. If Y is a subset of X, we write $Y \subset X$. If $Y \subset X$ and $X \subset Y$, then we say that the sets X and Y are *equal* and write $X = Y$. Thus two sets are equal if they contain exactly the same members.

It is convenient to introduce the set containing no elements at all. We call it the empty set, and denote it by $\emptyset$. Thus, for every object x, $x \notin \emptyset$. For example, the set of all real numbers x for which the inequalities $x < 0$ and $x > 1$ hold simultaneously is the empty set. The reader will check that from our definition of subset it follows logically that the empty set $\varnothing$ is a subset of every set (Why?).

There are two important constructions which can be applied to subsets of a set and yield new subsets. Suppose U and V are subsets of a given set X. We define $U \cap V$ to be the set consisting of all elements belonging to both U and V and call $U \cap V$ the *intersection* of U and V. Question: What is the intersection of the set of real numbers x such that $x > 0$ with the set of real numbers y such that $y < 5$? If we have many subsets of X, their intersection is defined as the set of all elements which belong to all the given subsets.

The second construction is the *union* $U \cup V$ of U and V; this is the subset of X consisting of all elements which belong either to U or to V. (When we say "either . . . or" it is understood that we mean "either . . . or . . . or both.")

Finally we have the concept of *function*. A function $f : X \to Y$ (sometimes called a *mapping*) is a rule which assigns to each element of a set X a unique element of a set Y. We write $f(x)$ for the element of Y which the function f assigns to x. The set X is called the *domain* or *domain of definition* of f. Two functions f and f' are said to be *equal*, and we write $f = f'$ if they have the same domain X and if, for all $x \in X$, $f(x) = f'(x)$. The function f is said to be *one-to-one* if $x_1 \neq x_2$ in X implies that $f(x_1) \neq f(x_2)$. [Note that this is equivalent to the statement that $f(x_1) = f(x_2)$ implies $x_1 = x_2$.] The function f is said to be *onto* Y if every $y \in Y$ can be expressed in the form $y = f(x)$ for some $x \in X$; we shall say that f is a function of X *into* Y when we want to allow the possibility that f is not onto Y. A one-to-one function f of a set X onto a set Y is called a *one-to-one correspondence* of X onto Y.

It is frequently useful to illustrate statements about sets by drawing diagrams. Although they have no mathematical significance, they do give us confidence that we are making sense and sometimes

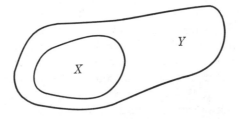

Figure 1.1

will suggest important steps in an argument. For example, the statement $X \subset Y$ is illustrated by Figure 1.1. In Figure 1.2 the shaded portion indicates $U \cup V$, while the cross-hatched portion

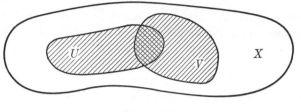

Figure 1.2

denotes $U \cap V$. Mappings (or functions) may be visualized by pictures such as that in Figure 1.3, which illustrates a function that

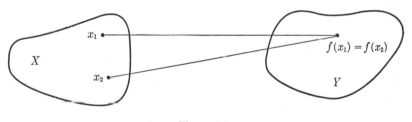

Figure 1.3

is not one-to-one. The reader will find it useful to construct far more diagrams than we have given in the book. It should be emphasized that a correct mathematical argument can never consist of a diagram alone, but must be a sequence of sentences with whatever symbolic abbreviations are appropriate to the context.

Now we are ready to discuss some important subsets of the system of real numbers.

The first subset to be considered is the *system of natural numbers* $1, 2 = 1 + 1, 3 = 2 + 1, 4 = 3 + 1$, etc. Because of the vague "etc.," it is necessary to give a more precise description.

(3.1) Definition.   The *system of natural numbers* is the unique subset N of the real numbers with the following properties:

(1) $1 \in N$;

(2) if $x \in N$, then $x + 1 \in N$; and

(3) If S is any subset of the real numbers satisfying (1) and (2), then $N \subset S$.

Before we can be sure that this definition is satisfactory, we must show that a set N satisfying conditions (1), (2), and (3) exists. First we observe that there exist subsets of R satisfying (1) and (2), for example the set of all real numbers. Let N be the intersection of all such subsets. Then by its construction, N satisfies conditions (1), (2), and (3). Moreover, N is uniquely determined, because if N' also satisfies (1), (2), and (3), then from (3) we obtain $N \subset N'$ and $N' \subset N$. Therefore $N = N'$, and the set N is uniquely determined.

It should be remarked that we have adopted this approach to the natural numbers only for the sake of economy. A more satisfying approach is to give axioms for the natural numbers, and then to construct the real numbers from them. For this rather lengthy construction, the reader is referred to the book of E. Landau, listed in the Bibliography.

We shall regard the next two statements as axioms about the system of natural numbers. It is impossible to overemphasize their importance; in fact almost all of the main results in this book are applications of one or the other.

(3.2)   Principle of Well-Ordering. *Let M be a nonempty subset of the set of natural numbers N. Then M has a least element, that is, for some element $m_0 \in M$, $m_0 \leq m$ for all $m \in M$.*

(3.3)   Principle of Mathematical Induction. *Suppose that for each natural number n there corresponds a statement $E(n)$ which is either true or false. Suppose, further, (A) $E(1)$ is true, and (B) if $E(n)$ is true then $E(n + 1)$ is true, for all $n \in N$. Then $E(n)$ is true for all natural numbers N.*

These statements are not independent; in fact either one can be derived from the other, using the definition we have given for N (see the exercises at the end of the section). Moreover, the principle of mathematical induction (3.3) is an easy consequence of Definition (3.1). To see this, suppose we are given statements $E(n)$ for each $n \in N$ such that (A) and (B) of (3.3) hold. Let S be the subset of N consisting of all $s \in N$ such that $E(s)$ is true. By (A), $1 \in S$; and by

(B), if $x \in S$, then $x + 1 \in S$. By (3) of Definition (3.1), it follows that $S = N$.

Some variations on the principle of induction are often useful, and we list one of them explicitly.

(3.4) *Let $\{E(n)\}$ be a family of statements defined for each natural number n. Suppose (A) $E(1)$ is true, and (B) if $E(r)$ is true for all natural numbers $r < n$, then $E(n)$ is true. Then $E(n)$ is true for all $n \in N$.*

In discussions where mathematical induction is involved, the statement which plays the role of $E(n)$ will often be called the *induction hypothesis*.

As a first application of mathematical induction, we prove the following statement.

(3.5) *If m and $n \in N$, then $m + n \in N$ and $mn \in N$.*

Proof. For the first statement, let us take as an induction hypothesis the statement

$$E(n): \quad \text{For a fixed } m \in N, \quad m + n \in N.$$

Then $E(1)$ is true by definition of N. Suppose $E(n)$ is true. Then

$$m + (n + 1) = (m + n) + 1 \in N$$

by the associative law for addition and by the induction hypothesis $E(n)$. This proves that $E(n)$ implies $E(n + 1)$, and the first result is established. The second is proved in a similar way.

As another illustration of the use of the principle of mathematical induction, we prove one or two facts about exponents.

Let a be a real number, and define

$$a = a^1, \qquad a^2 = (a^1)a, \qquad a^3 = a^2 a$$

and, in general, $a^{n+1} = a^n \cdot a$ for all natural numbers n. Then by mathematical induction a^n is defined for all positive integers n. Next we may prove

(3.6) $a^m a^n = a^{m+n}$ *for all $m, n \in N$.*

Proof. The result is true for $n = 1$ by definition. As an induction hypothesis we take:

$$E(n): \quad \text{For fixed } m \in N, \qquad a^m a^n = a^{m+n}.$$

We have already said that $E(1)$ is true. Suppose $E(n)$ is true, and consider $E(n + 1)$. The associative law together with $E(n)$ gives us

$$a^m a^{n+1} = a^m(a^n \cdot a) = (a^m a^n)a$$
$$= a^{m+n} \cdot a = a^{m+n+1}$$

which is $E(n + 1)$. By (3.3) we conclude that $E(n)$ is true for all n, and (3.6) is proved.

(3.7)★ $(a^m)^n = a^{mn}$ *for all* m *and* $n \in N$.

(3.8)★ $(ab)^n = a^n b^n$ *for all* a *and* $b \in R$, *and* $n \in N$.

We can also use the system of natural numbers to describe precisely what is meant by finite and infinite sets.

(3.9) Definition.   A set X is *finite* if for some natural number n there exists a one-to-one correspondence of the set of natural numbers m, such that $1 \leq m \leq n$, onto the set X. If, for all $n \in N$, no such correspondence exists, the set X is said to be *infinite*.

(3.10)★   *The set N of all natural numbers is an infinite set.*

Let X be a finite set. Then there is a natural number n and a one-to-one correspondence f of the natural numbers m, such that $1 \leq m \leq n$, onto the set X. Let us write $x_1 = f(1)$, $x_2 = f(2)$, $\cdots$, $x_n = f(n)$. Then we may write

$$X = \{x_1, x_2, \cdots, x_n\}.$$

The number n is called the *number of elements* in the set X.* Of course, for a given finite set there may be many choices of the function f. For example, if X is the set consisting of 3, -1, $\sqrt{2}$, when we write $X = \{3, -1, \sqrt{2}\}$ we are selecting the function $f: \{1, 2, 3\} \to X$ such that $f(1) = 3$, $f(2) = -1$, $f(3) = \sqrt{2}$. In other words, $X = \{x_1, x_2, x_3\}$ where $x_1 = 3$, $x_2 = -1$, $x_3 = \sqrt{2}$. When we write $X = \{-1, 3, \sqrt{2}\}$ we are selecting the function g such that $g(1) = -1$, $g(2) = 3$, $g(3) = \sqrt{2}$.

(3.11) Definition.   An *n-tuple* is a fixed mapping f from the set of natural numbers m such that $1 \leq m \leq n$, into a set X. We usually

---

* It can be proved that n is uniquely determined; that is, it is impossible to set up a one-to-one correspondence between the sets $X = \{1, 2, \cdots, n\}$ and $Y = \{1, 2, \cdots, q\}$ unless $n = q$.

write $\langle x_1, \cdots, x_n \rangle$ to denote an n-tuple where $f(1) = x_1, \cdots, f(n) = x_n$. An *ordered pair* is a 2-tuple $\langle x_1, x_2 \rangle$. Two n-tuples, $\langle x_1, \cdots, x_n \rangle$ and $\langle x_1', \cdots, x_n' \rangle$, are said to be *equal* if and only if $x_1 = x_1', \cdots, x_n = x_n'$. A *sequence* is a fixed mapping from the set of all natural numbers into a set X. We denote a sequence by $\{x_1, x_2, \cdots\}$. Note that functions defining n-tuples or sequences are not assumed to be one-to-one. For example, $\langle 0, 0, 0 \rangle$ is a 3-tuple which maps $\{1, 2, 3\}$ onto the single real number zero.

We conclude this section with the definitions of some other important subsets of the real numbers: the *integers* and the *rational numbers*.

(3.12)   Definition.   The *system of integers* Z is the union

$$N \cup \{0\} \cup N^-$$

where N^- is the set of all real numbers $-n$, where $n \in N$.

(3.13)★   *If a and $b \in Z$, then $a \pm b$, $ab \in Z$.*

(3.14)★   *There is no integer x such that $2x = 1$.*

Finally we come to the system of rational numbers.

(3.15)   Definition.   The system of *rational numbers* Q is the subset of the real numbers consisting of all real numbers a/b where a and $b \in Z$ and $b \neq 0$.

(3.16)★   *If q and $r \in Q$, so are $q \pm r$, qr, and q/r, where $r \neq 0$.*

(3.17)★   *If q and $r \in Q$, $q \neq 0$, then the equation $qx = r$ has a unique solution in Q.*

From (3.16) it follows that the system Q satisfies all the algebra axioms; in other words, Q is itself a field with respect to the operations of addition and multiplication defined in the real numbers R of which Q is a subset. We may express this fact by the assertion that Q is a *subfield* of R.

(3.18)★   *The field of rational numbers is the smallest subfield of the real numbers; that is, if F is any subfield of R, then $Q \subset F$.*

Note also that Q inherits the order axioms because $Q \subset R$. Therefore Q is an ordered field. We remark finally that there do exist real numbers which do not belong to the field of rational numbers. One way to settle this point is given by the following two theorems, which we state without proof.

(3.19) *There exists no rational number x such that $x^2 = 2$.*

(3.20) *There does exist a real number r such that $r^2 = 2$.*

For a complete and painstaking discussion of the real number system the reader may again consult Landau's book. Later in this book we shall need the fact (which can be proved by a fairly straightforward application of the completeness axiom) that every real number $a > 0$ has a unique positive square root $\sqrt{a}$.

EXERCISES

1. Prove the following statements by mathematical induction:
   a. $1 + 2 + \cdots + n = \frac{1}{2}(n + 1)n$.
   b. $1 + 3 + 5 + \cdots + (2k - 1) = k^2$.
   c. $1^2 + 2^2 + \cdots + n^2 = \dfrac{n(n + 1)(2n + 1)}{6}$.
   d. The number of distinct subsets of the set $\{1, 2, \cdots, n\}$ is 2^n.

2. How many distinct mappings are there of the set $\{1, 2, 3\}$ into itself? How many one-to-one mappings are there? How many n-tuples $\langle x_1, \cdots, x_n \rangle$ are there such that $x_i \in \{1, 2, 3\}$ for all i?

3. Discuss whether the mapping $x \to x^n$ (of R into R) is one-to-one for $n = 1, 2, \cdots$.

4. Let X be a set and let F be the set of all mappings of X into X. If f and $g \in F$, define $fg \in F$ by the rule

   $$(fg)(x) = f[g(x)], \qquad x \in X.$$

   Define the mapping $i \in F$ by the rule

   $$i(x) = x, \qquad x \in X.$$

   Prove that the mappings in F satisfy the associative law

   $$f(gh) = (fg)h, \qquad f, g, h \in F,$$

   and that

   $$fi = if = f, \qquad f \in F.$$

   Do the elements of F satisfy the commutative law $fg = gf$?

5. Let X be a set, and let f be a mapping of X into X. Prove that f is onto if there exists a mapping g of X into X such that $fg = i$.

6. Prove that a mapping f of X into X is one-to-one if there exists a mapping h such that $hf = i$.

7. Prove that there exists no natural number x such that $1 < x < 2$.

8. Prove that there exists no natural number x such that $n < x < n + 1$, for each natural number n.

9. Prove that the principle of mathematical induction implies the well-ordering principle. (*Hint:* Let M be a set of natural numbers which has no least element. Prove by mathematical induction, and exercise 8, that for all natural numbers n, $n \notin M$. Thus M is empty, and the well-ordering principle holds.)

10. Prove that the well-ordering principle implies the principle of mathematical induction.

11. Prove that the principle of mathematical induction (3.3) implies the alternate version (3.4).

CHAPTER **2**

VECTOR SPACES
and SYSTEMS
OF LINEAR EQUATIONS

This chapter contains the basic definitions and facts about vector spaces, together with a thorough discussion of the application of the general results on vector spaces to the determination of the solutions of systems of linear equations. The chapter concludes with an optional section on the geometrical interpretation of the theory of systems of linear equations.

4. FIELDS

For much of linear algebra, the only facts required about the real number system are the algebra axioms. This means that no additional work is required to develop a large part of linear algebra in case the underlying number system is an arbitrary field. Therefore we begin with the definition of a field, which is simply a repetition of the algebra axioms of the real numbers. The full force of all the axioms for the real numbers will not be needed until Chapter 4, on vector spaces with an inner product.

(4.1) Definition. A *field* is a mathematical system F consisting of a nonempty set F together with two operations, addition and multiplication, which assign to each pair of elements* α, $\beta \in F$ uniquely determined elements $\alpha + \beta$ and $\alpha\beta$ of F, such that the following conditions are satisfied for α, β, $\gamma \in F$.

Closure

(1) $\alpha + \beta = \beta + \alpha$, $\alpha\beta = \beta\alpha$ (commutative laws).
(2) $\alpha + (\beta + \gamma) = (\alpha + \beta) + \gamma$, $(\alpha\beta)\gamma = \alpha(\beta\gamma)$ (associative laws).
(3) $\alpha(\beta + \gamma) = \alpha\beta + \alpha\gamma$ (distributive law).
(4) There exists an element 0 such that $\alpha + 0 = \alpha$ for all $\alpha \in F$.
(5) For each element $\alpha \in F$ there exists an element $-\alpha$ such that $\alpha + (-\alpha) = 0$.
(6) There exists an element $1 \in F$ such that $1 \neq 0$ and such that $\alpha \cdot 1 = \alpha$ for all $\alpha \in F$.
(7) For each nonzero $\alpha \in F$ there exists an element $\alpha^{-1} \in F$ such that $\alpha\alpha^{-1} = 1$.

In any field, the consequences of the algebra axioms derived in Chapter 1 [Statements (2.3)–(2.14)] are valid, since only the above axioms are used in their proof.

The most important example of a field to have in mind at this stage is the field of real numbers. Another important example is the field of rational numbers, introduced in Chapter 1. Other examples are given in the exercises for this section; still others, such as the field of complex numbers, will play important parts later in the book.

EXERCISES

1. Show that the following systems are examples of fields.

   a. The set $Q(\sqrt{2})$ of all real numbers of the form $\alpha + \beta\sqrt{2}$, where α and β belong to the field of rational numbers Q. Addition and multiplication in $Q(\sqrt{2})$ are the operations already defined for the field of real numbers. In particular, compute $(\frac{1}{2} - \frac{3}{4}\sqrt{2})(1 - \sqrt{2})$, and $(\frac{1}{3} + \frac{1}{2}\sqrt{2})^{-1}$, and show that they belong to $Q(\sqrt{2})$. In general it must be checked that if $a, b \in Q(\sqrt{2})$ then $a \pm b$, ab, and a/b, for $b \neq 0$, also belong to $Q(\sqrt{2})$, in other words, that $Q(\sqrt{2})$ is a *subfield* of R.

   b. Let q be a rational number > 0 such that the equation $x^2 - q = 0$ has no rational solutions. Show that the set $Q(\sqrt{q})$

---

* See the list of Greek letters on p. 243.

of all real numbers $\alpha + \beta\sqrt{q}$, for α, β, $\in Q$, forms a field, the operations being as given in **a**. In particular, what is the formula for $(\alpha + \beta\sqrt{q})^{-1}$? Note that, since $\sqrt{q} \notin Q$, $Q(\sqrt{q})$ does not coincide with the field of rational numbers.

c. Let F be the system consisting of two elements $\{0, 1\}$, with the operations defined by the tables

+	0	1
0	0	1
1	1	0

·	0	1
0	0	0
1	0	1

Show that F is a field, with the property $2\alpha = \alpha + \alpha = 0$ for all $\alpha \in F$.

d. For an arbitrary natural number n, let $Z(n)$ be the system consisting of the natural numbers $\{0, 1, 2, \cdots, n - 1\}$, with the operations of addition and multiplication defined as follows. If a, $b \in Z(n)$, then the sum $a \oplus b$ is the remainder left after dividing the usual sum $a + b$ by n, while the product $a \otimes b$ is defined to be the remainder after dividing the usual product $a \cdot b$ by n. For example, in $Z(5)$, $3 \oplus 4 = 2$, $3 \otimes 3 = 4$. Write out tables for addition and multiplication in $Z(3)$, $Z(4)$, $Z(5)$, $Z(6)$. Which are fields?

5.   VECTOR SPACES

(5.1)   Definition.   Let F be an arbitrary field. A *vector space V over F* is a nonempty set V of objects $\{v\}$, called *vectors*, together with two operations, one of which assigns to each pair of vectors v and w a vector $v + w$ called the *sum* of v and w, and the other of which assigns to each element $\alpha \in F$ and each vector $v \in V$ a vector αv called the *product* of v by the element $\alpha \in F$. The operations are assumed to satisfy the following axioms, for α, $\beta \in F$ and for u, $v \in V$.

(1) $u + (v + w) = (u + v) + w$,   and $u + v = v + u$.
(2) There is a vector 0 such that $u + 0 = u$ for all $u \in V$.*
(3) For each vector u there is a vector $-u$ such that $u + (-u) = 0$.
(4) $\alpha(u + v) = \alpha u + \alpha v$.
(5) $(\alpha + \beta)u = \alpha u + \beta u$.
(6) $(\alpha\beta)u = \alpha(\beta u)$.
(7) $1u = u$.

---

* See the footnote on p. 21.

In this book we shall generally use Roman letters $\{x, y, u, v\}$ etc., to denote vectors, and Greek letters (see p. 243) $\{\alpha, \beta, \gamma, \delta, \xi, \eta, \theta, \lambda\}$ etc., to denote elements of the field involved. Elements of the field are often called *scalars*. We list a few facts about vectors which can be proved by the same arguments used to prove the corresponding facts for a field in Chapter 1, Section 2.

If $u + v = u + w$, then $v = w$.

The equation $u + x = v$ has a unique solution which we denote by $v - u$.

$$-(-u) = u, \quad u \in V.$$
$$0u = 0.*$$
$$-(\alpha u) = (-\alpha)u = \alpha(-u).$$
$$(-\alpha)(-u) = \alpha u, \quad \alpha \in F, u \in V.$$

EXAMPLES OF VECTOR SPACES

(5.2) The Vector Space R_n. The *vector space R_n* over the field of real numbers R is the algebraic system consisting of all n-tuples $a = \langle \alpha_1, \cdots, \alpha_n \rangle$ with $\alpha_i \in R$, together with the operations of addition, and multiplication of n-tuples by real numbers, to be defined below. The n-tuples $a \in R_n$ are called *vectors* and the real numbers α_i are called the *components* of the vector $a = \langle \alpha_1, \cdots, \alpha_n \rangle$. Two vectors $a = \langle \alpha_1, \cdots, \alpha_n \rangle$ and $b = \langle \beta_1, \cdots, \beta_n \rangle$ are said to be equal, and we write $a = b$ if and only if $\alpha_i = \beta_i$, $i = 1, \cdots, n$. The *sum* $a + b$ of the vectors $a = \langle \alpha_1, \cdots, \alpha_n \rangle$ and $b = \langle \beta_1, \cdots, \beta_n \rangle$ is defined by

$$a + b = \langle \alpha_1 + \beta_1, \cdots, \alpha_n + \beta_n \rangle.$$

The product of the vector a by the real number λ is defined by

$$\lambda a = \langle \lambda \alpha_1, \cdots, \lambda \alpha_n \rangle.$$

It is straightforward to verify that R_n is a vector space over R, according to Definition (5.1). In particular, the vector 0 is given by $0 = \langle 0, \cdots, 0 \rangle$, and if $a = \langle \alpha_1, \cdots, \alpha_n \rangle$, then $-a = \langle -\alpha_1, \cdots, -\alpha_n \rangle$.

REMARKS ON THE DEFINITIONS.   In elementary physics, for example, vectors are defined as directed line segments, and the operations of addition and multiplication by real numbers are defined geometri-

---

* For simplicity we use the same notation for the zero vector and the real number zero. The meaning of "0" will always be clear from the context.

cally. We briefly interrupt our discussion of vector spaces such as R_n to show that our definition of the vector space R_n is consistent with the interpretation of vectors used in physics. We shall not make use of this interpretation in this book. The proofs of theorems about the vector space R_n are based on the algebraic properties of the real numbers and do not rest on any results from geometry. Nevertheless, the geometrical way of thinking can often suggest the correct procedure in a purely algebraic problem.

We shall restrict ourselves to vectors in R_3. A vector $a = \langle \alpha_1, \alpha_2, \alpha_3 \rangle$ in R_3 is represented geometrically by the directed line segment $\overrightarrow{OP}$ in three-dimensional space from the origin O to the point P with coordinates $\alpha_1, \alpha_2, \alpha_3$. Thus a vector is determined by a length and a direction. In order not to make the definition of a vector depend on the particular choice of the coordinate system in three-dimensional space, we identify $\overrightarrow{OP}$ with all other directed line segments $\overrightarrow{QR}$ such that under a translation of axes which carries the origin into the point Q, the point P is carried into the point R. For example, we have $\overrightarrow{OP} = \overrightarrow{QR}$, where O is the origin, $P = (3, 1, -2)$, $Q = (1, -1, 2)$, and $R = (4, 0, 0)$.

Now let the vectors $a = \langle \alpha_1, \alpha_2, \alpha_3 \rangle$ and $b = \langle \beta_1, \beta_2, \beta_3 \rangle$ in R_3 be represented by $\overrightarrow{OP}$ and $\overrightarrow{OQ}$ respectively, where O is the origin. We define the geometric sum $\overrightarrow{OP} + \overrightarrow{OQ}$ to be $\overrightarrow{OS}$, where $\overrightarrow{PS}$ is a vector equal to $\overrightarrow{OQ}$, with initial point P. Thus $\overrightarrow{OP} + \overrightarrow{OQ} = \overrightarrow{OP} + \overrightarrow{PS} = \overrightarrow{OS}$, and vector addition is simply the parallelogram law, as in the accompanying figure. It thus follows that the geometric sum $\overrightarrow{OS}$ of $\overrightarrow{OP}$

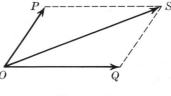

Figure 2.1

and $\overrightarrow{OQ}$ represents $a + b = \langle \alpha_1 + \beta_1, \alpha_2 + \beta_2, \alpha_3 + \beta_3 \rangle$.

Now let λ be a positive real number, and let $a = \langle \alpha_1, \alpha_2, \alpha_3 \rangle$ be represented by the directed line segment $\overrightarrow{OP}$ with O the origin and P the point $(\alpha_1, \alpha_2, \alpha_3)$. Let R be the point with coordinates $(\lambda\alpha_1, \lambda\alpha_2, \lambda\alpha_3)$. Then $\overrightarrow{OR}$ represents the vector λa. Geometrically R can be located on the ray from O passing through P, and is such that the distance from the origin to R is λ times the distance from the origin to P. We leave as an exercise the geometrical interpretation of λa, where $a \in R_3$, and λ is a negative real number.

(5.3)   The Vector Space F_n.   Let F be an arbitrary field. The *vector space* F_n is the set of all vectors $\langle\alpha_1, \cdots, \alpha_n\rangle$ with *components* $\alpha_i \in F$. If $a = \langle\alpha_1, \cdots, \alpha_n\rangle$, $b = \langle\beta_1, \cdots, \beta_n\rangle$, then we define

$$a = b, \quad \text{if and only if } \alpha_1 = \beta_1, \cdots, \alpha_n = \beta_n,$$
$$a + b = \langle\alpha_1 + \beta_1, \cdots, \alpha_n + \beta_n\rangle,$$
$$\alpha \cdot a = \langle\alpha\alpha_1, \cdots, \alpha\alpha_n\rangle, \quad \alpha \in F, \quad a \in F_n.$$

Then, exactly as in the case of R_n, it can be shown that F_n is a vector space over the field F.

(5.4)   The Vector Space of Continuous Functions.   Let $C[R]$ be the set of continuous real-valued functions f defined on the set of all real numbers R. Then $C[R]$ becomes a vector space V over the field of real numbers R if we define

$$(f + g)(x) = f(x) + g(x), \quad x \in R, \quad f, g \in V,$$
$$(\alpha f)(x) = \alpha f(x), \quad x \in R, \quad \alpha \in R.$$

From calculus we know that one of the basic facts concerning continuous functions is that $f + g$ and αf belong to $C[R]$ for all f, $g \in C[R]$ and $\alpha \in R$. We omit the verification of the vector space axioms. More generally, the set $C[a, b]$ of all continuous functions on a closed interval $[a, b]$, with the operations of addition and scalar multiplication of functions, is a vector space over R.

(5.5)   The Vector Space of Polynomial Functions.   Let $P[R]$ be the set of real valued polynomial functions on the real numbers R. Then $f \in P$ if f is a function, which assigns to each $x \in R$, a real number

$$f(x) = \alpha_0 + \alpha_1 x + \alpha_2 x^2 + \cdots + \alpha_r x^r,$$

where $\alpha_0, \alpha_1, \cdots, \alpha_n$ are real numbers depending only on f, and not on x. For example $f: f(x) = 2 - x^2$ is an element of $P[R]$. Let $f, g \in P$ and $\alpha \in R$, then $f + g$ and αf are defined as in Example (5.4), and it follows that with these definitions, $f + g \in P$, $\alpha f \in P$, and P is a vector space over R.

(5.6)   A Field, Viewed as a Vector Space Over a Subfield. Let E be a field that contains F as a *subfield;* that is, F is a subset of E such that the operations on F are the operations of E restricted to pairs of elements in F. Then E becomes a vector space over F if for a and b in E we define $a + b$ as the sum of a and b, as elements of the field E, and define αa, where $a \in E$ and $\alpha \in F$, as the result of multiplying a by α in E. To check the axioms for a vector space, it is necessary to show that the identity element $1 \in F$ is also the identity element in E.

These examples show the nature of abstraction in mathematics. The theorems we shall prove in this chapter were originally discovered for the vector space R_n. They are valid for arbitrary vector spaces in the sense of Definition (5.1) and thus apply to all the examples (5.2)–(5.6), as well as to the vector space R_n.

We conclude this section with some further consequences of Definition (5.1), which will be needed in the next section. The associative law states that, for a_1, a_2, a_3 in V,

$$(a_1 + a_2) + a_3 = a_1 + (a_2 + a_3).$$

If we have four vectors a_1, a_2, a_3, a_4, there are the following possible sums we can form:

$$a_1 + [a_2 + (a_3 + a_4)],$$
$$a_1 + [(a_2 + a_3) + a_4],$$
$$[a_1 + (a_2 + a_3)] + a_4,$$
$$[(a_1 + a_2) + a_3] + a_4.$$

The reader may check that all these expressions represent the same vector. More generally, it can be proved by mathematical induction that all possible ways of adding n vectors a_1, $\cdots$, a_n together to form a single sum yield a uniquely determined vector which we shall denote by

$$a_1 + \cdots + a_n = \sum_{i=1}^{n} a_i.$$

The commutative law together with this "generalized associative law" imply by a further application of mathematical induction that

$$(a_1 + \cdots + a_n) + (b_1 + \cdots + b_n) = (a_1 + b_1) + \cdots + (a_n + b_n)$$

or, more briefly,

(5.7) $$\sum_{i=1}^{n} a_i + \sum_{i=1}^{n} b_i = \sum_{i=1}^{n} (a_i + b_i).$$

The other rules can also be generalized to sums of more than two vectors:

$$\left(\sum_{i=1}^{n} \lambda_i\right) a = \sum_{i=1}^{n} \lambda_i a,$$

$$\lambda \left(\sum_{i=1}^{n} a_i\right) = \sum_{i=1}^{n} \lambda a_i,$$

We have also by (5.7):

$$\left(\sum_{i=1}^{n} \lambda_i a_i\right) + \left(\sum_{i=1}^{n} \mu_i a_i\right) = \sum_{i=1}^{n} (\lambda_i + \mu_i) a_i.$$

The main point is that these rules do require proof from the basic rules (5.1), and the reader will find it an interesting exercise in the use of mathematical induction to supply, for example, a proof of (5.7).

EXERCISES

1. With reference to the discussion of directed line segments following Example (5.2), find the point Q such that the vector $\overrightarrow{PQ}$ has components $\langle 3, 1, -1 \rangle$, in the following cases. Note that in this discussion we distinguish between the point $(3, 1, -1)$ and the vector $\langle 3, 1, -1 \rangle$. The reason for the distinction is that the points (α, β, γ) have no algebraic operations defined on them, while the vectors $\langle \alpha, \beta, \gamma \rangle$ are elements of a vector space, and can be added and multiplied by scalars.
   a. $P = (0, 0, 0)$
   b. $P = (1, 1, -1)$
   c. $P = (2, 1, 1)$.

2. Let $P = (1, -1, 1)$, $Q = (2, 1, 1)$, $R = (0, 1, 1)$, $S = (-1, 1, 0)$. Find T such that $\overrightarrow{QT} = \overrightarrow{RS}$. Find the components of $\overrightarrow{PT}$, and show that they are the sums of the corresponding components of $\overrightarrow{PQ}$ and $\overrightarrow{RS}$. Draw a figure to illustrate what you have done.

3. Let $P = (0, 2, 1)$ and $Q = (1, 0, 1)$ in R_3. Determine whether or not $\overrightarrow{PS} = \lambda \overrightarrow{PQ}$ for some real number λ, and if so, find λ, in the following cases.
   a. $S = (0, 0, 0)$

    b. $S = (-2, 6, 1)$

    c. $S = (\frac{1}{2}, 1, 1)$.

4. In the vector space R_3, compute (that is, express in the form $\langle \lambda, \mu, v \rangle$), the following vectors formed from $a = \langle -1, 2, 1 \rangle$, $b = \langle 2, 1, -3 \rangle$, $c = \langle 0, 1, 0 \rangle$:

    a. $a + b + c$

    b. $2a - b + c$

    c. $-a + 2b$

    d. $\alpha a + \beta b + \gamma c$.

5. Verify that the axioms for a vector space are satisfied for Examples (5.3), (5.4), and (5.5).

6. LINEAR DEPENDENCE

In this section we introduce the basic ideas needed to study vector spaces. The most important idea is the concept of linear dependence. The definition of linear dependence and its use are rather subtle, and it will be essential for the reader to study all the details in this section with particular care. One helpful way to study the material for the first time is to find a numerical example to illustrate each point. Many numerical examples are included in the text, but the reader will almost certainly need to make up some of his own.

    In this section, let V be a vector space over a field F. From Section 5, we shall assume familiarity with some of the elementary facts about vectors, including the possibility of forming arbitrary finite sums $\sum a_i$, with $a_i \in V$.

(6.1) Definition. Let $\{a_1, \cdots, a_m\}$ be an arbitrary finite set of vectors in V. The set of vectors $\{a_1, \cdots, a_m\}$ is said to be *linearly dependent* if there exist elements of F, $\lambda_1, \cdots, \lambda_m$, not all zero, such that

$$\lambda_1 a_1 + \lambda_2 a_2 + \cdots + \lambda_m a_m = 0.$$

Such a formula will be called a *relation of linear dependence*. A set of vectors which is not linearly dependent is said to be *linearly independent*. Thus, the set $\{a_1, \cdots, a_m\}$ is linearly independent if and only if

$$\lambda_1 a_1 + \cdots + \lambda_m a_m = 0, \qquad \lambda_i \in F,$$

implies that $\lambda_1 = \cdots = \lambda_m = 0$.

Before proceeding, let us look at a few simple cases of linear dependence.

First of all, the set consisting of the zero vector $\{0\}$ in V always forms a linearly dependent set, since for any $\lambda \neq 0$ in F we have

$$\lambda 0 = 0.$$

But if $a \neq 0$ in V, then the set $\{a\}$ alone is a linearly independent set. To see this, we have to prove that if

$$\lambda a = 0, \qquad \lambda \in F,$$

then $\lambda = 0$. This statement is equivalent to proving that if the conclusion ($\lambda = 0$) is false then the hypothesis ($\lambda a = 0$, $a \neq 0$) is false also. If $\lambda \neq 0$, then by Axiom 7 of Definition (4.1) there is an element λ^{-1} such that $\lambda^{-1}\lambda = 1$. Since $\lambda a = 0$, we obtain

$$\lambda^{-1}(\lambda a) = \lambda^{-1}0 = 0,$$

and by the "associative law" for multiplication of vectors by elements of F, we have

$$\lambda^{-1}(\lambda a) = (\lambda^{-1}\lambda)a = 0.$$

However, $\lambda^{-1}\lambda = 1$, and hence we have shown that $\lambda a = 0$, where $\lambda \neq 0$, implies $1 \cdot a = a = 0$, contrary to the hypothesis that $a \neq 0$. (The reader will be spared most of these agonizing details in the future, but it does no harm to see what goes into even such a simple statement as the one we have just established.)

Now let $\{a, b\}$ be a set consisting of two vectors in V. We shall prove:

(6.2) $\{a, b\}$ *is a linearly dependent set if and only if* $a = \lambda b$ *or* $b = \lambda'a$ *for some* λ *or* λ' *in* F.

Proof.   First suppose $a = \lambda b$, $\lambda \in F$. Then we have

$$a + [-(\lambda b)] = 0.$$

From the axioms for a vector space it follows, as in (2.12) of Chapter 1, that

$$-(\lambda b) = (-\lambda)b$$

and we have

$$1 \cdot a + (-\lambda)b = 0.$$

Since $1 \neq 0$, we have proved that $\{a, b\}$ is a linearly dependent set. Similarly, $b = \lambda'a$ implies that $\{a, b\}$ is a linearly dependent set.

Now suppose that

(6.3) $\alpha a + \beta b = 0, \qquad \alpha, \beta \in F$

where either α or $\beta \neq 0$. If $\alpha \neq 0$, then we have

$$\alpha a = (-\beta)b$$

and

$$a = \alpha^{-1}(\alpha a) = \alpha^{-1}(-\beta)b = (-\alpha^{-1}\beta)b,$$

as we wish to prove. If, on the other hand, $\alpha = 0$ and $\beta \neq 0$, the equation (6.3) becomes $\beta b = 0$, and hence $b = 0$. In that case we have $b = \lambda' a$ for $\lambda' = 0$, and (6.2) is completely proved.

Let us have a more concrete illustration. Let $a = \langle 1, -1 \rangle$ in R_2. Then $\{a, b\}$ is a linearly independent set if $b = \langle 1, 1 \rangle$ or $\langle 1, 0 \rangle$, and a linearly dependent set if $b = \langle -2, 2 \rangle$ or $\langle 0, 0 \rangle$.

Consider $a = \langle 1, -1 \rangle$, $b = \langle 1, 1 \rangle$, and $c = \langle 2, 1 \rangle$ in R_2. Are $\{a, b, c\}$ linearly dependent or not? Consider a possible relation of linear dependence, $\alpha a + \beta b + \gamma c = 0$, with α, β, γ real numbers. Then

$$\alpha a + \beta b + \gamma c = \langle \alpha + \beta + 2\gamma, -\alpha + \beta + \gamma \rangle.$$

In order for this vector to be zero, we must have

$$\alpha + \beta + 2\gamma = 0$$
$$-\alpha + b + \gamma = 0.$$

Do there exist numbers α, β, γ not all zero, satisfying these equations? Note that if $\{\alpha, \beta, \gamma\}$ solve the equations, so do $\{5\alpha, 5\beta, 5\gamma\}$. Try setting $\gamma = 1$; then the equations become

$$\alpha + \beta + 2 = 0$$
$$-\alpha + \beta + 1 = 0,$$

and we can solve for α and β, obtaining

$$\alpha = -\tfrac{1}{2}, \qquad \beta = -\tfrac{3}{2}, \qquad \gamma = 1.$$

Thus the vectors are linearly dependent. We shall demonstrate a more systematic way for carrying out this sort of test in the next section.

Now we give a few more consequences of the definitions. The first is left as an exercise.

(6.4)⋆   *The empty set is a linearly independent set.*⋆ *Any subset of a*

---

* This fact is sometimes useful in that it permits results to be stated in a general form without one's having to make exceptions.

linearly independent set is linearly independent. Any finite set of vectors containing a linearly dependent set of vectors as a subset is itself linearly dependent.

✳ **(6.5) Definition.** Let $\{a_1, \cdots, a_m\}$ be a set of vectors in V. A vector $a \in V$ is said to be a *linear combination* of $a_1, \cdots, a_m$ if a can be expressed, for some elements of F, $\lambda_1, \cdots, \lambda_m$, in the form

$$a = \lambda_1 a_1 + \cdots + \lambda_m a_m.$$

This concept can be used to restate the definition of linear independence. Thus, a set of vectors $\{a_1, \cdots, a_m\}$ is linearly independent if the only linear combination of $a_1, \cdots, a_m$ which is equal to 0 is $0a_1 + \cdots + 0a_m$.

The next theorem is an important generalization of (6.2).

✳ **(6.6) Theorem.** *A set of vectors $\{a_1, \cdots, a_m\}$ is linearly dependent if and only if there is some a_i, for $1 \leq i \leq m$, that is a linear combination of the remaining vectors a_j, $j \neq i$.*

Proof. First suppose that $\{a_1, \cdots, a_m\}$ is a linearly dependent set. Then for some elements of F, $\lambda_1, \cdots, \lambda_m$, not all zero, we have

(6.7) $$\lambda_1 a_1 + \cdots + \lambda_m a_m = 0.$$

By reindexing the a_i's, if necessary, we may assume that $\lambda_1 \neq 0$. Then λ_1^{-1} exists, and we obtain from (6.7)

$$\begin{aligned} a_1 &= \lambda_1^{-1}(\lambda_1 a_1) = \lambda_1^{-1}[(-\lambda_2)a_2 + \cdots + (-\lambda_m)a_m] \\ &= [\lambda_1^{-1}(-\lambda_2)]a_2 + \cdots + [\lambda_1^{-1}(-\lambda_m)]a_m \end{aligned}$$

as we wished to prove. Conversely, if a_1 is a linear combination of $\{a_2, \cdots, a_m\}$, then

$$a_1 = \mu_2 a_2 + \cdots + \mu_m a_m$$

for some real numbers μ_i. Then we have

$$(-1)a_1 + \mu_2 a_2 + \cdots + \mu_m a_m = 0$$

and, since $-1 \neq 0$, the set $\{a_1, \cdots, a_m\}$ is linearly dependent. The same argument applies if any other a_i is a linear combination of the remaining ones.

For example, let $a = \langle 1, -1 \rangle$, $b = \langle 1, 1 \rangle$ and $c = \langle 2, 1 \rangle$ in R_2. Then we have shown that the set $\{a, b, c\}$ is linearly dependent, and in fact

$$-\tfrac{1}{2}a - \tfrac{3}{2}b + c = 0.$$

Then $c = \frac{1}{2}a + \frac{3}{2}b$. We could in this case equally well solve for a in terms of b and c, or for b in terms of a and c.

A sharper version of (6.6) is the following useful result.

(6.8)   Lemma.   *If* $\{a_1, \cdots, a_m\}$ *is linearly dependent and if* $\{a_1, \cdots, a_{m-1}\}$ *is linearly independent, then* a_m *is a linear combination of* $a_1, \cdots, a_{m-1}$.

Proof.   By the hypothesis, we have

$$\lambda_1 a_1 + \cdots + \lambda_m a_m = 0$$

where some $\lambda_i \neq 0$. If $\lambda_m = 0$, then some $\lambda_i \neq 0$ for $1 \leq i \leq m - 1$, and the equation of linear dependence becomes

$$\lambda_1 a_1 + \cdots + \lambda_{m-1} a_{m-1} = 0,$$

contrary to the assumption that $\{a_1, \cdots, a_{m-1}\}$ is linearly independent. Therefore $\lambda_m \neq 0$, and we have

$$a_m = \lambda_m^{-1}[(-\lambda_1)a_1 + \cdots + (-\lambda_{m-1})a_{m-1}]$$

$$= \sum_{i=1}^{m-1} (-\lambda_m^{-1}\lambda_i)a_i$$

as we wished to prove.

To illustrate (6.8), let $a = \langle 0, 1 \rangle$, $b = \langle 1, -1 \rangle$, $c = \langle -2, 2 \rangle$ in R_2. Then a, b, c are linearly dependent (Why?). Moreover, a and b are linearly independent, so by (6.8), c must be a linear combination of a and b. (Show that this is correct.) But b and c are not linearly independent, and in this case it is easily shown that a is *not* a linear combination of b and c. Therefore the hypothesis in (6.8) is essential.

Finally, we define the important notion of a subspace of V.

(6.9)   Definition.   A *subspace* S of the vector space V is a nonempty set of vectors in V such that:

(1) If a and b are in S, then $a + b \in S$.
(2) If $a \in S$ and $\lambda \in F$, then $\lambda a \in S$.

The axioms (5.1) for a vector space are clearly satisfied for any subspace S or a vector space V, so that we see that a subspace is simply a vector space contained in a larger vector space.

REMARKS.   Clearly, the whole space V and the set consisting of the zero vector alone $\{0\}$ are examples of subspaces.

Note that if S is a subspace and if $a \in S$, then $-a = (-1)a \in S$. Therefore $a + (-a) \in S$, and we have shown that every subspace contains the zero vector. More generally, we have the following observation.

(6.10)   *If S is a subspace of V containing the vectors $a_1, \cdots, a_m$, then every linear combination of $a_1, \cdots, a_m$ belongs to S.*

Proof.   We prove the result by induction on m. If $m = 1$, the result is true by the definition of a subspace. Suppose that any linear combination of $m - 1$ vectors in S belongs to S, and consider a linear combination

$$a = \lambda_1 a_1 + \cdots + \lambda_m a_m$$

of m vectors belonging to S. Letting $a' = \lambda_2 a_2 + \cdots + \lambda_m a_m$, we have

$$a = \lambda_1 a_1 + a'$$

where $\lambda_1 a_1 \in S$ and $a' \in S$ by the induction hypothesis. By part 1 of the definition of subspace, $a \in S$, and (6.10) is proved.

The process of forming linear combinations leads to a method of constructing subspaces, as follows.

(6.11)   *Let $\{a_1, \cdots, a_m\}$ be a set of vectors in V, for $m \geq 1$; then the set of all linear combinations of the vectors $a_1, \cdots, a_m$ forms a subspace $S = S(a_1, \cdots, a_m)$. S is the smallest subspace containing $a_1, \cdots, a_m$ in the sense that if T is any subspace containing $a_1, \cdots, a_m$ then $S \subset T$.*

Proof.   Let $a = \displaystyle\sum_{i=1}^{m} \lambda_i a_i$ and $b = \displaystyle\sum_{i=1}^{m} \mu_i a_i$. Then

$$a + b = \sum_{i=1}^{m} (\lambda_i + \mu_i) a_i$$

is again a linear combination of $a_1, \cdots, a_m$. If $\lambda \in F$, then

$$\lambda a = \lambda \left(\sum_{i=1}^{m} \lambda_i a_i \right) = \sum_{i=1}^{m} \lambda(\lambda_i a_i) = \sum_{i=1}^{m} (\lambda \lambda_i) a_i.$$

These computations prove that S is a subspace, and the fact that it is the smallest one containing the given vectors is immediate by (6.10).

(6.12)   **Definition.**   The subspace $S = S(a_1, \cdots, a_m)$ defined in (6.11) is called the subspace *generated by* (or, sometimes, *spanned by*)

$a_1, \cdots, a_m$, and $a_1, \cdots, a_m$ are called *generators* of S. A subspace S of V is called *finitely generated* if there exist vectors $s_1, \cdots, s_k$ in S such that $S = S(s_1, \cdots, s_k)$.

EXERCISES

1. Test the following sets of vectors in R_2 and R_3 to determine whether or not they are linearly independent.
   a. $\langle 1, 1 \rangle, \langle 2, 1 \rangle$.
   b. $\langle 1, 1 \rangle, \langle 2, 1 \rangle, \langle 1, 2 \rangle$.
   c. $\langle 0, 1 \rangle, \langle 1, 0 \rangle$.
   d. $\langle 0, 1 \rangle, \langle 1, 0 \rangle, \langle \alpha, \beta \rangle$.
   e. $\langle 1, 1, 2 \rangle, \langle 3, 1, 2 \rangle, \langle -1, 0, 0 \rangle$.
   f. $\langle 3, -1, 1 \rangle, \langle 4, 1, 0 \rangle, \langle -2, -2, -2 \rangle$.
   g. $\langle 1, 1, 0 \rangle, \langle 0, 1, 1 \rangle, \langle 1, 0, 1 \rangle, \langle 1, 1, 1 \rangle$.

2. Prove that any two vectors in R_1 are linearly dependent.

3. Prove that any three vectors in R_2 are linearly dependent.

4. Determine which of the following subsets of R_n are subspaces.
   a. All vectors $\langle a_1, \cdots, \alpha_n \rangle$ such that $\alpha_1 = 1$.
   b. All vectors $\langle \alpha_1, \cdots, \alpha_n \rangle$ such that $\alpha_1 = 0$.
   c. All vectors $\langle \alpha_1, \cdots, \alpha_n \rangle$ such that $\alpha_1 + 2\alpha_2 = 0$.
   d. All vectors $\langle \alpha_1, \cdots, \alpha_n \rangle$ such that $\alpha_1 + \alpha_2 + \cdots + \alpha_n = 1$.
   e. All vectors $\langle \alpha_1, \cdots, \alpha_n \rangle$ such that $A_1\alpha_1 + \cdots + A_n\alpha_n = 0$ for fixed $A_1, \cdots, A_n$.
   f. All vectors $\langle \alpha_1, \cdots, \alpha_n \rangle$ such that $A_1\alpha_1 + \cdots + A_n\alpha_n = B$ for fixed $A_1, \cdots, A_n, B$.
   g. All vectors $\langle \alpha_1, \cdots, \alpha_n \rangle$ such that $\alpha_1^2 = \alpha_2$.

5. Determine which of the following subsets of $C[R]$ are subspaces of $C[R]$; see the example of vector spaces, (5.4).
   a. The set of polynomial functions in $C[R]$.
   b. The set of all $f \in C[R]$ such that $f(\frac{1}{2})$ is a rational number.
   c. The set of all $f \in C[R]$ such that $f(\frac{1}{2}) = 0$.
   d. The set of all $f \in C[R]$ such that $\int_0^1 f(t)\, dt = 1$.
   e. The set of all $f \in C[R]$ such that $\int_0^1 f(t)\, dt = 0$.
   f. The set of all $f \in C[R]$ such that $df/dt = 0$.
   g. The set of all $f \in C[R]$ such that
   $$\alpha \frac{d^2f}{dt^2} + \beta \frac{df}{dt} + \gamma f = 0, \qquad \alpha, \beta, \gamma \in R.$$

h. The set of all $f \in C[R]$ such that

$$\alpha \frac{d^2f}{dt^2} + \beta \frac{df}{dt} + \gamma f = g$$

for a fixed function $g \in C[R]$.

6. Show that the set of polynomial functions $P[R]$ [see (5.5)] is not a finitely generated vector space.

7. Is the intersection of two subspaces always a subspace? Prove your answer.

8. Is the union of two subspaces always a subspace? Explain.

9. Let a in R_n be a linear combination of vectors $b_1, \cdots, b_r$ in R_n, and let each vector b_i, $1 \le i \le r$, be a linear combination of vectors $c_1, \cdots, c_s$. Prove that a is a linear combination of $c_1, \cdots, c_s$.

7. THE CONCEPTS OF BASIS AND DIMENSION

We have seen that in R_2 (in Exercise 3 of Section 6) any three vectors are linearly dependent. Let us see what this gives us to say about the possible subspaces of R_2. These are:

$\{0\}$
$S(a)$, a subspace generated by a single vector a
$S(a_1, a_2)$, a subspace generated by two vectors
$S(a_1, a_2, a_3)$, etc.

In fact, we can prove a much sharper result, namely:

(7.1) *The only subspaces in R_2 are* $\{0\}$, *$S(a)$ for an arbitrary single vector a, and R_2.*

Proof. First of all consider $S = S(a_1, \cdots, a_m) \ne \{0\}$ where no pair $\{a_i, a_j\}$ of the vectors is linearly independent. Then, in particular, since $S \ne 0$ we may assume that $a_1 \ne 0$. For every $i > 1$ the linear dependence of the set $\{a_1, a_i\}$ implies by (6.2) that $a_i = \lambda_i a_1$ for some $\lambda_i \in R$. Therefore, $S \subset S(a_1)$ and, since $S(a_1) \subset S(a_1, \cdots, a_m)$ by (6.10), we have $S(a_1, \cdots, a_m) = S(a_1)$.

Next consider $S(a_1, \cdots, a_m)$ and suppose that some pair of the vectors, say $\{a_1, a_2\}$, forms a linearly independent set. We shall prove that

$$R_2 \subset S(a_1, a_2).$$

Let $b \in R_2$; then, by Exercise 3 of Section 6, $\{a_1, a_2, b\}$ is a linearly dependent set. By Lemma (6.8) we have $b \in S(a_1, a_2)$, and hence $R_2 \subset S(a_1, a_2)$. Finally, since $R_2 \subset S(a_1, a_2) \subset S(a_1, a_2, \cdots, a_m)$ we have

$$S(a_1, a_2, \cdots, a_m) = R_2.$$

By the result of Exercise 3 of Section 6, it follows that every subspace S of R_2 is finitely generated, and contains at most two linearly independent vectors. Thus (7.1) is proved.

The possible subspaces of R_n for $n > 2$ are more numerous. In this section we determine all subspaces of an arbitrary finitely generated vector space. All the results fall out almost effortlessly when we find the right place to start. We shall choose, as our key result, the following "replacement theorem," whose importance was first realized early in this century.

The idea is deceptively simple, and can be illustrated by the following example in R_3. Consider the subspace $S(a_1, a_2)$ where $a_1 = \langle 1, 0, 0 \rangle$ and $a_2 = \langle 0, 1, 0 \rangle$. The vector $b = \langle 2, -1, 0 \rangle$ belongs to $S(a_1, a_2)$, and in fact $b = 2a_1 - a_2$. The set consisting of $\{b\}$ is a linearly independent set, and the replacement theorem states, in this special case, that $S(a_1, a_2) = S(b, a_i)$ for $i = 1$ or 2; in other words b replaces one of the generators. In this case we see that $a_1 = \frac{1}{2}b + \frac{1}{2}a_2$, so that $S(a_1, a_2) = S(b, a_1)$. It can also be checked that $S(a_1, a_2) = S(b, a_2)$. The general result can be stated as follows.

(7.2) Replacement Theorem.   *Let $V = S(a_1, \cdots, a_m)$ be a finitely generated vector space over a field F, with generators $\{a_1, \cdots, a_m\}$. Suppose that $\{b_1, \cdots, b_q\}$ is a linearly independent set of vectors contained in V. Then, first $q \leq m$; and, second, there are $m - q$ of the vectors $a_1, \cdots, a_m$, which we will denote (upon changing some subscripts if necessary) by $a_{q+1}, \cdots, a_m$, such that these vectors together with $b_1, \cdots, b_q$ generate V; in other words*

$$V = S(b_1, \cdots, b_q, a_{q+1}, \cdots, a_m).$$

REMARK.   The possibility that $q = m$ is not excluded; in such a case it is understood that the set $\{a_{q+1}, \cdots, a_m\}$ is empty, and the conclusion then reads $S = S(b_1, \cdots, b_q)$. Also, it should be clear to the reader why the theorem is called the "replacement theorem": it says that a set of linearly independent vectors in a subspace can always be used to replace some of the generators in a given set of generators of the subspace.

Proof. This theorem will be proved by mathematical induction. Among the several possible positive integers appearing in the statement of the theorem, namely n, m, and q, it will be convenient to make the induction on $q + 1$. In other words, we are to think of m as fixed and to think of q as taking on the values $0, 1, 2, \cdots$. The theorem is obviously true if $q = 0$ and the set $\{b_1, \cdots, b_q\}$ is empty.* As our induction hypothesis, we assume that the conclusion of the theorem holds for any linearly independent set of $q - 1$ vectors in V where $q - 1 \geq 0$, and we have to prove that the statement holds when we are given a set of q linearly independent vectors, $\{b_1, \cdots, b_q\}$. Applying the induction hypothesis to the subset $\{b_1 \cdots, b_{q-1}\}$, we obtain $q - 1 \leq m$, and

$$V = S(b_1, \cdots, b_{q-1}, a_q, \cdots, a_m).$$

Now consider b_q. Since $b_q \in V$ we have

(7.3) $b_q = \lambda_1 b_1 + \cdots + \lambda_{q-1} b_{q-1} + \mu_q a_q + \cdots + \mu_m a_m$

for some elements of F, $\lambda_1, \cdots, \lambda_{q-1}$ and $\mu_q, \cdots, \mu_m$. At this point we see that $q \leq m$, for if $q > m$ then $q - 1 \geq m$ and, since $q - 1 \leq m$ by the induction hypothesis, we have $q - 1 = m$. Thus if $q > m$ we have $V = S(b_1, \cdots, b_{q-1})$. Then (7.3) becomes $b_q = \lambda_1 b_1 + \cdots + \lambda_{q-1} b_{q-1}$, which contradicts the assumption that $\{b_1, \cdots, b_q\}$ is a linearly independent set.

Returning to (7.3), we prove next that some $\mu_i \neq 0$. Otherwise, $\mu_q - \cdots = \mu_n = 0$, which again contradicts the hypothesis that $b_1, \cdots, b_{q-1}$ are linearly independent. Therefore, some $\mu_i \neq 0$, and by renaming the a_i's, we may assume that $\mu_q \neq 0$. Then we can solve the equation (7.3) for a_q as follows:

(7.4) $a_q = \mu_q^{-1}[(-\lambda_1) b_1 + \cdots + (-\lambda_{q-1}) b_{q-1} + b_q \mid (\quad \mu_{q+1}) a_{q+1} + \cdots + (-\mu_m) a_m]$.

In other words, we have shown that:

(7.5) $a_q \in S(b_1, \cdots, b_{q-1}, b_q, a_{q+1}, \cdots, a_m)$.

Obviously, $b_1, \cdots, b_{q-1}$ and $a_{q+1}, \cdots, a_m \in S(b_1, \cdots, b_q, a_{q+1}, \cdots, a_m)$, and this fact combined with (7.5) and the induction hypothesis yields

$$V = S(b_1, \cdots, b_{q-1}, a_q, \cdots, a_m) \subset S(b_1, \cdots, b_q, a_{q+1}, \cdots, a_m).$$

---

* We have pointed out in (6.4) that the empty set is a linearly independent set.

Since the other inclusion,

$$S(b_1, \cdots, b_q, a_{q+1}, \cdots, a_m) \subset V,$$

is clear, we have

$$V = S(b_1, \cdots, b_q, a_{q+1}, \cdots, a_m),$$

and the theorem is proved.

The importance of the replacement theorem is not its intrinsic interest, but its use as a common source from which the following basic results about vector spaces follow easily. It is important to realize that since subspaces of vector spaces are vector spaces in their own right, that the following results apply in particular to subspaces of vector spaces.

(7.6) Theorem. *Let $V = S(a_1, \cdots, a_m)$ be a vector space with m generators. Then any set of $m + 1$ vectors in V is linearly dependent.*

Proof. If the result is false, we contradict the first statement ($q \leq m$) of the replacement theorem.

The next result has already been anticipated in some special cases [for example, in Exercise 3 of Section 6, which was used to derive (7.1)].

(7.7) Corollary. *Any set of $n + 1$ vectors in F_n is a linearly dependent set.*

Proof. By (7.6), it is sufficient to prove that F_n is generated by some set of n vectors. Let:

(7.8) $e_1 = \langle 1, 0, 0, \cdots, 0 \rangle$, $e_2 = \langle 0, 1, 0, \cdots, 0 \rangle$, $\cdots$, $e_n = \langle 0, \cdots, 0, 1 \rangle$.

The vectors e_i will be called the *unit vectors* in F_n. We prove that:

(7.9) $$F_n = S(e_1, \cdots, e_n).$$

Let $a = \langle \alpha_1, \cdots, \alpha_n \rangle \in F_n$. Then we have

$$a = \alpha_1 e_1 + \cdots + \alpha_n e_n$$

by an easy computation, and (7.9) is established. As we have observed, (7.9) and (7.6) imply (7.7).

(7.10) Definition. A finite set of vectors $b_1, \cdots, b_k$ is said to be a *basis* for a vector space V if $\{b_1, \cdots, b_k\}$ is a linearly independent set such that V is generated by $b_1, \cdots, b_k$.*

(7.11) *Every finitely generated vector space V has a basis.*

Proof. If $V = 0$, we agree that the empty set $\varnothing$ spans V and $\varnothing$ is a basis for V. Now let $V \neq 0$ be a vector space with n generators. By (7.6), any set of $n + 1$ vectors in V is linearly dependent, and since a set consisting of a single nonzero vector is linearly independent, it follows that, for some integer $m \geq 1$, V contains linearly independent vectors $b_1, \cdots, b_m$ such that any set of $m + 1$ vectors in V is linearly dependent. We prove that $\{b_1, \cdots, b_m\}$ is a basis for V, and for this it is sufficient to show, for any vector $b \in V$, that $b \in S(b_1, \cdots, b_m)$. Because of the properties of the set $\{b_1, \cdots, b_m\}$, $\{b_1, \cdots, b_m, b\}$ is a linearly dependent set. Since $\{b_1, \cdots, b_m\}$ is linearly independent, (6.8) implies that $b \in S(b_1, \cdots, b_m)$, and the theorem is proved.

(7.12) Theorem. *Any two bases of a finitely generated vector space V contain the same number of vectors.*

Proof. The result is obvious if $V = 0$. Let $V \neq 0$ and let $\{b_1, \cdots, b_r\}$ and $\{b_1', \cdots, b_s'\}$ be bases of V. Applying the replacement theorem to $V = S(b_1, \cdots, b_r)$ and the linearly independent set $\{b_1', \cdots, b_s'\}$ in V, we obtain $s \leq r$. Reversing the argument, we have $r \leq s$. Combining our results, we have (7.12).

(7.13) Definition. Let V be a finitely generated vector space. The uniquely determined number of vectors in a basis for V is called the *dimension* of V (notation: dim V). In particular the subspace $\{0\}$ has dimension 0. A vector space V which is not finitely generated is said to be infinite dimensional (example: $P[R]$, discussed in Exercise 6 of Section 6).

We have now shown that a finitely generated vector space is determined as soon as we know a basis for it—the space then consists of the set of all linear combinations of the basis vectors. The next

---

* The concept of basis used in this book refers only to finitely generated vector spaces. There is a satisfactory theory of basis and dimension for vector spaces which are not finitely generated (see, for example, Chapter 9 of Jacobson's book, listed in the Bibliography).

two theorems give some idea of where to look for a basis if we know a set of generators for the vector space, or at least, some linearly independent vectors in it.

(7.14)   Theorem.   *Let $V = S(a_1, \cdots, a_m)$ be a finitely generated vector space with generators $\{a_1, \cdots, a_m\}$. Then a basis for V can be selected from among the set of generators $\{a_1, \cdots, a_m\}$. In other words, a set of generators for a finitely generated vector space always contains a basis.*

Proof.   The result is clear if $V = 0$. Now let $V \neq 0$. For some index r, where $1 \leq r \leq m$, we may assume, for a suitable ordering of $a_1, \cdots, a_m$, that $\{a_1, \cdots, a_r\}$ is linearly independent and that any larger set of the a_i's is linearly dependent. Then by (6.8) it follows that $a_{r+1}, \cdots, a_m$ all belong to $S(a_1, \cdots, a_r)$. Therefore $S(a_1, \cdots, a_m) = S(a_1, \cdots, a_r)$ and, since $\{a_1, \cdots, a_r\}$ is linearly independent, we conclude that it is a basis of V.

(7.15)   Theorem.   *Let $\{b_1, \cdots, b_q\}$ be a linearly independent set of vectors in a finitely generated vector space V. Then there exist other vectors $b_{q+1}, \cdots, b_m$ in V such that $\{b_1, \cdots, b_m\}$ is a basis of V.*

Proof.   By Theorem (7.11), V has a basis $\{a_1, \cdots, a_m\}$ where $m = \dim V$. By the replacement theorem we have $q \leq m$, and

(7.16) $$V = S(b_1, \cdots, b_q, a_{q+1}, \cdots, a_m)$$

for suitably chosen vectors $a_{q+1}, \cdots, a_m$ from the original basis. Then $\{b_1, \cdots, b_q, a_{q+1}, \cdots, a_m\}$ is the required basis of V if we can show that these vectors are linearly independent. If, on the contrary, they are linearly dependent, then (7.16) together with Theorem (7.14) implies that V has a basis of fewer than m vectors. This is impossible by Theorem (7.12). Therefore $\{b_1, \cdots, b_q, a_{q+1}, \cdots, a_m\}$ forms a basis for V and (7.15) is proved.

The thoughtful reader should not have been so overwhelmed with the relentless sequence of theorems that he failed to notice an important gap in the whole development, namely, that the theorems given so far are purely descriptive in nature and give no computational procedure, or algorithm, for testing sets of vectors for linear dependence or for explicitly finding bases of subspaces with given sets of generators. This gap is filled at the end of this section, where we give a computational procedure for testing for linear dependence of sets of vectors which can be used to handle many of the numerical problems in the book.

We next consider certain operations on subspaces of vector space V that lead to new subspaces. If S, T are subspaces of vector space V, it follows at once, from the definition, that $S \cup T$ is not always a subspace, as the following example in R_2 shows (see Exercise 8 of Section 6):

$$S = \{\langle 0, \beta \rangle, \quad \beta \in R\}, \qquad T = \{\langle \alpha, 0 \rangle, \quad \alpha \in R\}.$$

Because of this example, we define, for subspaces S and T of V,

$$S + T = \{s + t; \quad s \in S, t \in T\}.$$

It is easy to show that $S + T$ is a subspace and is, in fact, the smallest subspace containing $S \cup T$. On the other hand, if S and T are subspaces, $S \cap T$ is always a subspace. It is natural to ask for the dimensions of $S \cap T$ and $S + T$, given the dimensions of S and T. The answer is provided by the following result, suggested by a counting procedure for finite sets: if A and B are finite sets, then the number of objects in $A \cup B$ is the sum of the numbers of objects in A and B, less the number of objects in the overlap $A \cap B$.

(7.17)   Theorem.   *Let S and T be finitely generated subspaces of a vector space V. Then $S \cap T$ and $S + T$ are finitely generated subspaces, and we have*

memorize!

$$\dim (S + T) + \dim (S \cap T) = \dim S + \dim T.$$

Proof.   We shall give a sketch of the proof, leaving some of the details to the reader. Although it is not actually necessary, we consider first the special case $S \cap T = \{0\}$. Let $\{s_1, \cdots, s_d\}$ be a basis of S and $\{t_1, \cdots, t_e\}$ be a basis of T. Then it is easily checked that the vectors $s_1, \cdots, s_d, t_1, \cdots, t_e$ generate $S + T$, and (7.17) will follow in this case if we can show that these vectors are linearly independent. Suppose we have

$$\alpha_1 s_1 + \cdots + \alpha_d s_d + \beta_1 t_1 + \cdots + \beta_e t_e = 0.$$

Then

$$\alpha_1 s_1 + \cdots + \alpha_d s_d = -\beta_1 t - \cdots - \beta_e t_e \in S \cap T = \{0\}.$$

Since the s's and t's are linearly independent, we have $\alpha_1 = \cdots = \alpha_d = 0$ and $\beta_1 = \cdots = \beta_e = 0$.

Now suppose that $S \cap T \neq 0$. Then $S \cap T$ is finitely generated (Why?). By Theorem (7.11), $S \cap T$ has a basis $\{u_1, \cdots, u_c\}$

where $c = \dim S \cap T$. By Theorem (7.15) we can find sets of vectors $\{v_1, \cdots, v_d\}$ and $\{w_1, \cdots, w_e\}$ such that

$$\{u_1, \cdots, u_c, v_1, \cdots, v_d\} \text{ is a basis for } S,$$
$$\{u_1, \cdots, u_c, w_1, \cdots, w_e\} \text{ is a basis for } T.$$

Then $S + T = S(u_1, \cdots, u_c, v_1, \cdots, v_d, w_1, \cdots, w_e)$, and Theorem (7.17) will be proved if we can show that these vectors are linearly independent. Suppose we have

(7.18) $\xi_1 u_1 + \cdots + \xi_c u_c + \lambda_1 v_1 + \cdots + \lambda_d v_d + \mu_1 w_1 + \cdots + \mu_e w_e = 0.$

Then

$$\lambda_1 v_1 + \cdots + \lambda_d v_d = -\left(\sum \xi_i u_i\right) - \left(\sum \mu_i w_i\right) \in S \cap T$$

and hence there exist elements of F, $\zeta_1, \cdots, \zeta_c$, such that

$$\lambda_1 v_1 + \cdots + \lambda_d v_d = \zeta_1 u_1 + \cdots + \zeta_c u_c.$$

Since $\{v_1, \cdots, v_d, u_1, \cdots, u_c\}$ are linearly independent, we have $\lambda_1 = \cdots = \lambda_d = 0$. Then from (7.18) we have $\xi_1 = \cdots = \xi_c = \mu_1 = \cdots = \mu_e = 0$, and the proof is completed.

We now take up, for the special case of the vector space R_n, a computational procedure for testing sets of vectors for linear dependence, and for finding bases of subspaces.

We shall first derive some general results and then give an example to show how the procedure works.

(7.19) Lemma.

(1) *For any set of vectors $\{a_1, \cdots, a_p\}$ in R_n, $S(a_1 + \lambda a_i, a_2, \cdots, a_p)$ $= S(a_1, a_2, \cdots, a_p)$ for all $\lambda \in R$ and $i \neq 1$.*

(2) $S(a_1, a_2, \cdots, a_p) = S(\lambda a_1, a_2, \cdots, a_p)$ *for all $\lambda \neq 0$ in R.*

Proof. Since $a_1 + \lambda a_i \in S(a_1, \cdots, a_p)$, every linear combination of $a_1 + \lambda a_i, a_2, \cdots, a_p$ is in $S(a_1, \cdots, a_p)$ by (6.10). Therefore $S(a_1 + \lambda a_i, a_2, \cdots, a_p) \subset S(a_1, \cdots, a_p)$. Conversely, $a_1 = (a_1 + \lambda a_i) - \lambda a_i \in S(a_1 + \lambda a_i, a_2, \cdots, a_p)$, and it follows that $S(a_1, \cdots, a_p) \subset S(a_1 + \lambda a_i, a_2, \cdots, a_p)$. Combining our results, we obtain (1). The proof of (2) is left to the reader.

(7.20) Definition. An ordered collection of vectors $\{a_1, \cdots, a_p\}$ in R_n is said to be in *echelon form* if each $a_i \neq 0$ and if the position of the first nonzero entry in a_i is to the left of the position of the first non-zero entry in a_{i+1}, for $i = 1, 2, \cdots, p - 1$. For example,

$$\langle 1, 0, -2, 3 \rangle, \qquad \langle 0, 1, 2, 0 \rangle, \qquad \langle 0, 0, 0, 1 \rangle$$

are in echelon form, while

$$\langle 0, 1, 0, 0 \rangle, \qquad \langle 1, 0, 0, 0 \rangle$$

are not.

(7.21) Lemma. *Every finite set of vectors $(in \ R_n)$ in echelon form is a linearly independent set.*

Proof. Let $\{a_1, \cdots, a_p\}$ be a set of vectors in echelon form. We use induction on p, the result being obvious if $p = 1$. As an induction hypothesis, we may assume that any set of $p - 1$ vectors in echelon form is linearly independent. Since $\{a_2, \cdots, a_{p-1}\}$ are in echelon form (Why?), we may assume that $\{a_2, \cdots, a_{p-1}\}$ is a linearly independent set. Now suppose we have a possible relation of linear dependence

$$\lambda_1 a_1 + \lambda_2 a_2 + \cdots + \lambda_p a_p = 0, \qquad \lambda_i \in R.$$

We show that $\lambda_1 = 0$. Let α be the first nonzero entry in a_1, appearing in the kth position. Then the kth entry in $a_2, \cdots, a_p$ is zero, by the definition of echelon form, and the kth entry in $\lambda_1 a_1 + \cdots + \lambda_p a_p$ is $\lambda_1 \alpha = 0$. Therefore $\lambda_1 = 0$. By the induction hypothesis, $a_2, \cdots, a_p$ are linearly independent and we have $\lambda_2 = \cdots = \lambda_p = 0$. This completes the proof of the lemma.

(7.22) Theorem. *For every subspace $S = S(a_1, \cdots, a_p) \neq 0$ of R_n, it is possible to find vectors $\{b_1, \cdots, b_q\}$ in echelon form such that $S(a_1, \cdots, a_p) = S(b_1, \cdots, b_q)$. Then $dim \ S = q$ and $\{b_1, \cdots, b_q\}$ is a basis for S.*

Proof. We may assume that all the generators $a_i \neq 0$. We use induction on p, the case $p = 1$ being immediate since a single nonzero vector is always in echelon form. We may assume* that given any set of $m \leq p - 1$ nonzero vectors $\{a_1, \cdots, a_m\}$, we can find vectors $\{b_1, \cdots, b_q\}$ in echelon form such that $S(a_1, \cdots, a_m) = S(b_1, \cdots, b_q)$. By rearranging the vectors $a_1, \cdots, a_p$, we may assume that a_1 has a nonzero entry as far to the left as any of the a_i. Then by applying (1) of Lemma (7.19), we can find real numbers $\lambda_2, \cdots, \lambda_p$ successively such that

---

* We are using the version (3.4) in Chapter 1 of the principle of mathematical induction.

$$S(a_1, \cdots, a_p) = S(a_1, a_2 + \lambda_2 a_1, \cdots, a_p + \lambda_p a_p)$$
$$= S(a_1, a_2', \cdots, a_p'),$$

where $a_i' = a_i + \lambda_i a_1$, $i = 2, \cdots, p$, and the first nonzero entry of a_i' is farther to the right than the first nonzero entry in a_1. For example, let $a_1 = \langle 0, 3, 0, -1, 2 \rangle$, $a_2 = \langle 0, -1, 1, 0, 2 \rangle$ in R_5; then for a_2' we can take $a_2 = a_2 + \frac{1}{3} a_1 = \langle 0, 0, 1, -\frac{1}{3}, \frac{8}{3} \rangle$. By the induction hypothesis, there exist vectors $b_1, \cdots, b_q$ in echelon form such that

$$S(a_2', \cdots, a_p') = S(b_1, \cdots, b_q).$$

Since every vector b_i is a linear combination of $a_2', \cdots, a_p'$, no b_i has a nonzero entry as far to the left as a_1. Therefore $\{a_1, b_1, \cdots, b_q\}$ is a set of vectors in echelon form, and

$$S(a_1, \cdots, a_p) = S(a_1, a_2', \cdots, a_p') = S(a_1, b_1, \cdots, b_q).$$

This completes the proof of the theorem.

The next example shows how Theorem (7.22) is used in numerical work.

(7.23) Example.   Test the following vectors for linear dependence:

$$a = \langle -3, 2, 1, 4 \rangle, \qquad b = \langle 4, 1, 0, 2 \rangle, \qquad c = \langle -10, 3, 2, 6 \rangle.$$

Solution.   By Theorem (7.14) the vectors a, b, and c are linearly independent or dependent, according to whether the dimension of the subspace $S(a, b, c)$ is 3 or less than 3. We can test the dimension of $S(a, b, c)$ by Theorem (7.22). We pick a vector with a nonzero entry as far to the left as possible. In our example, any one of the vectors can be chosen. But if we had $\langle 0, 1 \rangle$, $\langle 2, 3 \rangle$ we would start from $\langle 2, 3 \rangle$. Let us start with a.

The next step is to apply Lemma (7.19) to express

$$S = S(a, b, c) = S(a, b', c')$$

where $b' = \lambda a + b$ and $c' = \mu a + c$ are determined so that the first components of b' and c' are zero. Thus we will have a start on putting the vectors in echelon form. Then we repeat the process with $\{b', c'\}$, etc. Specifically, we have

$$b' = \tfrac{4}{3} a + b = \langle 0, \tfrac{11}{3}, \tfrac{4}{3}, \tfrac{22}{3} \rangle,$$
$$c' = -\tfrac{10}{3} a + c = \langle 0, -\tfrac{11}{3}, -\tfrac{4}{3}, -\tfrac{22}{3} \rangle.$$

Since $b' = -c'$, we see that

$$S(a, b, c) = S(a, b')$$

and a and b' are in echelon form. Therefore $\{a, b, c\}$ is linearly dependent. Notice that the method also gives a basis for $S(a, b, c)$, namely $\{a, b'\}$, and the relation of linear dependence connecting a, b, and c which we obtain from $b' = -c'$. Thus we have

$$\tfrac{4}{3}a + b = +\tfrac{10}{3}a - c,$$

or

$$2a - b - c = 0.$$

SUMMARY. The preceding two sections contain results which are used constantly throughout the book. We shall list, in outline form, the main results about bases and dimension which the reader should remember in solving problems and understanding theoretical material to come later. For more complete statements, see the theorems stated earlier in the sections.

(A) Every finitely generated vector space V has a finite basis. The vectors in V are all linear combinations of the basis vectors. Two bases of a finitely generated vector space always contain the same number of vectors.

(B) Any set of $q + 1$ vectors in a vector space with q generators is linearly dependent.

(C) Every set of linearly independent vectors in a finitely generated vector space can be completed to a basis.

(D) Every finite set of generators of a finitely generated vector space contains a basis.

(E) If S and T are finitely generated subspaces of a vector space V, then

$$\dim (S + T) + \dim (S \cap T) = \dim S + \dim T.$$

(F) The numerical procedure given in Theorem (7.22) and Example (7.23) is used to test sets of vectors in R_n for linear dependence.

EXERCISES

1. Test the following sets of vectors for linear dependence, and find a relation of linear dependence (with nonzero coefficients) if one exists. Assume the vectors all belong to R_n.

   a. $\langle -1, 1 \rangle$, $\langle 1, 2 \rangle$, $\langle 1, 3 \rangle$.
   b. $\langle 2, 1 \rangle$, $\langle 1, 0 \rangle$, $\langle -2, 1 \rangle$.
   c. $\langle 1, 3, 4 \rangle$, $\langle 4, 0, 1 \rangle$, $\langle 3, 1, 2 \rangle$.
   d. $\langle 1, 1, 2 \rangle$, $\langle 2, 1, 3 \rangle$, $\langle 4, 0, -1 \rangle$, $\langle -1, 0, 1 \rangle$.
   e. $\langle 0, 1, 1, 2 \rangle$, $\langle 3, 1, 5, 2 \rangle$, $\langle -2, 1, 0, 1 \rangle$, $\langle 1, 0, 3, -1 \rangle$.
   f. $\langle 1, 1, 0, 0, 1 \rangle$, $\langle -1, 1, 1, 0, 0 \rangle$, $\langle 2, 1, 0, 1, 1 \rangle$, $\langle 0, -1, -1, -1, 0 \rangle$.

2. Find bases in echelon form for the vector spaces with the sets of vectors as generators given in parts **a–f** of Exercise 1.

3. Prove that the set of all $f \in C[R]$ such that $df/dt = 0$ is a one-dimensional subspace of $C[R]$. Can you generalize this result? For example, what is the dimension of the subspace consisting of all f such that $d^2f/dt^2 = 0$?

4. In Example (5.6) of vector spaces, a field was shown to be a vector space over any subfield. What is the dimension of the vector space $Q(\sqrt{2})$ (see Exercise 1a of Section 4) over the field of rational numbers Q? What is a basis for this vector space?

5. Determine whether $\langle 1, 1, 1 \rangle$ belongs to the subspace of R_3 generated by $\langle 1, 3, 4 \rangle$, $\langle 4, 0, 1 \rangle$, $\langle 3, 1, 2 \rangle$. Explain your reasoning.

6. Determine whether $\langle 2, 0, -4, -2 \rangle$ belongs to the subspace of R_4 generated by $\langle 0, 2, 1, -1 \rangle$, $\langle 1, -1, 1, 0 \rangle$, $\langle 2, 1, 0, -2 \rangle$.

7. Prove that every subspace S of a finitely generated subspace T of a vector space V is finitely generated, and that dim $S \leq$ dim T, with equality if and only if $S = T$.

8. Let $a_1, \cdots, a_m$ be linearly independent vectors in V. Prove that $\alpha_1 a_1 + \cdots + \alpha_m a_m = \alpha_1' a_1 + \cdots + \alpha_m' a_m$ if and only if $\alpha_1 = \alpha_1', \cdots, \alpha_m = \alpha_m'$. In other words, the coefficients of a vector expressed as a linear combination of linearly independent vectors are uniquely determined.

9. Let F be the field of 2 elements,* and let V be a two-dimensional vector space over F. How many vectors are there in V? How many one-dimensional subspaces? How many different bases are there?

10. Let S and T be two-dimensional subspaces of R_3. Prove that dim $(S \cap T) \geq 1$.

11. Let

$$a_1 = \langle 2, 1, 0, -1 \rangle \quad a_3 = \langle 1, -3, 2, 0 \rangle \quad a_5 = \langle -2, 0, 6, 1 \rangle$$
$$a_2 = \langle 4, 8, -4, -3 \rangle \quad a_4 = \langle 1, 10, -6, -2 \rangle \quad a_6 = \langle 3, -1, 2, 4 \rangle$$

and let

$$S = S(a_1, a_2, a_3, a_4), \qquad T = S(a_4, a_5, a_6).$$

Find dim S, dim T, dim $(S + T)$, and, using Theorem (7.17), find dim $(S \cap T)$.

---

* See Exercise 1c of Section 4.

8.   SYSTEMS OF LINEAR EQUATIONS

The rest of this chapter is devoted to the problem of solving systems of linear equations with real coefficients. This problem, as we have mentioned before, is one of the sources of linear algebra, and it would be an interesting, but lengthy, project to survey the rich variety of methods and ideas which appeared in the historical development of the subject. We shall content ourselves with one direct approach to the main facts, using the full force of our general theorems in Section 7, applied to the vector space R_n.

We shall describe a *system of m linear equations in n unknowns* by the notation

(8.1)
$$\begin{array}{c}
\alpha_{11}x_1 + \alpha_{12}x_2 + \cdots + \alpha_{1n}x_n = \beta_1 \\
\alpha_{21}x_1 + \alpha_{22}x_2 + \cdots + \alpha_{2n}x_n = \beta_2 \\
\cdots\cdots\cdots\cdots\cdots\cdots\cdots\cdots\cdots\cdots \\
\cdots\cdots\cdots\cdots\cdots\cdots\cdots\cdots\cdots\cdots \\
\cdots\cdots\cdots\cdots\cdots\cdots\cdots\cdots\cdots\cdots \\
\alpha_{m1}x_1 + \alpha_{m2}x_2 + \cdots + \alpha_{mn}x_n = \beta_m
\end{array}$$

where the α_{ij} and β_i are fixed real numbers and the $x_1, \cdots, x_n$ are the *unknowns*. The indexing is chosen such that for $1 \leq i \leq m$, the ith equation is

$$\alpha_{i1}x_1 + \cdots + \alpha_{in}x_n = \beta_i$$

where the first index appearing with α_{ij} stands for the equation in which α_{ij} appears and the second index j denotes the unknown x_j of which α_{ij} is the coefficient. Thus α_{21} is the coefficient of x_1 in the second equation, etc. The function or rule that assigns the real number α_{ij} to each pair (i, j), for $1 \leq i \leq m$ and $1 \leq j \leq n$, is called the *coefficient matrix* of the system (8.1). In general, an "*m-by-n*" (or $m \times n$) matrix is any rule which assigns to each ordered pair of natural numbers (i, j), where $1 \leq i \leq m$ and $1 \leq j \leq n$, a real number α_{ij}. An *m-by-n* matrix will be denoted by (α_{ij}) or simply by **A**. With any *m-by-n* matrix (α_{ij}) we can associate two sets of vectors in the vector spaces R_m and R_n respectively, viz., the *row vectors*

$$\{r_1, \cdots, r_m\} \subset R_n$$

where the ith row vector is

$$r_i = \langle \alpha_{i1}, \cdots, \alpha_{in} \rangle, \qquad 1 \leq i \leq m$$

and the *column vectors*

$$\{c_1, \cdots, c_n\} \subset R_m$$

where the jth column vector is

$$c_j = \langle \alpha_{1j}, \alpha_{2j}, \cdots, \alpha_{mj} \rangle.$$

We should also notice that row and column vectors are special kinds of matrices, and we shall often write

$$\mathbf{r}_i = (\alpha_{i1}, \cdots, \alpha_{in}), \qquad \mathbf{c}_j = \begin{pmatrix} \alpha_{1j} \\ \alpha_{2j} \\ \cdot \\ \cdot \\ \cdot \\ \alpha_{mj} \end{pmatrix}.$$

The *row subspace* of the m-by-n matrix (α_{ij}) is the subspace $S(r_1, \cdots, r_m)$ of R_n, and the *column subspace* is the subspace $S(c_1, \cdots, c_n)$ of R_m.

A *solution* of the system (8.1) is an n-tuple of real numbers $\{\lambda_1, \cdots, \lambda_n\}$ such that

$$\alpha_{11}\lambda_1 + \cdots + \alpha_{1n}\lambda_n = \beta_1$$
$$\cdots\cdots\cdots\cdots\cdots\cdots\cdots\cdots\cdots$$
$$\cdots\cdots\cdots\cdots\cdots\cdots\cdots\cdots\cdots$$
$$\alpha_{m1}\lambda_1 + \cdots + \alpha_{mn}\lambda_n = \beta_m.$$

In other words, the numbers $\{\lambda_i\}$ in the solution satisfy the equations (8.1) upon being substituted for the unknowns. We may identify a solution with a vector in R_n and may therefore speak of a *solution vector* of the system (8.1). Recalling the definition of the column vectors, we see that $x = \langle \lambda_1, \cdots, \lambda_n \rangle$ is a solution of the system (8.1) if and only if

(8.2) $$\lambda_1 c_1 + \lambda_2 c_2 + \cdots + \lambda_n c_n = b$$

where $b = \langle \beta_1, \cdots, \beta_n \rangle$, and we may describe the original system of equations by the more economical notation:

(8.3) $$x_1 c_1 + \cdots + x_n c_n = b.$$

A system of *homogeneous equations*, or a homogeneous system, is a system (8.3) in which the vector $b = 0$; if we allow the possibility $b \neq 0$, we speak of a *nonhomogeneous system*. If we have a homogeneous system,

(8.4) $$x_1 c_1 + \cdots + x_n c_n = 0,$$

then the zero vector $\langle 0, \cdots, 0 \rangle$ is always a solution vector, called the *trivial solution*. A solution different from $\langle 0, \cdots, 0 \rangle$ is called a *nontrivial solution*.

To clarify these concepts, consider the system

$$3x_1 - x_2 + x_3 = 1$$
$$x_1 + x_2 - x_3 = 2.$$

The matrix of the system is

$$\begin{pmatrix} 3 & -1 & 1 \\ 1 & 1 & -1 \end{pmatrix};$$

the row vectors are

$$r_1 = \langle 3, -1, 1 \rangle, \qquad r_2 = \langle 1, 1, -1 \rangle;$$

and the column vectors are

$$c_1 = \langle 3, 1 \rangle, \qquad c_2 = \langle -1, 1 \rangle, \qquad c_3 = \langle 1, -1 \rangle.$$

A solution vector is $\langle \frac{3}{4}, 0, -\frac{5}{4} \rangle$, as we check by substitution:

$$3(\tfrac{3}{4}) - 0 - \tfrac{5}{4} = 1$$
$$\tfrac{3}{4} + 0 + \tfrac{5}{4} = 2.$$

In terms of the column vectors, the system is written

$$x_1 c_1 + x_2 c_2 + x_3 c_3 = b,$$

where $b = \langle 1, 2 \rangle$, and the solution expressed in the form

$$b = \tfrac{3}{4} c_1 - \tfrac{5}{4} c_3.$$

By this time the reader should be beside himself in a wish to apply the results of the preceding section to systems of equations. Rather than give any more definitions, we dispose of some theoretical points of fundamental importance.

(8.5)   Theorem.   *A nonhomogeneous system* $x_1 c_1 + \cdots + x_n c_n = b$ *has a solution if and only if either of the following conditions is satisfied:*

(1) *b belongs to the column space* $S(c_1, \cdots, c_n)$.
(2) $\dim S(c_1, \cdots, c_n) = \dim S(c_1, \cdots, c_n, b)$.

Proof.   The fact that the first statement is equivalent to the existence of a solution is immediate from (8.2). To prove that condition 2 is equivalent to condition 1, we proceed as follows. If $b \in S(c_1, \cdots, c_n)$, then clearly $S(c_1, \cdots, c_n, b) = S(c_1, \cdots, c_n)$ and condition 2 holds. Conversely, if condition 2 holds, then since

$$S(c_1, \cdots, c_n) \subset S(c_1, \cdots, c_n, b),$$

we have by Exercise 7 of Section 7

$$S(c_1, \cdots, c_n) = S(c_1, \cdots, c_n, b)$$

and $b \in S(c_1, \cdots, c_n)$. This completes the proof.

REMARK.   Since we have in Section 7 a computational procedure for finding dim $S(a_1, \cdots, a_m)$ for any set of vectors $\{a_1, \cdots, a_m\}$, part 2 of (8.5) gives us a practical method of testing nonhomogeneous systems for existence of solutions. The equation (8.2) tells us that to find an actual solution we have to express b as a linear combination of the column vectors; this can be done by putting $\{c_1, \cdots, c_n, b\}$ in echelon form and keeping track of the results.

EXAMPLE.   We use Example (7.23) of Section 7 to illustrate this procedure. Letting the vectors a, b, c be column vectors, we consider the system

$$\begin{array}{rcr} -3x_1 + 4x_2 &=& -10 \\ 2x_1 + x_2 &=& 3 \\ x_1 + 0x_2 &=& 2 \\ 4x_1 + 2x_2 &=& 6 \end{array}$$

with column vectors c_1 and c_2, where $b = \langle -10, 3, 2, 6 \rangle$. From the results of Example (7.23) we have

$$S(c_1, c_2) = S(c_1, c_2, b)$$

and hence the system has a solution. In that exercise we also obtained the relation of linear dependence

$$2c_1 - c_2 - b = 0$$

which asserts that $\langle 2, -1 \rangle$ is a solution of the system.

The result of Theorem (8.4) can be restated in a convenient way by using the following concepts.

(8.6)   Definition.   Let (α_{ij}) be an m-by-n matrix with column vectors $\{c_1, \cdots, c_n\}$. The *rank* of the matrix is defined as the dimension of the column space $S(c_1, \cdots, c_n)$.

(8.7)   Definition.   If $x_1c_1 + \cdots + x_nc_n = b$ is a nonhomogeneous system whose coefficient matrix has columns $c_1, \cdots, c_n$, then the m-by-$(n + 1)$ matrix with columns $\{c_1, \cdots, c_n, b\}$ is called the *augmented matrix* of the system.

The next result is immediate from our definitions and Theorem (8.5).

(8.8)   Theorem.   *A nonhomogeneous system has a solution if and only if the rank of its coefficient matrix is equal to the rank of the augmented matrix.*

We have now settled the question of whether a nonhomogeneous system has a solution or not. If it does possess a solution, then we should ask to determine *all* solutions of the system. The key to this problem is furnished by the next theorem.

(8.9)   Theorem.   *Suppose that a nonhomogeneous system*

(8.10) $$x_1 c_1 + \cdots + x_n c_n = b$$

has a solution x_0; then for all solutions x of the homogeneous system

(8.11) $$x_1 c_1 + \cdots + x_n c_n = 0,$$

$x_0 + x$ is a solution of (8.10) and all solutions of (8.10) can be expressed in this form.

Proof.   Suppose first that $x = \langle \alpha_1, \cdots, \alpha_n \rangle$ is a solution of the homogeneous system and that $x_0 = \langle \alpha_1^{(0)}, \cdots, \alpha_n^{(0)} \rangle$ is a solution of (8.10). Then we have:

(8.12) $$\alpha_1^{(0)} c_1 + \cdots + \alpha_n^{(0)} c_n = b$$

and

$$\alpha_1 c_1 + \cdots + \alpha_n c_n = 0.$$

Adding these equations, we obtain

$$(\alpha_1^{(0)} + \alpha_1) c_1 + \cdots + (\alpha_n^{(0)} + \alpha_n) c_n = b,$$

which asserts that $x_0 + x$ is a solution of (8.10).

Now let $y = \langle \beta_1, \cdots, \beta_n \rangle$ be an arbitrary solution of (8.10), so that we have

(8.13) $$\beta_1 c_1 + \cdots + \beta_n c_n = b.$$

Subtracting (8.12) from (8.13), we obtain

$$(\beta_1 - \alpha_1^{(0)}) c_1 + \cdots + (\beta_n - \alpha_n^{(0)}) c_n = 0.$$

This asserts that $u = y - x_0$ is a solution of the homogeneous system, and we have

$$y = x_0 + u$$

as required. This completes the proof.

As an illustration of this theorem, let us return to the system

$$3x_1 - x_2 + x_3 = 1$$
$$x_1 + x_2 - x_3 = 2,$$

considered at the beginning of the section. There we observed that

$$\langle \tfrac{3}{4}, 0, -\tfrac{5}{4} \rangle$$

is a solution, as is easily derived by putting the column vectors c_1, c_3, and $b = \langle 1, 2 \rangle$ in echelon form. Another solution is obtained by putting c_1, c_2, and b in echelon form. This solution is

$$\langle \tfrac{3}{4}, \tfrac{5}{4}, 0 \rangle.$$

Theorem (8.9) tells us that the difference of these solutions must be a solution of the homogeneous system

$$3x_1 - x_2 + x_3 = 0$$
$$x_1 + x_2 - x_3 = 0.$$

The difference is $\langle 0, \tfrac{5}{4}, \tfrac{5}{4} \rangle$, and is a solution of the homogeneous system.

Thus the problem of finding all solutions of a nonhomogeneous system comes down to finding one solution of the nonhomogeneous system, and solving a homogeneous system. We shall show how to solve homogeneous systems in the next section, and content ourselves here with a few preliminary remarks.

(8.14)   Theorem.   *The set S of all solution vectors of a homogeneous system $x_1 c_1 + \cdots + x_n c_n = 0$ forms a subspace of R_n.*

Proof.   Let $a = \langle \lambda_1, \cdots, \lambda_n \rangle$ and $b = \langle \mu_1, \cdots, \mu_n \rangle$ belong to S. Then we have

$$\lambda_1 c_1 + \cdots + \lambda_n c_n = 0, \qquad \mu_1 c_1 + \cdots + \mu_n c_n = 0.$$

Adding these equations, we obtain

$$(\lambda_1 + \mu_1)c_1 + \cdots + (\lambda_n + \mu_n)c_n = 0,$$

which shows that $a + b \in S$. If $\lambda \in R$, then we have also

$$\lambda(\lambda_1 c_1 + \cdots + \lambda_n c_n) = (\lambda\lambda_1)c_1 + \cdots + (\lambda\lambda_n)c_n = 0$$

and $\lambda a \in S$. This completes the proof.

From this theorem and the results of the preceding sections, we will know all solutions of a homogeneous system as soon as we find a basis for the *solution space*, that is, the set of solutions of the system.

EXERCISES

1. Test for solvability of the following systems of equations, and if solvable, find a solution:

a. $x_1 + x_2 + x_3 = 8.$
  $\quad x_1 + x_2 + x_4 = 1.$
  $\quad x_1 + x_3 + x_4 = 14.$
  $\quad x_2 + x_3 + x_4 = 14.$

b. $x_1 + x_2 - x_3 = 3.$
  $\quad x_1 - 3x_2 + 2x_3 = 1.$
  $\quad 2x_1 - 2x_2 + x_3 = 4.$

c. $x_1 + x_2 - 5x_3 = -1.$

d. $2x_1 + x_2 + 3x_3 - x_4 = 1.$
  $\quad 3x_1 + x_2 - 2x_3 + x_4 = 0.$
  $\quad 2x_1 + x_2 - x_3 + 2x_4 = -1.$

e. $-x_1 + x_2 \quad\quad + x_4 = 0.$
  $\quad\quad x_2 + x_3 \quad\quad = 1.$

f. $x_1 + 2x_2 + 4x_3 = 1.$
  $\quad 2x_1 + x_2 + 5x_3 = 0.$
  $\quad 3x_1 - x_2 + 5x_3 = 0.$

g. $3x_1 + 4x_2 = -1.$
  $\quad -x_1 - x_2 = 1.$
  $\quad x_1 - 2x_2 = 0.$
  $\quad 2x_1 + 3x_2 = 0.$

2. For what values of α does the following system of equations have a solution?

$$3x_1 - x_2 + \alpha x_3 = 1$$
$$3x_1 - x_2 + x_3 = 5$$

3. Prove that a system of m homogeneous equations in $n > m$ unknowns always has a nontrivial solution.

4. Prove that a system of homogeneous equations $x_1 c_1 + \cdots + x_n c_n$ in n unknowns has a nontrivial solution if and only if the rank of the coefficient matrix is less than n.

9. SYSTEMS OF HOMOGENEOUS EQUATIONS

In Section 8 we showed that the problem of solving a nonhomogeneous system was reduced to solving a homogeneous system and that the set of solutions of a homogeneous system of m equations in n unknowns is a subspace of R_n. The system will be solved if we give a method of finding a basis of the solution space, for then the set of all solutions will be precisely the set of linear combinations of the basis vectors. The whole question is settled by the following theorem.

(9.1)   Theorem. *Let*

$$\alpha_{11}x_1 + \cdots + \alpha_{1n}x_n = 0$$
$$\cdots\cdots\cdots\cdots\cdots\cdots$$
$$\cdots\cdots\cdots\cdots\cdots\cdots$$
$$\cdots\cdots\cdots\cdots\cdots\cdots$$
$$\alpha_{m1}x_1 + \cdots + \alpha_{mn}x_n = 0$$

be a homogeneous system of m equations in n unknowns, with column vectors $c_1, \cdots, c_n$ arranged such that, for some r, $\{c_1, \cdots, c_r\}$ is a basis for the subspace $S(c_1, \cdots, c_n)$. Then for each i, if $r + 1 \le i \le n$, there exists a relation of linear dependence

$$\lambda_1^{(i)}c_1 + \cdots + \lambda_r^{(i)}c_r - c_i = 0, \qquad \lambda_j^{(i)} \in R.$$

Then for $r + 1 \le i \le n$

$$u_i = \langle \lambda_1^{(i)}, \cdots, \lambda_r^{(i)}, 0, \cdots, 0, \underbrace{-1}_{i}, 0, \cdots, 0 \rangle$$

(where it is to be understood that the -1 appears in the ith position in u_i) is a solution of the system, and $\{u_{r+1}, \cdots, u_n\}$ is a basis for the solution space of the system.

Proof. By Theorem (7.14) it is indeed possible to select a basis for $S(c_1, \cdots, c_n)$ from among the vectors $c_1, \cdots, c_n$ themselves. Rearranging the indices so that these vectors occupy the $1, \cdots, r$th positions changes the solution space only in that a corresponding change of position has been made in the components of the solution vectors.

Since $\{c_1, \cdots, c_r\}$ forms a basis for $S(c_1, \cdots, c_n)$, each vector c_i where $r + 1 \le i \le n$ is a linear combination of the basis vectors, and we have a relation of linear dependence

$$\lambda_1^{(i)}c_1 + \cdots + \lambda_r^{(i)}c_r - c_i = 0, \qquad \lambda_j^{(i)} \in R, \quad r + 1 \le i \le n,$$

as in the statement of the theorem.

As we saw in Formula (8.4), the vectors

$$u_i = \langle \lambda_1^{(i)}, \cdots, \lambda_r^{(i)}, \cdots, -1, \cdots, 0 \rangle, \qquad r + 1 \le i \le n,$$

with the -1 in the ith position of u_i, are solutions of the system. It remains to show that the $\{u_i\}$ are linearly independent, and that they generate the solution space.

To show that they are linearly independent, suppose we have a possible relation of linear dependence:

(9.2) $$\mu_{r+1}u_{r+1} + \cdots + \mu_n u_n = 0, \quad \text{for } \mu_i \in R.$$

The left side is a vector in R_n all of whose components are zero. For $r + 1 \leq i \leq n$, the ith component of (9.2) is $-\mu_i$ (Why?), and it follows that $\mu_{r+1} = \cdots = \mu_n = 0$. Now let $x = \langle \alpha_1, \cdots, \alpha_n \rangle$ be an arbitrary solution of the original system. From the definition of $u_{r+1}, \cdots, u_n$, we have

$$x + \sum_{k=r+1}^{m} \alpha_k u_k = \langle \xi_1, \cdots, \xi_r, 0, \cdots, 0 \rangle$$

where $\xi_1, \cdots, \xi_r$ are some elements of R. Since the set of solutions is a subspace of R_n, the vector $y = \langle \xi_1, \cdots, \xi_r, 0, \cdots, 0 \rangle$ is a solution of the original system and we have, by (8.4),

$$\xi_1 c_1 + \cdots + \xi_r c_r + 0 c_{r+1} + \cdots + 0 c_n = 0.$$

Since $c_1, \cdots, c_r$ are linearly independent, we have $\xi_1 = \cdots = \xi_r = 0$ and hence

$$x = \sum_{k=r+1}^{m} (-\alpha_k) u_k \in S(u_{r+1}, \cdots, u_n).$$

This completes the proof of the theorem.

(9.3) Corollary. *The dimension of the solution space of a homogeneous system in n unknowns is $n - r$, where r is the rank of the coefficient matrix.*

This result is immediate from our definition of the rank as the dimension of the column space of the coefficient matrix.

REMARKS AND EXAMPLE.   We wish to emphasize that Theorem (9.1) is a good theorem in the sense that each step in the proof can be carried out in a particular case by the computational procedures developed earlier in this chapter. Specifically, we have a method of finding the dimension of the space $S(c_1, \cdots, c_n)$—that of putting $c_1, \cdots, c_n$ in echelon form; and when we have found the dimension of the column space we can find by trial and error a subset of $\{c_1, \cdots, c_n\}$ containing the correct number of linearly independent vectors. We know that these form a basis for $S(c_1, \cdots, c_n)$ (Why?). Finally, the problem of finding the solution vector u_i is solved by putting $c_1, \cdots, c_r, c_i$ in echelon form and keeping track of the result. For example, let us solve the system

$$3x_1 - 2x_2 + x_3 - x_4 = 0$$
$$x_1 + x_2 + x_3 + x_4 = 0$$

with column vectors

$$c_1 = \begin{pmatrix} 3 \\ 1 \end{pmatrix}, \quad c_2 = \begin{pmatrix} -2 \\ 1 \end{pmatrix}, \quad c_3 = \begin{pmatrix} 1 \\ 1 \end{pmatrix}, \quad c_4 = \begin{pmatrix} -1 \\ 1 \end{pmatrix}.$$

Since $S(c_1, c_2, c_3, c_4) \subset R_2$, and since c_1 and c_2 are linearly independent, $\{c_1, c_2\}$ forms a basis for the column space (Why?). Putting c_1, c_2, c_3 in echelon form we obtain

$$2c_1 + 3c_2 = \begin{pmatrix} 0 \\ 5 \end{pmatrix},$$

$$c_1 - 3c_3 = \begin{pmatrix} 0 \\ -2 \end{pmatrix},$$

$$2(2c_1 + 3c_2) = -5(c_1 - 3c_3),$$

which gives us

$$-9c_1 - 6c_2 + 15c_3 = 0.$$

Thus one solution is

$$u_3 = \langle -9, -6, 15, 0 \rangle,$$

which could be normalized in the form of the u_i in Theorem (9.1) by multiplying by $-1/15$. Putting c_1, c_2, c_4 in echelon form, we obtain

$$c_1 + 3c_4 = \begin{pmatrix} 0 \\ 4 \end{pmatrix}$$

and

$$5(c_1 + 3c_4) = 4(2c_1 + 3c_2).$$

This gives us, for the second solution,

$$u_4 = \langle -3, -12, 0, 15 \rangle.$$

By Theorem (9.1), $\{u_3, u_4\}$ is a basis for the solution space.

We shall now apply our result to derive a useful and unexpected result about the rank of a matrix

$$\mathbf{A} = \begin{pmatrix} \alpha_{11} & \cdots & \alpha_{1n} \\ \cdots\cdots\cdots\cdots \\ \cdots\cdots\cdots\cdots \\ \cdots\cdots\cdots\cdots \\ \alpha_{m1} & \cdots & \alpha_{mn} \end{pmatrix}$$

with columns $c_1, \cdots, c_n$ and rows $r_1, \cdots, r_m$. Let us define the *row rank* of $\mathbf{A}$ as the dimension of the row space $S(r_1, \cdots, r_m)$. Some writers call the rank as we have defined it the "column rank" but, as the next theorem shows, the row rank and the column rank are always equal.

With the matrix $\mathbf{A}$, let us consider the homogeneous system

$$
\begin{aligned}
\alpha_{11}x_1 + \cdots + \alpha_{1n}x_n &= 0 \\
&\cdots \\
&\cdots \\
&\cdots \\
\alpha_{m1}x_1 + \cdots + \alpha_{mn}x_n &= 0
\end{aligned}
$$

(9.4)

It is convenient for this proof and for some arguments in the next section to use the notation

$$r_i \cdot x = \alpha_{i1}x_1 + \cdots + \alpha_{in}x_n$$

for the two vectors r_i and x, so that the system (9.4) can be described also by the system of equations

$$
\begin{aligned}
r_1 \cdot x &= 0 \\
&\cdots \\
&\cdots \\
&\cdots \\
r_m \cdot x &= 0
\end{aligned}
$$

(9.5)

The "inner product" $r \cdot x$ has the property that

(9.6) $(\lambda r + \mu s) \cdot x = \lambda(r \cdot x) + \mu(s \cdot x),$ for λ and $\mu \in R,$
and for r and $s \in R_n.$

(9.7)   **Theorem.**   *The row rank of an m-by-n matrix $\mathbf{A}$ is equal to the rank of $\mathbf{A}$.*

Proof.   We shall use the notations we have just introduced. Now, without changing the column rank we may assume that $\{r_1, \cdots, r_t\}$ forms a basis for the row space of $\mathbf{A}$, where t is the row rank of $\mathbf{A}$. Then from (9.6) it follows easily that the system of equations

$$
\begin{aligned}
r_1 \cdot x &= 0 \\
&\cdots \\
&\cdots \\
&\cdots \\
r_t \cdot x &= 0
\end{aligned}
$$

(9.8)

has the same solution space as (9.5). To see this, it is sufficient to prove that any solution x of (9.8) is a solution of (9.5). For $t + 1 \leq i \leq m,$ we have

$$r_i = \xi_1 r_1 + \cdots + \xi_t r_t, \qquad \xi_j \in R.$$

Then, by (9.6),

$$r_i \cdot x = \sum_{k=1}^{t} \xi_k (r_k \cdot x) = 0$$

since x is a solution of (9.8), and our assertion is proved.

The columns of the matrix $\mathbf{A}'$ whose rows are $r_1, \cdots, r_t$ are in R_t; hence

$$\operatorname{rank} \mathbf{A}' \leq t$$

and

$$n - \operatorname{rank} \mathbf{A}' \geq n - t.$$

Since (9.6) and (9.8) have the same solution space, we have by Corollary (9.3)

$$n - \operatorname{rank} \mathbf{A} = n - \operatorname{rank} \mathbf{A}' \geq n - t,$$

and hence rank $\mathbf{A} \leq t$. Interchanging the rows and columns of $\mathbf{A}$, we obtain an n-by-m matrix $\mathbf{A}^*$; repeating the argument with $\mathbf{A}^*$, we have rank $\mathbf{A}^* \leq$ row rank of $\mathbf{A}^*$. But rank $\mathbf{A}^* = t$ and row rank $\mathbf{A}^* =$ rank $\mathbf{A}$. Combining our results, we have

$$\operatorname{rank} \mathbf{A} = \operatorname{row\ rank} \mathbf{A}$$

and Theorem (9.7) is proved.

Finally we remark that the theorems and proofs in Sections 8 and 9 are valid for systems of equations and matrices with coefficients in an arbitrary field F, since only the field properties of R were used in the discussion.

EXERCISES

1. Find a basis for the solution space of the system

$$\begin{aligned} 3x_1 - x_2 \quad\ + x_4 &= 0 \\ x_1 + x_2 + x_3 + x_4 &= 0. \end{aligned}$$

2. Find bases for the solution spaces of the homogeneous systems associated with the systems given in Exercise 1 of Section 8.

3. Describe all solutions of the system

$$\begin{aligned} -x_1 + 2x_2 + x_3 + 4x_4 &= 0 \\ 2x_1 + x_2 - x_3 + x_4 &= 1. \end{aligned}$$

4. In plane analytic geometry, given two points, such as (3, 1) and (−1, 0), a method is given for finding an equation

$$Ax + By + C = 0$$

such that both points are solutions of the equation. Show that this problem is equivalent to solving the homogeneous system

$$A \begin{pmatrix} 3 \\ -1 \end{pmatrix} + B \begin{pmatrix} 1 \\ 0 \end{pmatrix} + C \begin{pmatrix} 1 \\ 1 \end{pmatrix} = 0,$$

to find a nontrivial solution. Prove that if $\langle A', B', C' \rangle$ is another nontrivial solution, then $\langle A', B', C' \rangle$ is a scalar multiple of the first solution $\langle A, B, C \rangle$.

5. With reference to Exercise 4, let (α, β) and (γ, δ) be distinct points in the plane. Prove that there exist real numbers A, B, C, not all zero, such that both points satisfy the equation

$$Ax + By + C = 0,$$

and that if both points also satisfy

$$A'x + B'y + C' = 0,$$

then $\langle A', B', C' \rangle = \lambda \langle A, B, C \rangle$ $\lambda \in R$. A *line* in R_2 is defined as the set of solutions of an equation $Ax + By + C = 0$. Show that the above result proves that two distinct points in R_2 lie on a unique line.

10. LINEAR MANIFOLDS *

In this section we shall apply the results of Sections 7 to 9 to a discussion of the generalizations in R_n of lines and planes in two and three dimensions.

We define a *line* in R_n as a one-dimensional subspace $S(a)$ or, more generally, a translate $b + S(a)$ of a one-dimensional subspace by some fixed vector b. Thus a vector p belongs to the line $b + S(a)$ if, for some $\lambda \in R$ (see Figure 2.2),

$$p = b + \lambda a.$$

---

* This section is optional. For an elegant presentation of the material of this section, and the whole connection between geometry and linear algebra, see the book by Gruenberg and Weir listed in the Bibliography.

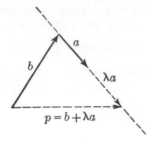

Figure 2.2

By analogy we might then define a *plane* in R_n as a two-dimensional subspace $S \subset R_n$ or, more generally, a translate $b + S$ of a two-dimensional space S by a fixed vector b. If $\{a_1, a_2\}$ is a basis of S, then $p \in b + S$ if and only if (see Figure 2.3),

$$p = b + \lambda_1 a_1 + \lambda_2 a_2, \qquad \lambda_i \in R.$$

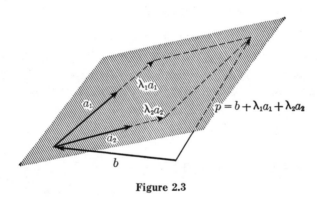

Figure 2.3

The general concept we are looking for is the following generalization of the concept of subspace.

(10.1) Definition. A *linear manifold* V in R_n is the set of all vectors in $b + S$, where b is a fixed vector and S is a fixed subspace of R_n. Thus $p \in V$ if and only if $p = b + a$ for some $a \in S$. The subspace S is called the *directing space* of V. The *dimension* of V is the dimension of the subspace S.

(10.2) Theorem. *Let $V = b + S$ be a linear manifold in R_n; then the directing space of V is the set of all vectors $p - q$ where $p, q \in V$.*

Proof.   Let p, $q \in V$; then there exist vectors a, $a' \in S$ such that

$$p = b + a, \qquad q = b + a'.$$

Then

$$p - q = (b + a) - (b + a') = a - a' \in S.$$

On the other hand, if $a \in S$, then $a = b - (b - a)$, so that $a = p - q$ where $p = b$ and $q = b - a$ both belong to V. This completes the proof.

This theorem shows that the directing space of $V = b + S$ is determined independently of the vector b.

We know that lines and planes in R_2 and R_3 are also described as the sets of solutions of certain linear equations. The definition of a linear manifold $V = b + S$ suggests that a linear manifold can be described by equations in the general case. From Section 8 we know that vectors in $b + S$ have the form we obtained for the solutions of a nonhomogeneous system of linear equations, where b is the particular solution and S is the solution space of the associated homogeneous system.

In working out this idea we begin by indicating how to describe a subspace S by a system of linear equations.

(10.3)   Lemma.   *Let S be an r-dimensional subspace of R_n; then there exists a set of $n - r$ homogeneous linear equations in n unknowns whose solution space is exactly S.*

REMARK.   No set of less than $n - r$ equations can have S as solution space. Why?

Proof of Lemma (10.3).   Let $\{b_1, \cdots, b_r\}$ be a basis for S. The only system of equations which are possibly relevant to the problem is [in the notation of (9.5)]:

(10.4)

$$
\begin{aligned}
b_1 \cdot x &= 0 \\
&\cdots \\
&\cdots \\
&\cdots \\
b_r \cdot x &= 0
\end{aligned}
$$

But these obviously do not solve the problem, since it may happen (and usually does) that, say, $b_1 \cdot b_1 \neq 0$, so that b_1 is not, in general, a solution vector of (10.4). Let S^* be the solution space of (10.4). By (9.7) the rank of the matrix whose rows are $b_1, \cdots, b_r$ is r; hence

S^* has dimension $n - r$, by (9.3). Let $\{c_1, \cdots, c_{n-r}\}$ be a basis for S^* and consider the system of equations

$$c_1 \cdot x = 0$$
$$\cdots\cdots\cdots$$
$$\cdots\cdots\cdots$$
$$c_{n-r} \cdot x = 0$$

By the same reasoning, the solution space S^{**} of this system has dimension r and, clearly, $S \subset S^{**}$ (Why?). Since dim $S = r$, we have by Exercise 7 of Section 7 the result that $S = S^{**}$, and the lemma is proved.

REMARK.   Note that our computational procedures in Sections 7 to 9 can be applied to carrying out each of the steps in the proof of Lemma (10.3). For example, let us find a system of equations whose solution space in R_4 has a basis consisting of the vectors $b_1 = \langle 1, 1, 0, 1 \rangle$ and $b_2 = \langle 1, 0, 1, 1, \rangle$. Letting x denote $\langle x_1, x_2, x_3, x_4 \rangle$, we form the system

(10.5)
$$b_1 \cdot x = 0$$
$$b_2 \cdot x = 0.$$

The column vectors of the system are

$$c_1 = \langle 1, 1 \rangle, \qquad c_2 = \langle 1, 0 \rangle, \qquad c_3 = \langle 0, 1 \rangle, \qquad c_4 = \langle 1, 1 \rangle.$$

By inspection a basis for the solution space of the system (10.5) is

$$\langle 1, 0, 0, -1 \rangle$$
$$\langle -1, 1, 1, 0 \rangle,$$

and according to Lemma (10.3), the desired system of equations is

$$x_1 \qquad\qquad - x_4 = 0$$
$$-x_1 + x_2 + x_3 \qquad = 0.$$

The next result completes our geometrical interpretation of systems of linear equations.

(10.6)   Theorem. *A necessary and sufficient condition for a set of vectors $V \subset R_n$ to form a linear manifold of dimension r is that V be the set of all solutions of a system of $n - r$ nonhomogeneous equations in n unknowns whose coefficient matrix has rank $n - r$.*

Proof.   First let

$$x_1 c_1 + \cdots + x_n c_n = b, \qquad c_i \in R_{n-r}$$

be a system of $n - r$ equations in n unknowns whose coefficient matrix has rank $n - r$. By Theorem (8.9) the set V of all solutions is a linear manifold $x_0 + S$ where S is the solution space of the homogeneous system $x_1 c_1 + \cdots + x_n c_n = 0$. By Corollary (9.3), dim $S = n - (n - r)$ and hence dim $V = r$.

To prove the converse, let $V = y + S$ be a linear manifold of dimension r. By Lemma (10.3) there exists a system of $n - r$ equations whose solution space is S:

$$x_1 c_1 + \cdots + x_n c_n = 0.$$

If $y = \langle \eta_1, \cdots, \eta_n \rangle$, let

$$b = \eta_1 c_1 + \cdots + \eta_n c_n.$$

Then the nonhomogeneous system $x_1 c_1 + \cdots + x_n c_n = b$ has for its solutions exactly the set $y + S = V$. This completes the proof of the theorem.

For example, let us find a system of equations for the linear manifold V whose directing space S has a basis

$$b_1 = \langle 1, 1, 0, 1 \rangle \quad \text{and} \quad b_2 = \langle 1, 0, 1, 1 \rangle,$$

and contains the vector $\langle 1, 2, 3, 4 \rangle$. As we showed in the first example in this section, S is a solution space of the system

$$\begin{aligned} x_1 \qquad\quad - x_4 &= 0 \\ -x_1 + x_2 + x_3 \qquad &= 0. \end{aligned}$$

As in the proof of Theorem (10.6), we substitute the vector $\langle 1, 2, 3, 4 \rangle$ in the system to obtain

$$\begin{aligned} 1 \qquad\quad - 4 &= -3 \\ -1 + 2 + 3 \qquad &= 4. \end{aligned}$$

Then the equations whose solutions form the linear manifold V are

$$\begin{aligned} x_1 \qquad\quad - x_4 &= -3 \\ -x_1 + x_2 + x_3 \qquad &= 4, \end{aligned}$$

by Theorem (10.6).

EXERCISES

1. Find a set of homogeneous linear equations whose solution space is generated by the vectors:
   a. $\langle 2, 1, -3 \rangle$, $\langle 1, -1, 0 \rangle$, $\langle 1, 3, -4 \rangle$;
   b. $\langle 2, 1, 1, -1 \rangle$, $\langle -1, 1, 0, 4 \rangle$, $\langle 1, 1, 2, 1 \rangle$.

2. Find a set of homogeneous equations whose solution space S is generated by the vectors $\langle 3, -1, 1, 2 \rangle$, $\langle 4, -1, -2, 3 \rangle$, $\langle 10, -3, 0, 7 \rangle$, $\langle -1, 1, -7, 0 \rangle$. Find a system of nonhomogeneous equations whose set of solutions is the linear manifold with directing space S and which passes through $\langle 1, 1, 1, 1 \rangle$.

3. A *hyperplane* is a linear manifold of dimension $n - 1$ in R_n. Prove that a linear manifold is a hyperplane if and only if it is the set of solutions of a single linear equation $\alpha_1 x_1 + \cdots + \alpha_n x_n = \beta$, with some $\alpha_i \neq 0$. Prove that a linear manifold of dimension r is the intersection of exactly $n - r$ hyperplanes.

4. A *line* is defined as a one-dimensional linear manifold in R_n. Prove that if p and q are distinct vectors belonging to a line L, then L consists of all vectors of the form

$$p + \lambda(q - p), \qquad \lambda \in R.$$

5. Prove that a line in R_n is the intersection of $n - 1$ hyperplanes. Find a system of linear equations whose set of solutions is the line passing through the points:
   a. $p = \langle 1, 1 \rangle$, $q = \langle 2, -1 \rangle$ in R_2;
   b. $p = \langle 1, 1, 2 \rangle$, $q = \langle -1, 2, -1 \rangle$ in R_3;
   c. $p = \langle 1, -1, 0, 2 \rangle$, $q = \langle 2, 0, 1, 1 \rangle$ in R_4.

6. Find two distinct vectors on the line belonging to the intersection of the hyperplanes:

$$x_1 + 2x_2 - x_3 = -1, \qquad 2x_1 + x_2 + 4x_3 = 2 \text{ in } R_3;$$
$$x_1 + x_2 = 0, \qquad x_2 - x_3 = 0, \qquad x_2 - 2x_4 = 0 \text{ in } R_4.$$

7. Prove that, if p and q are vectors belonging to a linear manifold V, then the line through p and q is contained in V.

8. Let S and T be subspaces of R_n, which are represented as the solution spaces of homogeneous systems

$$a_1 \cdot x = 0, \quad \cdots, \quad a_r \cdot x = 0$$

and

$$b_1 \cdot x = 0, \quad \cdots, \quad b_s \cdot x = 0$$

respectively. Prove that $S \cap T$ is the solution space of the system

$$a_1 \cdot x = 0, \quad \cdots, \quad a_r \cdot x = 0, \qquad b_1 \cdot x = 0, \quad \cdots, \quad b_s \cdot x = 0.$$

Use this remark to find a basis for $S \cap T$, where S and T are as in Exercise 11 of Section 7.

9. Let $S_1 = S(e_1, e_2, e_3)$ in R_4, where $e_1 = \langle 1, 0, 0, 0 \rangle$, $e_2 = \langle 0, 1, 0, 0 \rangle$, and $e_3 = \langle 0, 0, 1, 0 \rangle$. Let $S_2 = S(a_1, a_2, a_3)$, where $a_1 = \langle 1, 1, 0, 1 \rangle$,

$a_2 = \langle 2, -1, 3, -1 \rangle$, $a_3 = \langle -1, 0, 0, 2 \rangle$. Find dim $(S_1 + S_2)$, dim $(S_1 \cap S_2)$. Find a basis for $S_1 \cap S_2$.

10. Find the point in R_3 where the line joining the points $\langle 1, -1, 0 \rangle$ and $\langle -2, 1, 1 \rangle$ pierces the plane

$$3x_1 - x_2 + x_3 - 1 = 0.$$

CHAPTER 3

LINEAR TRANSFORMATIONS and MATRICES

In order to compare different mathematical systems of the same type, it is essential to study the functions from one system to another which preserve the operations of the system. Thus in calculus we study functions f which preserve the limit operation: if $\lim_{i \to \infty} x_i = x$, then $\lim_{i \to \infty} f(x_i) = f(x)$. These are the continuous functions. For vector spaces, we investigate functions that preserve the vector space operations of addition and scalar multiplication. These are the linear transformations. In this chapter we develop the language of linear transformations and the connection between linear transformations and matrices. Deeper results about linear transformations appear later.

11. LINEAR TRANSFORMATIONS

In this section, F denotes an arbitrary field.

(11.1) Definition. Let V and W be vector spaces over F. A *linear transformation of V into W* is a function $T: V \to W$ which assigns to each vector $v \in V$ a unique vector $w = T(v) \in W$ such that

mapping

$$T(v_1 + v_2) = T(v_1) + T(v_2), \qquad v_i \in V,$$
$$T(\alpha v) = \alpha T(v), \qquad \alpha \in F, \quad v \in V.$$

$\alpha \circ T(v)$

We shall often use the notation Tv instead of $T(v)$, in order to avoid a forest of parentheses.

We first consider some examples of linear transformations.

EXAMPLE A.   A system of linear equations

$$y_1 = \alpha_{11}x_1 + \cdots + \alpha_{1n}x_n$$

(11.2)

$$\vdots$$

$$y_m = \alpha_{m1}x_1 + \cdots + \alpha_{mn}x_n$$

with $\alpha_{ij} \in F$, can be regarded in two ways. In Chapter 2, we assumed $\{y_1, \cdots, y_m\}$ to be given, and asked how to solve for $\{x_1, \cdots, x_n\}$. This operation, however, is not a function, because the solution $\{x_1, \cdots, x_n\}$ is not uniquely determined by $\{y_1, \cdots, y_m\}$. For example both $\langle 1, -1 \rangle$ and $\langle 2, -2 \rangle$ are solutions of the equation $x_1 + x_2 = y$, when $y = 0$. On the other hand, we may think of $\langle y_1, \cdots, y_m \rangle$ as a function of $\langle x_1, \cdots, x_n \rangle$, for a given coefficient matrix $\mathbf{A} = (\alpha_{ij})$. Thus the equation

$$x_1 + x_2 = y$$

defines a function of $R_2 \to R_1$, namely, the function $T: \langle \alpha_1, \alpha_2 \rangle \to \langle \alpha_1 + \alpha_2 \rangle$. For example $\langle 2, -3 \rangle \to \langle -1 \rangle$, $\langle 1, 1 \rangle \to \langle 2 \rangle$, $\langle 1, -1 \rangle \to \langle 0 \rangle$.

In general, the system (11.2) defines a function T from F_n into F_m, which assigns to each n-tuple $\langle x_1, \cdots, x_n \rangle$ in R_n the m-tuple $\langle y_1, \cdots, y_m \rangle$ in R_m. We leave it to the reader to verify that the function defined by a system (11.2), with a fixed coefficient matrix, is always a linear transformation of $F_n \to F_m$.

EXAMPLE B.   Let f be a continuous real valued function on the real numbers. Then the rule which assigns to f the integral $I(f) = \int_0^1 f(t)\, dt$ is a linear transformation from the vector space $C[R]$ into the vector space R_1 [see Example (5.4)]. This fact is expressed by the rules

$$I(f_1 + f_2) = I(f_1) = I(f_2),$$
$$I(\alpha f) = \alpha I(f),$$

for $f_1, f_2, f \in C[R]$ and $\alpha \in R$.

EXAMPLE C.   Let $P[R]$ be the vector space of polynomial functions defined on R [see (5.5)]. Then the derivative function D, which assigns to each polynomial function its derivative, is a linear transformation of $P[R] \rightarrow P[R]$. We have to check that the derivative of a polynomial function is a polynomial function, and that the conditions

$$D(f_1 + f_2) = D(f_1) + D(f_2)$$
$$D(\alpha f) = \alpha(Df)$$

hold for all polynomial functions f_1, f_2, f and scalars α.

These illustrations show that some of the operations studied in the theory of linear equations, and in calculus, are all examples of linear transformations.

The importance of linear transformations comes partly from the fact that they can be combined by certain algebraic operations, and the resulting algebraic system has many properties not to be found in the other algebraic systems we have studied so far.*

(11.3) Definition.   Let F be an arbitrary field and let V and W be vector spaces over F. Let S and T be linear transformations of $V \rightarrow W$. Define a mapping $S + T$ of $V \rightarrow W$ by the rule

$$(S + T)v = S(v) + T(v), \qquad v \in V.$$

Then $S + T$ is a linear transformation of $V \rightarrow W$ called the *sum* of the linear transformations S and T.

(11.4) Definition.   Let M, N, P be vector spaces over F and let S be a linear transformation of $M \rightarrow N$ and T a linear transformation of $N \rightarrow P$; then the mapping $TS: M \rightarrow P$ defined by

$$(TS)(m) = T[S(m)]$$

is a linear transformation of $M \rightarrow P$ called the *product* of the linear transformations T and S.

(11.5) Theorem.   *Let V, W be vector spaces over F and let $L(V, W)$ denote the set of all linear transformations of V into W; then $L(V, W)$ is a vector space over F, with respect to the operations*

$$S + T, \qquad S, T \in L(V, W), \quad see \ Definition \ (11.3),$$

and

$$\alpha S, \qquad \alpha \in F, \quad S \in L(V, W),$$

where $(\alpha S)(v) = \alpha[S(v)]$.

Proof.   We check first that $S + T$ and αS actually belong to $L(V, W)$; the argument is simply a thorough workout with the axioms for a vector space. Let v_1, $v_2 \in V$; then

---

* At this point the reader should review some of the definitions concerning functions on sets in Section 3.

$$(S + T)(v_1 + v_2) = S(v_1 + v_2) + T(v_1 + v_2)$$
$$= [S(v_1) + S(v_2)] + [T(v_1) + T(v_2)]$$
$$= [S(v_1) + T(v_1)] + [S(v_2) + T(v_2)]$$
$$= (S + T)(v_1) + (S + T)(v_2).$$

For $\xi \in F$ we have

$$(S + T)(\xi v) = S(\xi v) + T(\xi v) = \xi[S(v)] + \xi[T(v)]$$
$$= \xi[S(v) + T(v)] = \xi[(S + T)(v)].$$

Turning to the mapping αS, we have

$$(\alpha S)(v_1 + v_2) = \alpha[S(v_1) + S(v_2)] = \alpha S(v_1) + \alpha S(v_2)$$

and, for $\xi \in F$,

$$(\alpha S)(\xi v) = \alpha[S(\xi v)] = \alpha[\xi S(v)]$$
$$= (\alpha \xi)S(v) = (\xi \alpha)S(v)$$
$$= \xi[(\alpha S)(v)],$$

since F satisfies the commutative law for multiplication.

The linear transformation 0, which sends each $v \in V$ into the zero vector, satisfies the condition that*

$$T + 0 = T, \qquad T \in L(V, W)$$

and the transformation $-T$, defined by

$$(-T)v - -T(v)$$

satisfies the condition that

$$T + (-T) = 0.$$

The verification of the other axioms is left to the reader.

The set of linear transformations of a vector space V into itself admits three operations: addition, scalar multiplication, and multiplication of linear transformations. The next result shows what algebraic properties these operations have.

(11.6) Theorem. *Let V be a vector space over F, and let S, $T \in L(V, V)$ and $\alpha \in F$; then*

$$S + T, \qquad ST, \qquad \alpha S$$

are all elements of $L(V, V)$. With respect to the operations $S + T$ and αS, $L(V, V)$ is a vector space. Moreover, $L(V, V)$ has the further properties:

$$S(TU) = (ST)U \qquad (associative\ law);$$

---

* The symbol 0 is given still another meaning, but the context will always indicate which meaning is intended.

there is a linear transformation 1 *called the* identity transformation *on V such that*

$$1v = v, \qquad v \in V$$

and

$$1T = T1 = T, \qquad T \in L(V, V).$$

Finally, we have the distributive laws

$$S(T + U) = ST + SU, \qquad (S + T)U = SU + TU.$$

Proof. Because the properties of $L(V, V)$ relative to the operations $S + T$ and αS were already described in the preceding theorem, it is sufficient to consider the properties of ST. First we check that ST is a linear transformation. For $v_1, v_2 \in V$ and $\alpha \in F$ we have

$$\begin{aligned}(ST)(v_1 + v_2) &= S[T(v_1 + v_2)] = S[T(v_1) + T(v_2)] \\ &= S[T(v_1)] + S[T(v_2)] = (ST)v_1 + (ST)v_2\end{aligned}$$

and

$$\begin{aligned}(ST)(\alpha v_1) &= S[T(\alpha v_1)] = S[\alpha T(v_1)] \\ &= \alpha\{S[T(v_1)]\} = \alpha[ST(v_1)].\end{aligned}$$

This completes the proof that $ST \in L(V, V)$. The same argument shows that TS in Definition (11.4) is a linear transformation.

Now let S, T, U be elements of $L(V, V)$. The associative and distributive laws are verified by checking that the transformations $S(TU)$ and $(ST)U$, for example, have the same effect on an arbitrary vector in V. Let $v \in V$; then

$$[S(TU)](v) = S[(TU)(v)] = S\{T[U(v)]\}$$

while

$$[(ST)U](v) = ST[U(v)] = S\{T[U(v)]\}.$$

Similarly,

$$\begin{aligned}[S(T + U)](v) &= S[(T + U)(v)] = S[T(v) + U(v)] \\ &= S[T(v)] + S[U(v)] = (ST + SU)(v)\end{aligned}$$

and

$$\begin{aligned}[(S + T)U](v) &= (S + T)U(v) = S[U(v)] + T[U(v)] \\ &= (SU)(v) + (TU)(v) = (SU + TU)(v).\end{aligned}$$

The properties of the identity transformation 1 are immediate. This completes the proof of the theorem.

The previous result leads to the following general concept.

(11.7) Definition. A *ring* $\mathcal{R}$ is a mathematical system consisting of a nonempty set $\mathcal{R} = \{a, b, \cdots\}$ together with two operations, addition and multiplication, each of which assigns to a pair of elements a and b in $\mathfrak{R}$ other elements of $\mathfrak{R}$, denoted by $a + b$ in the case of addition and ab in the case of multiplication, such that the following conditions hold for all a, b, c in $\mathfrak{R}$.

(1) $a + b = b + a$.

(2) $(a + b) + c = a + (b + c)$.

(3) There is an element 0 such that $a + 0 = a$ for all $a \in \mathfrak{R}$.

(4) For each $a \in \mathfrak{R}$ there is an element $-a$ such that $a + (-a) = 0$.

(5) $(ab)c = a(bc)$.

(6) $a(b + c) = ab + ac$, $(a + b)c = ac + bc$.

(7) If the commutative law for multiplication ($ab = ba$, for $a, b \in \mathfrak{R}$) holds, then $\mathfrak{R}$ is called a *commutative ring*.

Any field is a commutative ring; the integers Z form a commutative ring which is not a field. In the exercises at the end of this section, the reader is asked to show that the commutative law for multiplication does not hold in general for the linear transformations in $L(V, V)$. Theorem (11.6) now can be stated more concisely:

(11.6′)   Theorem. $L(V, V)$ *is a ring*.

It is worth checking to what extent the proofs of the ring axioms for $L(V, V)$ depend on the assumption that the elements are *linear* transformations. To make this question more precise, let $M(V, V)$ be the set of *all* functions $T: V \to V$ and define $S + T$ and ST as for linear transformations. It can easily be verified that all the axioms for a ring hold for $M(V, V)$, with the exception of the one distributive law

$$S(T + U) = ST + SU,$$

which actually fails for suitably chosen S, T, and U in $M(V, V)$.

The mapping $T: \langle \alpha, \beta \rangle \to \langle \beta, 0 \rangle$, for $\alpha, \beta \in R$, is a linear transformation of R_2 such that $T^2 = 0$. It is impossible for T to have a reciprocal $\hat{T}$ such that $T\hat{T} = 1$, since $T\hat{T} = 1$ implies

$$T(T\hat{T}) = T \cdot 1 = T,$$

while, because of the associative law,

$$T(T\hat{T}) = T^2\hat{T} = 0 \cdot \hat{T} = 0,$$

which produces the contradiction $T = 0$. Because of this phenomenon, it is necessary to make the following definition.

(11.8)   Definition.   A linear transformation $T \in L(V, V)$ is said to be *invertible* (or *nonsingular*) if there exists a linear transformation $T^{-1} \in L(V, V)$ (called the *inverse* of T) such that

$$TT^{-1} = T^{-1}T = 1.$$

An exercise at the end of this section shows that $TU = 1$ does not imply always that $UT = 1$; so, if T' is to be shown the inverse of T, both the equations $TT' = 1$ and $T'T = 1$ must be checked.

Some other properties of invertible transformations can be best understood from the viewpoint of the following definition.

(11.9) Definition.   A *group* G is a mathematical system consisting of a nonempty set G, together with one operation which assigns to each pair of elements S, T in G a third element ST in G, such that the following conditions are satisfied.

(1) $(ST)U = S(TU)$,   for S, T, $U \in G$.
(2) There is an element $1 \in G$ such that $S1 = 1S = S$ for all $S \in G$.
(3) For each $S \in G$ there is an element $S^{-1} \in G$ such that $SS^{-1} = S^{-1}S = 1$.

(11.10)   Theorem.   *Let G be the set of invertible linear transformations in $L(V, V)$; then G is a group.*

Proof.   In view of the definition of invertible linear transformation and what has already been proved about $L(V, V)$, it is only necessary to check that if S, $T \in G$ then $ST \in G$. We have

$$(ST)T^{-1}S^{-1} = S \cdot 1S^{-1} = 1,$$
$$T^{-1}S^{-1}(ST) = T^{-1} \cdot 1T = 1.$$

Hence $ST \in G$ and $T^{-1}S^{-1}$ is an inverse of ST.

The next theorem, on the uniqueness of T^{-1}, etc., holds for groups in general.

(11.11)   Theorem.   *Let G be an arbitrary group; then the equations*

$$AX = B, \qquad XA = B$$

have unique solutions $A^{-1}B$ and BA^{-1} respectively. In particular, $AX = 1$ implies that $X = A^{-1}$. Similarly, $XA = 1$ implies $X = A^{-1}$.

Proof.   We have

$$A(A^{-1}B) = (AA^{-1})B = 1B = B$$

and

$$(BA^{-1})A = B(A^{-1}A) = B \cdot 1 = B,$$

proving that solutions of the equations do exist. For the uniqueness, suppose that

$$AX' = B.$$

Then $A^{-1}(AX') = A^{-1}B$ and, since
$$A^{-1}(AX') = (A^{-1}A)X' = 1 \cdot X' = X',$$
we have $X' = A^{-1}B$. Similarly, $X'A = B$ implies $X' = BA^{-1}$. This completes the proof of the theorem.

Other important examples of groups will be considered in the next chapter.

EXERCISES

1. Which of the following mappings of $R_2 \to R_2$ are linear transformations?
  a. $\langle x_1, x_2 \rangle \to \langle y_1, y_2 \rangle$, where $y_1 = 3x_1 - x_2 + 1$ and $y_2 = -x_1 + 2x_2$.
  b. $\langle x_1, x_2 \rangle \to \langle y_1, y_2 \rangle$, where $y_1 = 3x_1 + x_2^2$ and $y_2 = -x_1$.
  c. $\langle x_1, x_2 \rangle \to \langle x_2, x_1 \rangle$.
  d. $\langle x_1, x_2 \rangle \to \langle x_1 + x_2, x_2 \rangle$.
  e. $\langle x_1, x_2 \rangle \to \langle 2x_1, x_2 \rangle$.

2. Verify that the function $T: F_n \to F_m$ described in Example A is a linear transformation.

3. Let T be the linear transformation of $F_2 \to F_2$ defined by the system
$$y_1 = -3x_1 + x_2$$
$$y_2 = x_1 - x_2$$
and let U be the linear transformation defined by the system
$$y_1 = x_1 + x_2$$
$$y_2 = x_1$$
Find a system of linear equations defining the linear transformations
$$2T, \quad T - U, \quad T^2, \quad TU, \quad UT, \quad T^2 + 2U.$$
Is $TU = UT$?

4. Let D be the linear transformation of the polynomial functions $P[R]$ defined by $Df = $ derivative of f. Let M be the mapping of $P[R] \to P[R]$ defined by $(Mf)(x) = xf(x)$. Is M a linear transformation of $P[R]$? Find the transformations $M + D, DM, MD$. Is $MD = DM$?

5. Let T be a linear transformation of V into W. Prove that $T(0) = 0$ and that $T(-v) = -T(v)$ for all $v \in V$. If S is a sub-

space of V, prove that $T(S)$, which consists of all vectors $\{Ts, s \in S\}$, is a subspace of W.

6. A linear transformation $T: V \to W$ is called an *isomorphism* if T is a one-to-one mapping of V onto W. Let V be a vector space over F with a basis $\{v_1, \cdots, v_n\}$. Then every vector in V can be expressed in one and only one way in the form $\xi_1 v_1 + \cdots + \xi_n v_n$, $\xi_i \in F$. Prove that the mapping T which assigns to $\xi_1 v_1 + \cdots + \xi_n v_n$ the vector $\langle \xi_1, \cdots, \xi_n \rangle$ in F_n, is an isomorphism of V onto F_n.

7. Prove that an invertible transformation in $L(V, V)$ is an isomorphism of V onto V.

8. Consider the linear transformations T and U of $R_2 \to R_2$ described by the systems of equations

$$T: \begin{aligned} y_1 &= x_1 + x_2 \\ y_2 &= x_1 - x_2 \end{aligned} \qquad U: \begin{aligned} y_1 &= -x_1 + 2x_2 \\ y_2 &= x_1 - 2x_2 \end{aligned}$$

Is T an isomorphism? Is U an isomorphism? What about TU?

9. Prove that in order for a linear transformation defined by a system of equations

$$y_i = \sum_{j=1}^{n} \alpha_{ij} x_j, \qquad i = 1, \cdots, m,$$

to be one-to-one, it is necessary and sufficient that the homogeneous system

$$\sum_{j=1}^{n} \alpha_{ij} x_j = 0, \qquad i = 1, \cdots, m$$

have only the trivial solution.

10. Test the linear transformations defined by the following systems of equations to determine whether they are one-to-one.

    a. $\begin{aligned} y_1 &= 3x_1 - x_2 \\ y_2 &= x_1 + x_2 \end{aligned}$

    b. $\begin{aligned} y_1 &= 3x_1 - x_2 + x_3 \\ y_2 &= -x_1 \qquad\;\; + 2x_3 \end{aligned}$

    c. $\begin{aligned} y_1 &= x_1 + 2x_2 \\ y_2 &= x_1 - x_2 \\ y_3 &= -2x_1 \end{aligned}$

    d. $\begin{aligned} y_1 &= x_1 \qquad\;\; - x_3 \\ y_2 &= x_1 + x_2 \\ y_3 &= -x_1 - 3x_2 - 2x_3 \end{aligned}$

e. $y_1 = \quad x_1 + 2x_2 + \quad x_3$
    $y_2 = \quad x_1 + \quad x_2$
    $y_3 = \qquad\qquad x_2 + \quad x_3$

11. Let T be a linear transformation from F_n into F_m defined by a system of equations

$$y_i = \sum_{j=1}^{n} \alpha_{ij}x_j, \qquad i = 1, 2, \cdots, m.$$

Prove that a vector w in F_m is the image $T(v)$ of some vector $v \in F$, if and only if w is a linear combination of the column vectors of the matrix of the system.

12. Using Exercise 11, prove that a linear transformation defined by a system of equations carries F_n onto F_m if and only if the rank of the coefficient matrix of the system is m.

13. Using Exercise 11, test the linear transformations given in Exercise 10 to decide which ones map F_n onto F_m.

14. Let T be a linear transformation of F_n into F_n defined by a system of linear equations

$$y_i = \sum_{j=1}^{n} \alpha_{ij}x_j, \qquad i = 1, 2, \cdots, n.$$

Prove that the following statements about T are equivalent.
a. T is one-to-one.
b. T is onto.
c. T is an isomorphism of F_n onto F_n.
d. T is an invertible linear transformation.

15. Let I be the linear transformation of $P[R] \rightarrow P[R]$ defined by

$$I(f) = \alpha_0 x + \frac{\alpha_1 x^2}{2} + \cdots + \frac{\alpha_k x^{k+1}}{k+1},$$

for a polynomial function $f(x) = \alpha_0 + \alpha_1 x + \cdots + \alpha_k x^k$. Let D be the derivative operation in $P[R]$. Show that $DI = 1$, but that neither D nor I are isomorphisms. Is D one-to-one? Onto? Answer the same questions for I.

12. ADDITION AND MULTIPLICATION OF MATRICES

In Section 11 we defined the operations of addition, multiplication by scalars, and multiplication of linear transformations. In this section the corresponding operations are defined for matrices. In Section 13 we shall relate linear transformations of arbitrary finite dimensional vector spaces with matrices; Section 12 can be regarded as an introduction to that discussion.

First of all there is no difficulty in defining the vector space operations on matrices; we simply treat m-by-n matrices as $m \cdot n$-tuples.

(12.1) Definition. Let $\mathbf{A} = (\alpha_{ij})$ and $\mathbf{B} = (\beta_{ij})$ be two m-by-n matrices with coefficients in a field F. The sum $\mathbf{A} + \mathbf{B}$ is defined to be the m-by-n matrix whose (i, j) entry is $\alpha_{ij} + \beta_{ij}$. If $\alpha \in F$, then $\alpha\mathbf{A}$ is the m-by-n matrix whose (i, j) entry is $\alpha\alpha_{ij}$.

We can now state the following result.

(12.2) Theorem. *The set of all m-by-n matrices with coefficients in F forms a vector space over F, with respect to the operations given in Definition (12.1).*

The proof is the same as the verification that F_n is a vector space and is omitted.

The definition of matrix multiplication is not as obvious. In order to start, let us consider a problem similar to one discussed in the problems in Section 11.

Let $T: R_2 \to R_3$ be the linear transformation

$$(12.3) \qquad \begin{aligned} y_1 &= x_1 + x_2 \\ y_2 &= -x_1 + x_2 \\ y_3 &= x_1 \end{aligned}$$

and let $U: R_3 \to R_3$ be the linear transformation

$$\begin{aligned} y_1 &= -x_1 + x_3 \\ y_2 &= x_1 + x_2 \\ y_3 &= -x_1 + 2x_3. \end{aligned}$$

The matrices associated with these systems of equations are

$$T \leftrightarrow \mathbf{A} = \begin{pmatrix} 1 & 1 \\ -1 & 1 \\ 1 & 0 \end{pmatrix}, \qquad U \leftrightarrow \mathbf{B} = \begin{pmatrix} -1 & 0 & 1 \\ 1 & 1 & 0 \\ -1 & 0 & 2 \end{pmatrix}.$$

The linear transformation UT maps R_2 into R_3. Let us work out the system of equations defining it.

If

$$T(x) = y, \qquad U(y) = z$$

then
$$UT(x) = U(y) = z.$$
Rewriting the system for U so that it carries $\{y_1, y_2, y_3\} \rightarrow \{z_1, z_2, z_3\}$ we have the system

$$
(12.4) \qquad U: \begin{aligned} z_1 &= -y_1 & &+ y_3 \\ z_2 &= y_1 + y_2 \\ z_3 &= -y_1 & &+ 2y_3 \end{aligned}
$$

Now we can substitute for $\{y_1, y_2, y_3\}$ using (12.3) to find the system associated with UT:

$$
(12.5) \qquad \begin{aligned} z_1 &= -(x_1 + x_2) + x_1 & &= -x_2 \\ z_2 &= (x_1 + x_2) + (-x_1 + x_2) &&= 2x_2 \\ z_3 &= -(x_1 + x_2) + 2x_1 && = x_1 - x_2 \end{aligned}
$$

which is associated with the matrix

$$
\mathbf{C} = \begin{pmatrix} 0 & -1 \\ 0 & 2 \\ 1 & -1 \end{pmatrix}.
$$

It is natural to define the matrix $\mathbf{C}$ to be the product of the matrices $\mathbf{B}$ and $\mathbf{A}$. Then the product UT of linear transformations will correspond to the product $\mathbf{BA}$ of the corresponding matrices.

In order to see how the product $\mathbf{C} = \mathbf{BA}$ is formed, let us write the equations (12.3) and (12.4) in the form

$$
\begin{aligned} y_1 &= \alpha_{11}x_1 + \alpha_{12}x_2 \\ y_2 &= \alpha_{21}x_1 + \alpha_{22}x_2 \\ y_3 &= \alpha_{31}x_1 + \alpha_{32}x_2 \end{aligned}
$$

and

$$
\begin{aligned} z_1 &= \beta_{11}y_1 + \beta_{12}y_2 + \beta_{13}y_3 \\ z_2 &= \beta_{21}y_1 + \beta_{22}y_2 + \beta_{23}y_3 \\ z_3 &= \beta_{31}y_1 + \beta_{32}y_2 + \beta_{33}y_3 \end{aligned}
$$

respectively. Then (12.5) becomes

$$
\begin{aligned} z_1 &= \beta_{11}(\alpha_{11}x_1 + \alpha_{12}x_2) + \beta_{12}(\alpha_{21}x_1 + \alpha_{22}x_2) + \beta_{13}(\alpha_{31}x_1 + \alpha_{32}x_2) \\ z_2 &= \beta_{21}(\alpha_{11}x_1 + \alpha_{12}x_2) + \beta_{22}(\alpha_{21}x_1 + \alpha_{22}x_2) + \beta_{23}(\alpha_{31}x_1 + \alpha_{32}x_2) \\ z_3 &= \beta_{31}(\alpha_{11}x_1 + \alpha_{12}x_2) + \beta_{32}(\alpha_{21}x_1 + \alpha_{22}x_2) + \beta_{33}(\alpha_{31}x_1 + \alpha_{32}x_2). \end{aligned}
$$

Then the entry in the $(1, 1)$ position of the product matrix $\mathbf{BA}$ may be obtained by taking the first row of $\mathbf{B}$ and the first column of $\mathbf{A}$, multiplying corresponding elements together, and adding. The other entries are seen to be obtained by the same process.

We can now make a formal definition.

(12.6)   **Definition.**   Let $\mathbf{B} = (\beta_{ij})$ be a q-by-n matrix (q rows and n columns) with coefficients in F, $\mathbf{A} = (\alpha_{kl})$ an n-by-m matrix. Then the product matrix $\mathbf{C} = \mathbf{BA}$ is defined to be the q-by-m matrix whose (i, j) entry γ_{ij} is given by

$$\gamma_{ij} = \beta_{i1}\alpha_{1j} + \cdots + \beta_{in}\alpha_{nm} = \sum_{k=1}^{n} \beta_{ik}\gamma_{kj},$$

for $1 \leq i \leq q$, $1 \leq j \leq m$. In general, multiplication of a q-by-r matrix $\mathbf{B}$ and an s-by-t matrix $\mathbf{A}$ is defined if and only if $r = s$, and in that case results in a q-by-t matrix $\mathbf{BA}$ according to the rule we have given.

EXAMPLES.   In $\mathbf{a} - \mathbf{d}$, it is assumed that the matrices have real coefficients.

a. $\begin{pmatrix} -1 & 0 & 1 \\ 1 & 1 & 0 \\ -1 & 0 & 2 \end{pmatrix} \begin{pmatrix} 1 & 1 \\ -1 & 1 \\ 1 & 0 \end{pmatrix} = \begin{pmatrix} 0 & -1 \\ 0 & 2 \\ 1 & -1 \end{pmatrix}$

b. $\begin{pmatrix} 1 & 1 \\ -1 & 1 \\ 1 & 0 \end{pmatrix} \begin{pmatrix} -1 & 0 & 1 \\ 1 & 1 & 0 \\ -1 & 0 & 2 \end{pmatrix}$ not defined

c. $\begin{pmatrix} 2 & 1 \\ 0 & -1 \end{pmatrix} \begin{pmatrix} 1 \\ -1 \end{pmatrix} = \begin{pmatrix} 1 \\ 1 \end{pmatrix}$

d. $(1 \quad -1) \begin{pmatrix} 2 & 1 \\ 0 & -1 \end{pmatrix} = (2 \quad 2).$

e. Matrix multiplication can be used to rewrite the systems of equations themselves. For example the system

$$2x_1 - x_2 = 1$$
$$x_1 + x_2 = 0$$

can be written in matrix form

$$\begin{pmatrix} 2 & -1 \\ 1 & 1 \end{pmatrix} \begin{pmatrix} x_1 \\ x_2 \end{pmatrix} = \begin{pmatrix} 1 \\ 0 \end{pmatrix}.$$

More generally, a system

$$\alpha_{11}x_1 + \cdots + \alpha_{1n}x_n = \beta_1$$

(12.7)

$$\alpha_{m1}x_m + \cdots + \alpha_{mn}x_n = \beta_m$$

of m equations in n unknowns can be written in matrix form

$$\mathbf{Ax} = \mathbf{b}$$

where $\mathbf{A} = (\alpha_{ij})$, and

$$\mathbf{x} = \begin{pmatrix} x_1 \\ \cdot \\ \cdot \\ \cdot \\ x_n \end{pmatrix}, \qquad \mathbf{b} = \begin{pmatrix} \beta_1 \\ \cdot \\ \cdot \\ \cdot \\ \beta_n \end{pmatrix}.$$

The linear transformation defined by the system (12.7) can be described as follows:

$$T(\mathbf{x}) = \mathbf{A} \cdot \mathbf{x},$$

where $\mathbf{x}$ is the column vector with entries $x_1, \cdots, x_n$, regarded as an n-by-1 matrix, and $\mathbf{A} \cdot \mathbf{x}$ denotes matrix multiplication.

EXERCISES

The numerical problems refer to matrices with real coefficients.

1. Compute the following matrices:

$$\begin{pmatrix} -1 & 2 \\ -1 & 0 \end{pmatrix} \begin{pmatrix} 1 & 1 \\ 0 & 1 \end{pmatrix}, \qquad \begin{pmatrix} -1 & 2 & 3 \\ 1 & 1 & 1 \end{pmatrix} \begin{pmatrix} 1 & 1 \\ 1 & 0 \\ 2 & -1 \end{pmatrix},$$

$$\begin{pmatrix} 0 & 1 & 1 \\ -1 & 1 & 0 \end{pmatrix} \begin{pmatrix} 1 \\ 2 \\ 0 \end{pmatrix}, \qquad (1 \quad 1 \quad 2) \begin{pmatrix} -1 \\ 0 \\ 1 \end{pmatrix},$$

$$\begin{pmatrix} 0 & 1 \\ 0 & 0 \end{pmatrix} \begin{pmatrix} 0 & 1 \\ 0 & 0 \end{pmatrix}, \qquad \begin{pmatrix} 1 & 0 & 0 \\ 0 & -1 & 0 \\ 0 & 0 & 2 \end{pmatrix} \begin{pmatrix} 1 & 1 & 0 \\ -1 & 2 & 1 \\ 1 & 1 & 3 \end{pmatrix}$$

$$\begin{pmatrix} 1 & 1 & 0 \\ -1 & 2 & 1 \\ 1 & 1 & 3 \end{pmatrix} \begin{pmatrix} 1 & 0 & 0 \\ 0 & -1 & 0 \\ 0 & 0 & 2 \end{pmatrix}.$$

2. Let S and T be linear transformations of $F_n \to F_m$ defined by systems of equations with matrices $\mathbf{A}$ and $\mathbf{B}$ respectively. Show that the matrix of $S + T$ is $\mathbf{A} + \mathbf{B}$.

3. a. Prove that matrix multiplication is associative, whenever it is defined: $(\mathbf{AB})\mathbf{C} = \mathbf{A}(\mathbf{BC})$.
  b. Prove that $\alpha(\mathbf{AB}) = (\alpha\mathbf{A})\mathbf{B} = \mathbf{A}(\alpha\mathbf{B})$ for all $\alpha \in F$.

4. Letting $\mathbf{x}$ denote a column vector of appropriate size, solve the matrix equation $\mathbf{Ax} = \mathbf{b}$, in the following cases. Note that by the last example, the matrix equation $\mathbf{Ax} = \mathbf{b}$ is equivalent to a system of linear equations.

a. $\mathbf{A} = \begin{pmatrix} 1 & 1 \\ -1 & 0 \end{pmatrix}, \qquad \mathbf{b} = \begin{pmatrix} 2 \\ 1 \end{pmatrix}.$

b. $\mathbf{A} = \begin{pmatrix} 1 & 1 & 0 \\ -1 & 1 & 2 \end{pmatrix}, \qquad \mathbf{b} = \begin{pmatrix} 0 \\ 0 \end{pmatrix}.$

c. $\mathbf{A} = \begin{pmatrix} 1 & 0 & 0 & 0 & 0 \\ 0 & 1 & 0 & 1 & 0 \\ -1 & 0 & 0 & 0 & 1 \end{pmatrix} \quad \mathbf{b} = \begin{pmatrix} 1 \\ 0 \\ -1 \end{pmatrix}.$

d. $\mathbf{A} = \begin{pmatrix} 1 & 1 & 0 & 1 \\ 0 & 1 & -1 & 0 \end{pmatrix}, \qquad \mathbf{b} = \begin{pmatrix} 1 \\ 2 \end{pmatrix}.$

5. Define a *diagonal matrix* $\mathbf{D}$ over F to be an n-by-n matrix whose (i, j) entry is zero unless $i = j$. We usually write

$$\mathbf{D} = \begin{pmatrix} \delta_1 & & 0 \\ & \ddots & \\ 0 & & \delta_n \end{pmatrix}$$

to denote a diagonal matrix. Figure out the effect of multiplying an arbitrary matrix on the left and on the right by a diagonal matrix $\mathbf{D}$. In particular, the n-by-n *identity matrix* $\mathbf{I}$ is the diagonal matrix with 1's on the diagonal. Show that $\mathbf{IA} = \mathbf{AI} = \mathbf{A}$ for all $\mathbf{A}$.

6. Two matrices $\mathbf{A}$ and $\mathbf{B}$ are said to *commute* if $\mathbf{AB} = \mathbf{BA}$. Prove that the only n-by-n matrices which commute with all the n-by-n diagonal matrices over F are the diagonal matrices themselves.

7. An n-by-n matrix $\mathbf{A}$ is said to be *invertible* if there exists an n-by-n matrix $\mathbf{B}$ such that $\mathbf{AB} = \mathbf{BA} = \mathbf{I}$. Prove that if $\mathbf{A}$ is invertible, then $\mathbf{A}$ has a uniquely determined inverse $\mathbf{A}^{-1}$ such that $\mathbf{AA}^{-1} = \mathbf{A}^{-1}\mathbf{A} = \mathbf{I}$. Prove that the invertible n-by-n matrices form a group.

8. Let $\mathbf{A}$ denote an n-by-n matrix and $\mathbf{x}$ and $\mathbf{b}$ column vectors with n rows. Show that $\mathbf{A}$ is invertible if and only if the linear transformation $\mathbf{x} \rightarrow \mathbf{A} \cdot \mathbf{x}$ is invertible, and that in case $\mathbf{A}$ is invertible, the equation

$$\mathbf{Ax} = \mathbf{b}$$

has a unique solution $\mathbf{x} = \mathbf{A}^{-1} \cdot \mathbf{b}$. Prove that the ith column of a matrix $\mathbf{A}$ is given by $\mathbf{A}\mathbf{e}_i$, where $\mathbf{e}_i$ is the column vector with a 1 in the ith position and zeros elsewhere. Therefore show that if $\mathbf{A}$ is invertible, the column vectors of $\mathbf{A}^{-1}$ are the unique solutions of the equations $\mathbf{Ax} = \mathbf{e}_i$, $i = 1, 2, \cdots, n$. Use this method to find $\mathbf{A}^{-1}$ in case $\mathbf{A}$ is any one of the matrices:

a. $\begin{pmatrix} 1 & 1 \\ -1 & 1 \end{pmatrix}$ b. $\begin{pmatrix} 1 & 1 & 2 \\ 1 & 0 & 1 \\ 1 & 1 & 0 \end{pmatrix}$ c. $\begin{pmatrix} 1 & 1 & 0 & 1 \\ 1 & 0 & 1 & 1 \\ 1 & 1 & 0 & 1 \\ 0 & -1 & 1 & 1 \end{pmatrix}$.

9. Let $\mathbf{I}$ be the n-by-n identity matrix, that is, the matrix whose rows are the unit vectors in F_n. Define an *elementary matrix* as any one of the matrices $\mathbf{P}_{ij}$, $\mathbf{B}_{ij}(\lambda)$, $\mathbf{D}_i(\mu)$ for all $i, j = 1, \cdots, n$, and $\lambda, \mu \in F$. These matrices are defined as follows.

a. $\mathbf{P}_{ij}$ is obtained from $\mathbf{I}$ by interchanging the ith and jth rows.

b. $\mathbf{B}_{ij}(\lambda)$ is obtained from $\mathbf{I}$ by adding λ times the jth row of $\mathbf{I}$ to the ith row.

c. $\mathbf{D}_i(\mu)$ is obtained from $\mathbf{I}$ by multiplying the ith row of $\mathbf{I}$ by μ.

For example, in the set of 2-by-2 matrices we have

$$\mathbf{P}_{12} = \begin{pmatrix} 0 & 1 \\ 1 & 0 \end{pmatrix}, \qquad \mathbf{B}_{12}(\lambda) = \begin{pmatrix} 1 & \lambda \\ 0 & 1 \end{pmatrix}, \qquad \mathbf{D}_2(\mu) = \begin{pmatrix} 1 & 0 \\ 0 & \mu \end{pmatrix}.$$

Now let $\mathbf{A}$ be an arbitrary n-by-n matrix. Prove that:

a. $\mathbf{P}_{ij}\mathbf{A}$ is obtained from $\mathbf{A}$ by interchanging the ith and jth rows of $\mathbf{A}$.

b. $\mathbf{B}_{ij}(\lambda)\mathbf{A}$ is obtained from $\mathbf{A}$ by adding λ times the jth row of $\mathbf{A}$ to the ith row.

c. $\mathbf{D}_i(\mu)\mathbf{A}$ is obtained from $\mathbf{A}$ by multiplying the ith row of $\mathbf{A}$ by μ.

The operations on $\mathbf{A}$ described in **a**, **b**, and **c** above are called *elementary operations* and may be referred to as types 1, 2, and 3, respectively.

10. (Continuation of Exercise 9.) Let $\mathbf{A}$ be an arbitrary n-by-n matrix. Prove by methods similar to those used in Theorem (7.22) of Section 7 that there exists a sequence of elementary operations of types 1, 2, or 3 which reduces $\mathbf{A}$ to a matrix whose rows are in echelon form, and that the number of nonzero rows is the rank of $\mathbf{A}$. If $\mathbf{A}$ is invertible, show that there exists a sequence of elementary operations of types 1, 2, or 3, which reduces $\mathbf{A}$ to the identity matrix. In this case, Exercise 9 implies that there exist elementary matrices $\mathbf{E}_1 \cdots, \mathbf{E}_s$ of types A, B, C such that

$$\mathbf{E}_s\mathbf{E}_{s-1} \cdots \mathbf{E}_1\mathbf{A} = \mathbf{I}.$$

Prove that

$$\mathbf{A}^{-1} = \mathbf{E}_s\mathbf{E}_{s-1} \cdots \mathbf{E}_1\mathbf{I},$$

so that if the elementary operations given by $\mathbf{E}_1, \cdots, \mathbf{E}_s$ reduce $\mathbf{A}$ to $\mathbf{I}$, the same sequence of elementary operations applied to $\mathbf{I}$ will yield $\mathbf{A}^{-1}$. Apply this construction of $\mathbf{A}^{-1}$ to the matrices given below, which are invertible.

a. $\begin{pmatrix} 2 & -1 \\ -2 & 1 \end{pmatrix}$

b. $\begin{pmatrix} 2 & 1 \\ 1 & 1 \end{pmatrix}$

c. $\begin{pmatrix} 3 & 1 & 0 \\ 1 & 2 & 1 \\ 0 & -1 & 2 \end{pmatrix}$

d. $\begin{pmatrix} 1 & 1 & 0 \\ 0 & 1 & 1 \\ -1 & 1 & 0 \end{pmatrix}$

$$\text{e.} \quad \begin{pmatrix} 1 & 1 & 1 & 0 \\ 0 & 1 & 1 & 1 \\ 1 & 0 & 1 & 1 \\ 1 & 1 & 0 & 1 \end{pmatrix}.$$

13. LINEAR TRANSFORMATIONS AND MATRICES

Throughout the rest of this chapter, V and W denote finite-dimensional vector spaces over F. The first result asserts that a linear transformation is completely determined if we know its effect on a set of basis elements and that, conversely, we may define a linear transformation by assigning arbitrary images for a set of basis elements.

(13.1) Theorem. *Let $\{v_1, \cdots, v_n\}$ be a basis of V over F. If S and T are elements of $L(V, W)$ such that $S(v_i) = T(v_i)$, $1 \leq i \leq n$, then $S = T$. Moreover, let $w_1, \cdots, w_n$ be arbitrary vectors in W. Then there exists one and only one linear transformation $T \in L(V, W)$ such that $T(v_i) = w_i$.*

Proof. Let $v = \sum_{1}^{n} \xi_i v_i$. Then $S(v_i) = T(v_i)$, $1 \leq i \leq n$, implies that

$$S(v) = S\left(\sum \xi_i v_i\right) = \sum \xi_i S(v_i) = \sum \xi_i T(v_i) = T(v).$$

Since this holds for all $v \in V$, we have $S = T$, and the first part of the theorem is proved.

To prove the second part, let $w_1, \cdots, w_n$ be given and define a mapping $T: V \to W$ by setting

$$T\left(\sum \xi_i v_i\right) = \sum \xi_i w_i, \qquad \xi_i \in F.$$

Since $\{v_1, \cdots, v_n\}$ is a basis of V, $\sum \xi_i v_i = \sum \eta_i v_i$ implies $\xi_i = \eta_i$, $1 \leq i \leq n$, and hence $T(\sum \xi_i v_i) = T(\sum \eta_i v_i)$, and we have shown that T is a function. It is immediate from the definition that T is a linear transformation of $V \to W$ such that $T(v_i) = w_i$, $1 \leq i \leq n$, and the uniqueness of T is clear by the first part of the theorem. This completes the proof.

Now consider a fixed basis $\{v_1, \cdots, v_n\}$ of V over F and for simplicity let $T \in L(V, V)$. Then for each i, $T(v_i)$ is a linear combination of $v_1, \cdots, v_n$, and the coefficients can be used to define the rows or columns of an n-by-n matrix which together with the basis $\{v_1, \cdots, v_n\}$ determines completely the linear transformation T, because of the preceding theorem. The question whether we should let $T(v_i)$ give the rows or columns of the matrix corresponding to T is answered by requiring that the matrix of a product of two transformations be the product of their corresponding matrices.

For example, let V be a two-dimensional vector space over F with basis $\{v_1, v_2\}$. Let S and T in $L(V, V)$ be defined by

$$S(v_1) = -v_1 + 2v_2, \qquad T(v_1) = 2v_1 + 3v_2,$$
$$S(v_2) = v_1 + v_2, \qquad T(v_2) = -v_2.$$

Then ST is the linear transformation given by

$$ST(v_1) = S(2v_1 + 3v_2) = 2(-v_1 + 2v_2) + 3(v_1 + v_2)$$
$$= v_1 + 7v_2,$$
$$ST(v_2) = S(-v_2) = -(v_1 + v_2) = -v_1 - v_2.$$

The matrices corresponding to S, T, ST, if we let $S(v_i)$ correspond to the *rows* of the matrix of S, etc., are respectively

$$\begin{pmatrix} -1 & 2 \\ 1 & 1 \end{pmatrix}, \quad \begin{pmatrix} 2 & 3 \\ 0 & -1 \end{pmatrix}, \quad \begin{pmatrix} 1 & 7 \\ -1 & -1 \end{pmatrix}$$

and we have

$$\begin{pmatrix} -1 & 2 \\ 1 & 1 \end{pmatrix} \cdot \begin{pmatrix} 2 & 3 \\ 0 & -1 \end{pmatrix} \neq \begin{pmatrix} 1 & 7 \\ -1 & -1 \end{pmatrix}.$$

Let us see if we have better luck by letting $S(v_i)$ correspond to the columns of the matrix of S, etc. In this case the matrices corresponding to S, T, ST are respectively

$$\begin{pmatrix} -1 & 1 \\ 2 & 1 \end{pmatrix}, \quad \begin{pmatrix} 2 & 0 \\ 3 & -1 \end{pmatrix}, \quad \begin{pmatrix} 1 & -1 \\ 7 & -1 \end{pmatrix}$$

and this time it is true that

$$\begin{pmatrix} -1 & 1 \\ 2 & 1 \end{pmatrix} \cdot \begin{pmatrix} 2 & 0 \\ 3 & -1 \end{pmatrix} = \begin{pmatrix} 1 & -1 \\ 7 & -1 \end{pmatrix}.$$

All this suggests the following definition.

(13.2) Definition. Let $\{v_1, \cdots, v_n\}$ be a basis of V and let $T \in L(V, V)$. The *matrix of T with respect to the basis* $\{v_1, \cdots, v_n\}$ of

V is the n-by-n matrix whose ith column, for $1 \leq i \leq n$, is the set of coefficients obtained when $T(v_i)$ is expressed as a linear combination of $v_1, \cdots, v_n$. Thus the matrix (α_{rs}) of T is described by the equations

$$T(v_i) = \sum_{j=1}^{n} \alpha_{ji} v_j = \alpha_{1i} v_1 + \cdots + \alpha_{ni} v_n.$$

To give another example, let T be the linear transformation of a three-dimensional vector space with basis $\{v_1, v_2, v_3\}$ such that

$$\begin{aligned}
T(v_1) &= 2v_1 - 3v_3 \\
T(v_2) &= v_2 + 5v_3 \\
T(v_3) &= v_1 - v_2.
\end{aligned}$$

Then the matrix of T with respect to the basis $\{v_1, v_2, v_3\}$ is

$$\begin{pmatrix} 2 & 0 & 1 \\ 0 & 1 & -1 \\ -3 & 5 & 0 \end{pmatrix}.$$

Let us check whether Definition (13.2) is consistent with the interpretation of the matrix of a linear transformation given by a system of equations. For example, let T be defined by the system

$$\begin{aligned}
y_1 &= 3x_1 - x_2 \\
y_2 &= x_1 + 2x_2.
\end{aligned}$$

Let

$$e_1 = \begin{pmatrix} 1 \\ 0 \end{pmatrix}, \qquad e_2 = \begin{pmatrix} 0 \\ 1 \end{pmatrix};$$

then e_1 and e_2 form a basis for R_2, and we can compute the matrix of T with respect to this basis according to Definition (13.2). Using the results of the last example in the preceding section, we have

$$T(e_1) = \begin{pmatrix} 3 & -1 \\ 1 & 2 \end{pmatrix} \begin{pmatrix} 1 \\ 0 \end{pmatrix} = \begin{pmatrix} 3 \\ 1 \end{pmatrix} = 3e_1 + e_2$$

$$T(e_2) = \begin{pmatrix} 3 & -1 \\ 1 & 2 \end{pmatrix} \begin{pmatrix} 0 \\ 1 \end{pmatrix} = \begin{pmatrix} -1 \\ 2 \end{pmatrix} = -e_1 + 2e_2.$$

Thus the matrix of T is

$$\begin{pmatrix} 3 & -1 \\ 1 & 2 \end{pmatrix}.$$

The reader can easily check that for a general system of n equations in n unknowns with matrix $\mathbf{A}$, the matrix of the corresponding linear transformation with respect to the basis $\{e_1, \cdots, e_n\}$ defined as above, is $\mathbf{A}$, according to Definition (13.2).

We now give some general results on the connection between linear transformations and matrices.

We recall that if $\mathbf{A}$, $\mathbf{B}$ are n-by-n matrices with coefficients (α_{ij}) and (β_{ij}), respectively, their sum and product are defined by

$$(\alpha_{ij}) + (\beta_{ij}) = (\alpha_{ij} + \beta_{ij}),$$

$$(\alpha_{ij})(\beta_{ij}) = (\gamma_{ij}), \qquad \gamma_{ij} = \sum_{k=1}^{n} \alpha_{ik}\beta_{kj}.$$

In treating a matrix as an n^2-tuple, it is also natural to define

$$\alpha(\alpha_{ij}) = (\alpha\alpha_{ij}), \qquad \alpha \in F.$$

We come now to the result that links the algebraic structure of $L(V, V)$ introduced in the preceding section with the algebraic structure of the set $M_n(F)$ of all n-by-n matrices with coefficients in F.

(13.3) Theorem. *Let* $\{v_1, \cdots, v_n\}$ *be a fixed basis of* V *over* F. *The mapping* $T \to (\alpha_{ij})$ *which assigns to each linear transformation* T *its matrix* (α_{ij}) *with respect to the basis* $\{v_1, \cdots, v_n\}$ *is a one-to-one mapping of* $L(V, V)$ *onto* $M_n(F)$ *such that, if* $T \to (\alpha_{ij})$ *and* $S \to (\beta_{ij})$, *then*

$$T + S \to (\alpha_{ij}) + (\beta_{ij}),$$
$$TS \to (\alpha_{ij})(\beta_{ij}),$$
$$\alpha T \to \alpha(\alpha_{ij}).$$

Proof. The fact that the mapping is one-to-one and onto is clear by Theorem (13.1). The fact that $T + S$ and αT map onto the desired matrices is clear from the definition and, of course, the result on TS should be true because this property motivated our definition of the matrix corresponding to T. However, we should check the details. We have

$$Tv_i = \sum_{j=1}^{n} \alpha_{ji}v_j, \qquad Sv_i = \sum_{j=1}^{n} \beta_{ji}v_j.$$

Then

$$(TS)v_i = T(Sv_i) = T\left(\sum_{j=1}^{n} \beta_{ji}v_j\right)$$

$$= \sum_{j=1}^{n} \beta_{ji} T(v_j) = \sum_{j=1}^{n} \beta_{ji} \sum_{k=1}^{n} \alpha_{kj} v_k$$

$$= \sum_{k=1}^{n} \left(\sum_{j=1}^{n} \alpha_{kj} \beta_{ji} \right) v_k.$$

Thus the (k, i) entry of the matrix of TS is $\sum_{j=1}^{n} \alpha_{kj}\beta_{ji}$, which is also the (k, i) entry of the product $(\alpha_{ij})(\beta_{ij})$. This completes the proof.

(13.4) Corollary. *Let* A, B, C *be n-by-n matrices with coefficients in F; then*

$$\mathbf{A(BC) = (AB)C}$$
$$\mathbf{A(B + C) = AB + AC,} \qquad \mathbf{(A + B)C = AC + BC.}$$

The proof is immediate by Theorems (13.3) and (11.6) and does not require any computation at all.

Some remarks on (13.3) are appropriate at this point. First, Theorem (13.3) is simply the assertion that $L(V, V)$ is isomorphic with $M_n(F)$ as a ring and as a vector space over F. Theorem (13.3) asserts that all computations in $L(V, V)$ can equally well be carried out in $M_n(F)$. Experience shows that frequently the shortest and most elegant solution of a problem comes by working in $L(V, V)$, but the reader will find that there are times when calculations with matrices cannot be avoided. The preceding theorem also has the complication that the correspondence between $L(V, V)$ and $M_n(F)$ depends on the choice of a basis in V. Our next task is to work out this connection explicitly.

Let $\{v_1, \cdots, v_n\}$ be a basis of V over F and let $\{w_1, \cdots, w_n\}$ be a set of vectors in V. Then we have

(13.5) $$w_i = \sum_{j=1}^{n} \mu_{ji} v_j, \qquad 1 \le i \le n.$$

We assert that $\{w_1, \cdots, w_n\}$ is another basis of V if and only if the matrix (μ_{ij}) is invertible [the definition of invertible matrix is the same as for invertible transformation, (11.8); see also Exercise 7 of Section 12]. To see this, suppose first that $\{w_1, \cdots, w_n\}$ is a basis. Then we can express each

$$v_i = \sum_{j=1}^{n} \eta_{ji} w_j$$

where (η_{ij}) is an n-by-n matrix. Substituting in (13.5), we obtain

$$w_i = \sum_{j=1}^{n} \mu_{ji} v_j = \sum_{j=1}^{n} \mu_{ji} \left(\sum_{k=1}^{n} \eta_{kj} w_k \right) = \sum_{k=1}^{n} \left(\sum_{j=1}^{n} \eta_{kj} \mu_{ji} \right) w_k.$$

Since $\{w_1, \cdots, w_n\}$ are linearly independent, we obtain

$$\sum_{j=1}^{n} \eta_{kj} \mu_{ji} = \begin{cases} 1 & \text{if } i = k \\ 0 & \text{if } i \neq k \end{cases}$$

and we have proved that $(\eta_{ij})(\mu_{ij}) = \mathbf{I}$. Similarly, $(\mu_{ij})(\eta_{ij}) = \mathbf{I}$ and we have shown that (μ_{ij}) is an invertible matrix. We leave as an exercise the proof that if (μ_{ij}) is invertible then $\{w_1, \cdots, w_n\}$ is a basis.

(13.6) **Theorem.** *Let $\{v_1, \cdots, v_n\}$ be a basis of V and let $\{w_1, \cdots, w_n\}$ be another basis such that*

$$w_i = \sum_{j=1}^{n} \mu_{ji} v_j$$

where (μ_{rs}) is an invertible matrix. Let $T \in L(V, V)$, and let (α_{ij}) and (α'_{ij}) be the matrices of T with respect to the bases $\{v_1, \cdots, v_n\}$ and $\{w_1, \cdots, w_n\}$ respectively. Then we have

$$(\mu_{ij})(\alpha'_{ij}) = (\alpha_{ij})(\mu_{ij})$$

or

$$(\alpha'_{ij}) = (\mu_{ij})^{-1}(\alpha_{ij})(\mu_{ij}).$$

Proof. We have

$$T(w_i) = \sum_{j=1}^{n} \alpha'_{ji} w_j = \sum_{j=1}^{n} \alpha'_{ji} \sum_{k=1}^{n} \mu_{kj} v_k$$

$$= \sum_{k=1}^{n} \left(\sum_{j=1}^{n} \mu_{kj} \alpha'_{ji} \right) v_k,$$

while on the other hand we have

$$T(w_i) = T\left(\sum_{j=1}^{n} \mu_{ji} v_j \right) = \sum_{j=1}^{n} \mu_{ji} \left(\sum_{k=1}^{n} \alpha_{kj} v_k \right)$$

$$= \sum_{k=1}^{n} \left(\sum_{j=1}^{n} \alpha_{kj} \mu_{ji} \right) v_k.$$

Therefore

$$\sum_{j=1}^{n} \mu_{kj}\alpha'_{ji} = \sum_{j=1}^{n} \alpha_{kj}\mu_{ji}, \qquad 1 \leq i, \quad k \leq n,$$

and the theorem is proved.

(13.7) Definition. Two matrices $\mathbf{A}$ and $\mathbf{B}$ in $M_n(F)$ are *similar* if there exists an invertible matrix $\mathbf{X}$ in $M_n(F)$ such that

$$\mathbf{B} = \mathbf{X}^{-1}\mathbf{A}\mathbf{X}.$$

Theorem (13.6) asserts that, if $\mathbf{A}$ and $\mathbf{B}$ are matrices of $T \in L(V, V)$ with respect to different bases, then $\mathbf{A}$ and $\mathbf{B}$ are similar. The reader may verify that the converse of this statement is also true. Thus if $\mathbf{A}$ and $\mathbf{B}$ are similar matrices, then $\mathbf{A}$ and $\mathbf{B}$ can always be viewed as matrices of a single linear transformation with respect to different bases.

As an illustration of the preceding theorem, let $T \in L(R_2, R_2)$ be defined by:

$$T(e_1) = e_1 - e_2$$
$$T(e_2) = e_1 + 2e_2,$$

where $e_1 = \langle 1, 0 \rangle$, $e_2 = \langle 0, 1 \rangle$. The matrix $\mathbf{A}$ of T with respect to the basis $\{e_1, e_2\}$ is

$$\begin{pmatrix} 1 & 1 \\ -1 & 2 \end{pmatrix}.$$

Let us find the matrix $\mathbf{B}$ of T with respect to the basis $\{u_1 = e_1 + e_2, u_2 = e_1 - e_2\}$. We have

$$T(u_1) = T(e_1) + T(e_2) = 2e_1 + e_2,$$

and in order to express $T(u_1)$ as a linear combination of u_1 and u_2, we have to solve for e_1 and e_2 in terms of u_1 and u_2. We obtain

$$e_1 = \tfrac{1}{2}(u_1 + u_2), \qquad e_2 = \tfrac{1}{2}(u_1 - u_2),$$

and

$$T(u_1) = \tfrac{3}{2}u_1 + \tfrac{1}{2}u_2,$$
$$T(u_2) = -\tfrac{3}{2}u_1 + \tfrac{3}{2}u_2.$$

The matrix $\mathbf{B}$ of T with respect to the basis $\{u_1, u_2\}$ is

$$\mathbf{B} = \begin{pmatrix} \dfrac{3}{2} & -\dfrac{3}{2} \\ \dfrac{1}{2} & \dfrac{3}{2} \end{pmatrix}.$$

To find an invertible matrix S such that $S^{-1}AS = B$, we use the equations expressing $\{e_1, e_2\}$ in terms of $\{u_1, u_2\}$. For S we obtain the matrix

$$\begin{pmatrix} \dfrac{1}{2} & \dfrac{1}{2} \\[2mm] \dfrac{1}{2} & -\dfrac{1}{2} \end{pmatrix}.$$

To conclude this section, we apply our basic results about basis and dimension from Section 7, together with the results of this section, to obtain some useful theorems about linear transformations. Besides the results (A)–(F) given in the summary to Section 7, we emphasize particularly the following two results contained in Theorem (13.1).

(G) A linear transformation is uniquely determined by its action on a basis of the vector space.

(H) If $\{v_1, \cdots, v_n\}$ is a basis for a vector space V, and $w_1, \cdots, w_n$ are arbitrary vectors in W, there exists a linear transformation $T \in L(V, W)$ such that $T(v_i) = w_i$ $i = 1, \cdots, n$.

(13.8) Definition. Let V and W be finite-dimensional vector spaces over a field F, and let $T \in L(V, W)$. Then $T(V) = \{$all vectors $T(v)$, $v \in V\}$ is a subspace of W called the *range* of T; the dimension of $T(V)$ is called the *rank* of T. The set of vectors $v \in V$ such that $T(v) = 0$ is called the *null space* of T [notation: n(T)], and the dimension of $n(T)$ is called the *nullity* of T.

(13.9) Theorem. *Let $T \in L(V, W)$. Then*
$$\dim T(V) + \dim n(T) = \dim V.$$

In other words, the sum of the rank of T and the nullity of T is equal to the dimension of V.

Proof. Let $\{v_1, \cdots, v_k\}$ be a basis for the null space n(T) (with our convention that this set is empty if n$(T) = 0$). By one of the facts (A)–(H) (Which one?), there exist vectors $\{v_{k+1}, \cdots, v_n\}$ in V such that $\{v_1, \cdots, v_k, \cdots, v_n\}$ is a basis for V. It is sufficient to prove that $\{T(v_{k+1}), \cdots, T(v_n)\}$ is a basis for $T(V)$. We have first the fact that

$$T\left(\sum_{i=1}^{n} \xi_i v_i\right) = \sum_{i=k+1}^{n} \xi_i T(v_i), \qquad \xi_i \in F,$$

because $T(v_i) = 0$ for $1 \le i \le k$. Finally, suppose we have

$$\sum_{i=k+1}^{n} \eta_i T(v_i) = 0$$

for some $\eta_i \in F$. Then

$$T\left(\sum_{i=k+1}^{n} \eta_i v_i\right) = 0,$$

and $\sum_{i=k+1}^{n} \eta_i v_i \in n(T)$. Because of the way the basis $\{v_i\}$ for V was chosen, it follows that all the $\{\eta_i\}$ are zero, and the theorem is proved.

The next result should tie up some loose ends connected with the concept of invertible linear transformation.

(13.10)   Theorem.   *Let $T \in L(V, V)$ for some finite-dimensional space V over F. Then the following statements are equivalent:*

(1) T is invertible;
(2) T is one-to-one;
(3) T is onto.

Proof.   We prove that (1) implies (2), (2) implies (3), and (3) implies (1). First we assume (1). Then there exists $T^{-1} \in L(V, V)$ such that $TT^{-1} = T^{-1}T = 1$. Suppose $T(v_1) = T(v_2)$. Applying T^{-1} we obtain $T^{-1}T(v_1) = T^{-1}T(v_2)$, and $v_1 = v_2$. Thus (1) implies (2).

Next assume (2). Then the null space $n(T) = 0$. By Theorem (13.9) we have dim $T(V) = n$, and it follows that $T(V) = V$, and that T is onto.

Finally, assume T is onto. By Theorem (13.9) again, T is also one-to-one. It follows that if $\{v_1, \cdots, v_n\}$ is a basis for V, then $\{T(v_1), \cdots, T(v_n)\}$ is also a basis. By statement (H) above, there exists a linear transformation U such that $UT(v_i) = v_i, i = 1, \cdots, n$. By statement (G) we have $UT = 1$. On the other hand, $TU(Tv_i) = Tv_i$ for $i = 1, \cdots, n$, and since $\{Tv_i, \cdots, Tv_n\}$ is a basis, we have $TU = 1$. Therefore T is invertible and the theorem is proved.

Finally we introduce the important idea of characteristic vector for a linear transformation.

(13.11)   Definition.   Let $T \in L(V, V)$. An element $\alpha \in F$ is called a *characteristic root* (or *eigenvalue*, or *proper value*) of T if there exists a vector $v \ne 0$ in V such that $T(v) = \alpha v$. A nonzero vector v such that $T(v) = \alpha v$ is called a *characteristic vector* (*eigenvector* or *proper vector*) belonging to the characteristic root α.

There may be many characteristic vectors belonging to a given characteristic root. For example, the identity linear transformation 1 on V has $1 \in F$ as its only characteristic root, but every nonzero vector in V is a characteristic vector belonging to this characteristic root.

We can also define characteristic roots and characteristic vectors for matrices.

(13.12)   *Let* **A** *be an n-by-m matrix with entries in* F. *An element* $\alpha \in F$ *is called a* characteristic root *of* **A** *if there exists some nonzero column vector* **x** *in* F_n *such that* $\mathbf{Ax} = \alpha\mathbf{x}$; *such a vector* **x** *is called a* characteristic vector *belonging to* α.

The correspondence between linear transformations and matrices shows that α is a characteristic root of $T \in L(V, V)$ if and only if α is a characteristic root of the matrix of T with respect to any basis of the vector space.

Our last theorem is the following one, which shows how characteristic vectors with respect to different characteristic roots, behave.

(13.13)   **Theorem.**   *Let* $v_1, v_2, \cdots, v_r$ *be characteristic vectors belonging to distinct characteristic roots* $\alpha_1, \cdots, \alpha_r$ *of* $T \in L(V, V)$. *Then* $\{v_1, \cdots, v_r\}$ *are linearly independent.*

Proof.   We use induction on r. The result is clear if $r = 1$, and so we assume an induction hypothesis that any set of fewer than r of the $\{v_i\}$ is a linearly independent set. Suppose

(13.14) $\eta_1 v_1 + \eta_2 v_2 + \cdots + \eta_r v_r = 0, \qquad \eta_i \in F.$

We wish to prove that all $\eta_i = 0$. Suppose some $\eta_i \neq 0$; we prove that this contradicts the induction hypothesis. We may assume all $\eta_i \neq 0$, otherwise we have already contradicted the induction hypothesis. Applying T to (13.14), we obtain

$$\eta_1 \alpha_1 v_1 + \eta_2 \alpha_2 v_2 + \cdots + \eta_r \alpha_r v_r = 0.$$

Multiplying (13.14) by α_1 and subtracting, we obtain

$$\eta_1(\alpha_1 - \alpha_1)v_1 + \eta_2(\alpha_2 - \alpha_1)v_2 + \cdots + \eta_r(\alpha_r - \alpha_1)v_r = 0.$$

The term involving v_1 drops out. Since the $\{\alpha_i\}$ are distinct, the coefficients of $\{v_2, \cdots, v_r\}$ are different from zero, and we have contradicted the induction hypothesis. This completes the proof of the theorem.

The following corollaries are almost immediate and their proofs are left as exercises.

(13.15)⋆   Corollary.   *A linear transformation $T \in L(V, V)$ has at most $n = \dim V$ distinct characteristic roots.*

(13.16)⋆   Corollary.   *Let $T \in L(V, V)$ have the maximum number $n = \dim V$ characteristic roots. Then there exists a basis of V consisting of characteristic vectors.*

(13.17)⋆   *Let $\mathbf{A}$ be an n-by-n matrix with n distinct characteristic roots $\{\alpha_1, \cdots, \alpha_n\}$. Then $\mathbf{A}$ is similar to the diagonal matrix*

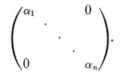

$$\begin{pmatrix} \alpha_1 & & 0 \\ & \cdot & \\ & & \cdot & \\ 0 & & \alpha_n \end{pmatrix}.$$

EXERCISES

In all the Exercises, all vector spaces involved are assumed to have finite bases, and the field F can be taken to be the field of real numbers in the numerical problems.

1. Let $S, T, U \in L(V, V)$ be given by

$$\begin{array}{lll} S(u_1) = u_1 - u_2, & T(u_1) = u_2, & U(u_1) = 2u_1 \\ S(u_2) = u_1, & T(u_2) = u_1, & U(u_2) = -2u_2 \end{array}$$

where $\{u_1, u_2\}$ is a basis for V. Find the matrices of S, T, U with respect to the basis $\{u_1, u_2\}$ and with respect to the new basis $\{w_1, w_2\}$ where

$$\begin{array}{l} w_1 = 3u_1 - u_2 \\ w_2 = u_1 + u_2. \end{array}$$

Find invertible matrices $\mathbf{X}$ in each case such that $\mathbf{X}\mathbf{A}\mathbf{X}^{-1} = \mathbf{A}'$ where $\mathbf{A}$ is the matrix of the transformation with respect to the old basis, and $\mathbf{A}'$ the matrix with respect to the new basis.

2. Let S, T, U be linear transformations such that (letting $\{u_1, u_2\}$ or $\{u_1, u_2, u_3\}$ be bases of the vector spaces)

$$S(u_1) = \quad u_1 + u_2, \qquad T(u_1) = \quad u_1 - u_2,$$
$$S(u_2) = -u_1 - u_2, \qquad T(u_2) = 2u_2,$$

$$U(u_1) = \quad u_1 + u_2 - u_3$$
$$U(u_2) = \quad u_2 - 3u_3$$
$$U(u_3) = -u_1 - 3u_2 - 2u_3.$$

a. Find the rank and nullity of S, T, U.

b. Which of these linear transformations are invertible?

c. Find bases for the null spaces of S, T, and U.

d. Find bases for the range spaces of S, T, and U.

3. Let V be the space of all polynomial functions $f(x) = \alpha_0 + \alpha_1 x + \cdots + \alpha_k x^k$, with real coefficients α_i and k fixed. Show that the derivative transformation D defined in Example C of Section 11, maps V into V. What is the matrix of D with respect to the basis 1, x, $\cdots$, x^k of V? What is the rank of $D: V \to V$? What is the nullity?

4. In R_4, with a basis e_1, e_2, e_3, e_4, does there exist a linear transformation $T: R_4 \to R_4$ such that

$$T(x) = e_1, \qquad T(y) = 0, \qquad T(z) = 0,$$

where

$$x = e_1 - e_2 + e_3, \qquad y = e_1 + e_2, \qquad z = e_3?$$

5. In R_4, with basis e_1, e_2, e_3, e_4, does there exist a linear transformation $U: R_4 \to R_4$ such that

$$U(x_1) = e_1, \qquad U(y_1) = 0, \qquad U(z_1) = 0$$

where

$$x_1 = e_1 + e_2 - e_3, \qquad y_1 = e_2 - 3e_2, \qquad z_1 = -e_1 - 2e_3?$$

6. Suppose T is a linear transformation of R_3 such that

$$T(e_1) = \quad 2e_1 - e_2 + e_3$$
$$T(e_2) = -e_1 \qquad + e_3$$
$$T(e_3) = \quad e_1 + e_2$$

where e_1, e_2, e_3, is a basis. Verify that

$$T(2e_1 + e_2)$$

can be found by multiplying the matrix of T with respect to the

basis (e_1, e_2, e_3) by the column vector $\begin{pmatrix} 2 \\ 1 \\ 0 \end{pmatrix}$.

7. Let $T \in L(V, W)$ and let $\{v_1, \cdots, v_n\}$, $\{w_1, \cdots, w_m\}$ be bases of V and W respectively. Let

$$T(v_i) = \sum_{j=1}^{m} \alpha_{ji} w_j, \qquad i = 1, 2, \cdots, n,$$

and let (α_{ij}) be called the matrix of T with respect to the two bases $\{v_1, \cdots, v_n\}$ and $\{w_1, \cdots, w_m\}$. Let V_1, V_2, V_3 be vector spaces of dimension 2, 3, 1 respectively with bases $\{u_1, u_2\}$, $\{v_1, v_2, v_3\}$, $\{w\}$ respectively. Let $T \in L(V_1, V_2)$ and $U \in L(V_2, V_3)$ be defined by

$$\begin{aligned} T(u_1) &= v_1 + v_2 & U(v_1) &= w \\ T(u_2) &= v_2 - v_3, & U(v_2) &= -w. \\ & & U(v_3) &= 0 \end{aligned}$$

What are the matrices of T and U with respect to the given bases? What is the matrix of UT with respect to the bases $\{u_1, u_2\}$ and $\{w\}$, and how is it related to the matrices of T and U?

8. Let $T \in L(V, W)$ and let (α_{ij}) be the matrix of T with respect to some bases of V and W as in Exercise 7. Show that the rank of T is equal to the rank of (α_{ij}) as it was defined in Chapter 2.

9. Give an example of a linear transformation $T : V \to V$ which shows that it can happen that $T(V) \cap n(T) \neq 0$.

10. Let $T \in L(V, V)$. Prove that there exists a nonzero linear transformation $S \in L(V, V)$ such that $TS = 0$ if and only if there exists a nonzero vector $v \in V$ such that $T(v) = 0$.

11. Let $S, T \in L(V, V)$ be such that $ST = 1$. Prove that $TS = 1$. (Exercise 15, Section 11, shows that this result is not true unless V is finite-dimensional.)

12. Prove that a nonzero vector $v \in V$ is a characteristic vector for some characteristic root if and only if the one-dimensional subspace $W = S(v)$ is carried into itself by T, that is $T(W) \subset W$.

13. Prove that similar matrices have the same characteristic roots.

14. Let $T \in L(V, V)$ be a linear transformation such that $T^m = 0$ for some $m > 0$. Prove that all the characteristic roots of T are zero.

15. Let A be a matrix such that $A \neq 0$ and $A^m = 0$ for some m $\left[\text{for example, } A \text{ could be } \begin{pmatrix} 0 & 1 \\ 0 & 0 \end{pmatrix}\right]$. Prove that A is not similar to any diagonal matrix.

CHAPTER 4

VECTOR SPACES
with an
INNER PRODUCT

This chapter begins with an optional section on symmetry of plane figures, which shows how some natural geometrical questions lead to the problem of studying linear transformations that preserve length. The concept of length in a general vector space over the real numbers is introduced in the next section, where it is shown how length is related to an inner product. The language of orthonormal bases and orthogonal transformations is developed with some examples from geometry and analysis. Besides the fact that the real numbers form a field, we shall use heavily in this chapter the order properties of the real numbers from Chapter 1, and the fact that every real number $a \geq 0$ has a unique nonnegative square root $\sqrt{a}$.

14. THE CONCEPT OF SYMMETRY

The word *symmetry* has rich associations for most of us. A person familiar with sculpture and painting knows the importance of symmetry to the artist and how the distinctive features of certain types of architecture and ornaments result from the use of symmetry. A geologist knows that crystals are classified according to the symmetry properties they possess. A naturalist knows the many appearances of symmetry in the shapes of plants, shells, and fish. The chemist knows that the symmetry properties of molecules are related to their chemical properties. In this section we shall consider the mathematical concept of symmetry, which will provide some worthwhile insight into all of the preceding examples.

Let us begin with a simple example from analytic geometry, Figure 4.1. What does it mean to say the graph of the parabola

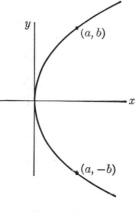

Figure 4.1

$y^2 = x$ is symmetric about the x-axis? One way of looking at it is to say that if we fold the plane along the x axis the two halves of the curve $y^2 = x$ fit together. But this is a little too vague. A more precise description comes from the observation that the operation of plane-folding defines a transformation T, of the points in the plane, which assigns to a point (a, b) the point $(a, -b)$ which meets it after the plane is folded. The symmetry of the parabola is now described by asserting that if (a, b) is a point on the parabola so is the transformed point $(a, -b)$. This sort of symmetry is called *bilateral symmetry*.

Now consider the example of a triod, Figure 4.2. What sort of symmetry does it possess? It clearly has bilateral symmetry about the three lines joining the center with the points a, b, and c. The triod has also a new sort of symmetry, *rotational symmetry*. If we rotate points in the plane through an angle of 120°, leaving the center fixed, then the triod is carried onto itself. Does the triod have the

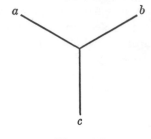

Figure 4.2

same symmetry properties as the winged triod of Figure 4.3? Clearly not; the winged triod has only rotational symmetry and does not possess the bilateral symmetry of the triod. Thus we see that the symmetry properties of figures may serve to distinguish them.

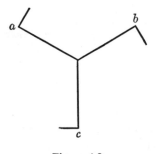

Figure 4.3

We have not yet arrived at a precise definition of symmetry. Another example suggests the underlying idea. The circle with center 0, Figure 4.4, possesses all the kinds of symmetry we have discussed so far. However, we can look at the symmetry of the circle from another viewpoint. The circle is carried onto itself by any transformation T which preserves distance and which leaves the center fixed, for the circle consists of precisely those points p whose distances from 0 are a fixed constant r and, if T is a distance preserving transformation such that $T(0) = 0$, then the distance of $T(p)$ from 0 will

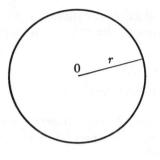

Figure 4.4

again be r and $T(p)$ is on the circle. This suggests the following definition.

(14.1) Definition. By a *figure* X we mean a set of points in the plane. A *symmetry* of a figure X is a transformation T of the plane into itself such that:

(1) $T(X) = X$; that is, T sends every point in X onto another point in X, and every point in X is the image of some point in X under T.

(2) T preserves distance; that is, if $d(p, q)$ denotes the distance between the points p and q, then

$$d[T(p),\ T(q)] = d(p,\ q)$$

for all points p and q.

(14.2) Theorem. *The set G of all symmetries of a figure X form a group G, called the symmetry group of the figure* [*see Definition* (11.9)].

Proof. We show first that if $S,\ T \in G$ then the product ST defined by

$$ST(p) = S[T(p)]$$

belongs to G. We have $ST(X) = S[T(X)] = S(X) = X$ and $d(ST(p),\ ST(q)) = d(S[T(p)],\ S[T(q)]) = d(T(p),\ T(q)) = d(p,\ q)$ and hence $ST \in G$. We have to check also that

$$S(TU) = (ST)U, \qquad \text{for } S,\ T,\ U \in G,$$

which is a consequence of the fact that both mappings send $p \rightarrow S\{T[U(p)]\}$. The transformation 1 such that $1(p) = p$ for all p belongs, clearly, to G and satisfies

$$S \cdot 1 = 1 \cdot S = S, \qquad S \in G.$$

Finally, if $S \in G$, there exists a symmetry S^{-1} of X which unwinds whatever S has done (the reader can give a more rigorous proof) such that

$$SS^{-1} = S^{-1}S = 1.$$

This completes the proof of the theorem.

The vague question, What kinds of symmetry can a figure possess? is now replaced by the precise mathematical question, What are the possible symmetry groups? We shall investigate a simple case of this problem in this section. First we look at some examples of symmetry groups.

The symmetry group of the triod, Figure 4.5, consists of the three bilateral symmetries about the arms of the triod and three

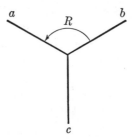

Figure 4.5

rotations through angles of 120°, 240°, and 360°. By means of the group operation we show that the symmetries of the triod all can be built up from two of the symmetries. For example, let R be the counterclockwise rotation through an angle of 120° and let S be the bilateral symmetry about the arm a. The reader may verify that the symmetry group G of the triod consists of the symmetries

$$\{1, R, R^2, S, SR, SR^2\}.$$

We may also verify that $S^2 = 1$, $R^3 = 1$, and $SR = R^{-1}S$ and that these rules suffice to multiply arbitrary elements of G.

The symmetry group of the winged triod is easily seen to consist of exactly the symmetries

$$\{1, R, R^2\}.$$

More generally, let X be the n-armed figure (Figure 4.6), S the bi-

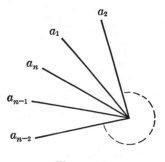

Figure 4.6

lateral symmetry about the arm a_1, and R the rotation carrying $a_2 \rightarrow a_1$. Then the group of X consists exactly of the symmetries

(14.3) $\{1, R, R^2, \cdots, R^{n-1}, S, SR, \cdots, SR^{n-1}\}$

and these symmetries are multiplied according to the rules

$$R^n = 1, \qquad S^2 = 1, \qquad SR = R^{-1}S.$$

The symmetry group of the corresponding winged figure consists of precisely the rotations

(14.4) $\{1, R, R^2, \cdots, R^{n-1}\}.$

The group (14.3) is called the *dihedral group* D_n; the group (14.4) is called the *cyclic group* C_n. We shall sketch a proof that these are the only *finite* symmetry groups of plane figures.

We require first some general remarks. It will be convenient to identify the plane with the vector space R_2 of all pairs of real numbers $\langle \alpha, \beta \rangle$. If p is a vector $\langle \alpha, \beta \rangle$, then the *length* $\|p\|$ is defined by

$$\|p\| = \sqrt{\alpha^2 + \beta^2}$$

and the distance from p to q (see Figure 4.7) is then given by

$$d(p, q) = \|p - q\|.$$

We require also the fact from plane analytic geometry that $p = \langle \alpha, \beta \rangle$ is perpendicular to $q = \langle \gamma, \delta \rangle$ (notation: $p \perp q$) if and only if

$$\alpha\gamma + \beta\delta = 0.$$

(14.5)   *A distance preserving transformation T of R_2 which leaves the zero element fixed is a linear transformation.*

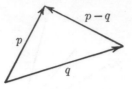

Figure 4.7

Proof. A point p in the plane is completely determined by its distances from 0, $e_1 = \langle 1, 0 \rangle$, and $e_2 = \langle 0, 1 \rangle$. Therefore $T(p)$ is completely determined by $T(e_1)$ and $T(e_2)$, since $T(0) = 0$. From Chapter 3 we can define a linear transformation $\tilde{T}$ such that

$$T(e_1) = \tilde{T}(e_1), \qquad T(e_2) = \tilde{T}(e_2).$$

Since both T and $\tilde{T}$ are determined by their action on e_1 and e_2, we have $T = \tilde{T}$.

We prove next the following characterization of a distance preserving transformation.

(14.6)   *A linear transformation T preserves distances if and only if:*

(14.7) $\|T(e_1)\| = \|T(e_2)\| = 1$ *and* $T(e_1) \perp T(e_2)$.

Proof. If T preserves distances, then it is clear that (14.7) holds. Conversely, suppose T is a linear transformation such that (14.7) holds. To prove that T preserves distances it is sufficient to prove that, for all vectors p,

$$\|T(p)\| = \|p\|,$$

for then

$$d[T(p), T(q)] = \|T(p) - T(q)\| = \|T(p - q)\| = \|p - q\| = d(p, q).$$

Now let $p = \xi e_1 + \eta e_2$ and let $T(e_1) = \langle \alpha, \beta \rangle$, $T(e_2) = \langle \gamma, \delta \rangle$. Then (14.7) implies that

$$\alpha^2 + \beta^2 = \gamma^2 + \delta^2 = 1, \qquad \alpha\gamma + \beta\delta = 0.$$

Then

$$
\begin{aligned}
\|T(p)\|^2 &= \|\xi T(e_1) + \eta T(e_2)\|^2 = \|\langle \xi\alpha + \eta\gamma, \xi\beta + \eta\delta \rangle\|^2 \\
&= (\xi\alpha + \eta\gamma)^2 + (\xi\beta + \eta\delta)^2 \\
&= \xi^2\alpha^2 + 2\xi\alpha\eta\gamma + \eta^2\gamma^2 + \xi^2\beta^2 + 2\xi\beta\eta\delta + \eta^2\delta^2 \\
&= \xi^2(\alpha^2 + \beta^2) + \eta^2(\gamma^2 + \delta^2) + 2\xi\eta(\alpha\gamma + \beta\delta) \\
&= \xi^2 + \eta^2 = \|p\|^2.
\end{aligned}
$$

This completes the proof of (14.6).

Now let T be a distance preserving transformation and leaving the origin fixed, and let $T(e_1) = \langle \alpha, \beta \rangle$. Then $T(e_2)$ is a point on the

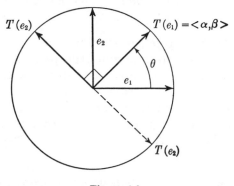

Figure 4.8

unit circle whose radius vector is perpendicular to $T(e_1)$, Figure 4.8. It follows that either

$$T(e_2) = \langle -\beta, \alpha \rangle$$

or

$$T(e_2) = \langle \beta, -\alpha \rangle.$$

In the former case the matrix of T with respect to $\{e_1, e_2\}$ is

$$\mathbf{A} = \begin{pmatrix} \alpha & -\beta \\ \beta & \alpha \end{pmatrix},$$

while in the latter case the matrix is

$$\mathbf{A} = \begin{pmatrix} \alpha & \beta \\ \beta & -\alpha \end{pmatrix}.$$

In the former case T is a rotation through an angle θ such that $\cos \theta = \alpha$, while in the latter case T is a bilateral symmetry about the line making an angle $\frac{1}{2}\theta$ with e_1. Notice that in the second case the matrix of T^2 is

$$\begin{pmatrix} \alpha & \beta \\ \beta & -\alpha \end{pmatrix} \begin{pmatrix} \alpha & \beta \\ \beta & -\alpha \end{pmatrix} = \begin{pmatrix} \alpha^2 + \beta^2 & 0 \\ 0 & \alpha^2 + \beta^2 \end{pmatrix} = \mathbf{I}$$

so that $T^2 = 1$. The second kind of transformation will be called a *reflection*, the first a *rotation*.

The next result shows how reflections and rotations combine.

(14.8)   *Let S and T be distance-preserving linear transformations; then:*

(1) *If S, T are rotations, then ST is a rotation.*
(2) *If S, T are reflections, ST is a rotation.*
(3) *If one of S, T is a rotation and the other is a reflection, then ST is a reflection.*

The proof of (14.8) is left to the Exercises.

Now we are ready to determine the possible finite symmetry groups G of plane figures. We assume that all the elements of G are linear transformations (and so leave the origin fixed). To determine a group means to show that it is *isomorphic* with a group that has previously been constructed, in the sense that a one-to-one correspondence exists between the two groups which preserves the multiplication laws of the two groups.

(14.9)   Theorem.   *Let G be a finite group of distance-preserving linear transformations. Then G is isomorphic with one of the following:*

(1) *The cyclic group $C_n = \{1, R, R^2, \cdots, R^{n-1}\}$, $R^n = 1$, consisting of the powers of a single rotation.*
(2) *The dihedral group $D_n = \{1, R, \cdots, R^{n-1}, S, SR, \cdots, SR^{n-1}\}$ where R is a rotation, S a reflection, and $R^n = 1$, $S^2 = 1$, $SR = R^{-1}S$.*

Proof.   We may suppose $G \neq \{1\}$. First suppose all the elements of G are rotations and let R be a rotation in G through the least positive angle. Consider the powers of R, $\{1, R, R^2, \cdots\}$. These exhaust G, as will be seen. Suppose $T \in G$ is a rotation different from all the powers of R. If φ is the angle of T and θ the angle of R, then, for some i, $i\theta < \varphi < (i + 1)\theta$, Figure 4.9. Then G contains TR^{-i}

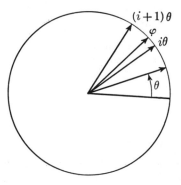

Figure 4.9

which is a rotation in G through an angle $\varphi - i\theta$ smaller than θ, contrary to our assumption. Therefore G consists of the powers of R and is a cyclic group.

Now suppose G contains a reflection S. Let H be the set of all rotations contained in G. Then H itself is a group and, by the first part of the proof, there exists a rotation R in H such that

$$H = \{1, R, R^2, \cdots, R^{n-1}\}, \qquad R^n = 1.$$

Now let $X \in G$; either $X \in H$, or X is a reflection. In the latter case SX is a rotation. Hence $SX = R^i$ for some i, and since $S^2 = 1$ we have

$$X = S(SX) = SR^i$$

and we have proved that

$$G = \{1, R, \cdots, R^{n-1}, S, SR, \cdots, SR^{n-1}\}.$$

Finally, SR is a reflection; hence $(SR)^2 = 1$ or $SRSR = 1$, and we have $SR = R^{-1}S$. It follows that G is isomorphic with a dihedral group, and the theorem is proved.

For further discussion of this topic, the reader is urged to consult the books of Weyl and of Coexter listed in the Bibliography.

EXERCISES

All exercises in this set refer to vectors in R_2. Figures should be drawn in order to see the point of most of the exercises.

1. For vectors $a = \langle \alpha_1, \alpha_2 \rangle$, $b = \langle \beta_1, \beta_2 \rangle$, define their inner product $(a, b) = \alpha_1\beta_1 + \alpha_2\beta_2$. Show that the inner product satisfies the following rules:
   a. $(a, b) = (b, a)$
   b. $(a, b + c) = (a, b) + (a, c)$
   c. $(\lambda a, b) = \lambda(a, b)$, for all $\lambda \in R$.
   d. $\|a\| = \sqrt{(a, a)}$
   e. $a \perp b$ if and only if $(a, b) = 0$.
   f. $a \perp b$ if and only if $\|a + b\| = \|a - b\|$. (Draw a figure to illustrate this statement.)

2. A *line* L in R_2 is defined to be the set of all vectors for the form $p + x$, where p is a fixed vector, and x ranges over some one-dimensional subspace S of R_2. Thus if $S = S(a)$, the line L consists

of all vectors of the form $p + \lambda a$, where $\lambda \in R$. We shall use the notation $p + S$ for the line L described above.*

a. Let $p + S$ and $q + S$ be two lines with the same one-dimensional subspace S. Show that $p + S$ and $q + S$ either coincide or have no vectors in common. In the latter case, we say that the lines are *parallel*.

b. Show that there is one and only one line L containing two distinct vectors p and q, and that L consists of all vectors of the form $p + \lambda(q - p)$, $\lambda \in R$.

c. Show that three distinct vectors p, q, r are collinear if and only if $S(q - p) = S(q - r)$.

d. Show that two distinct lines are either parallel or intersect in a unique vector.

3. Let L be the line containing two distinct vectors p and q, and let r be a vector not on L. Show that a vector u on L such that $(u - r) \perp (q - p)$ is a solution of the simultaneous equations

$$(u - r, q - p) = 0,$$
$$u = p + \lambda(q - p), \qquad \lambda \in R.$$

Show that there is a unique value of λ for which these equations are satisfied. Derive a formula for the perpendicular distance from a point to a line. Test your formula on some numerical examples.

4. Let

$$A = \begin{pmatrix} \alpha_{11} & \alpha_{12} \\ \alpha_{21} & \alpha_{22} \end{pmatrix}$$

by a 2-by-2 matrix with entries from R. Define the *determinant* of A, $D(A)$, by the formula

$$D(A) = \alpha_{11}\alpha_{22} - \alpha_{12}\alpha_{21}.$$

a. Show that if A is the matrix of a distance preserving linear transformation T of R_2, then

$$D(A) = \pm 1,$$

and that $D(A) = +1$ if and only if A is a rotation, while $D(A) = -1$ if and only if A is a reflection.

b. Prove that for any 2-by-2 matrices A and B, $D(AB) = D(A)D(B)$.

c. Derive the statements (1), (2), (3) in (14.8).

---

* This definition of a line in R_2 is identical with the definition given in Section 10; no results from Section 10 are needed to do any of these problems, however.

15. INNER PRODUCTS

Let V be a vector space over the real numbers R.

(15.1) Definition. An *inner product* on V is a function which assigns to each pair of vectors u, v in V a real number (u, v) such that the following conditions are satisfied.

(1) (u, v) is a *bilinear function*; that is,

$$(u + v, w) = (u, w) + (v, w),$$
$$(u, v + w) = (u, v) + (u, w),$$
$$(\alpha u, v) = (u, \alpha v) = \alpha(u, v),$$

for all u, v, $w \in V$ and $\alpha \in R$.

(2) The function (u, v) is *symmetric*; that is,

$$(u, v) = (v, u), \qquad u, v \in V.$$

(3) The function is *positive definite*; that is,

$$(u, u) \geq 0$$

and

$$(u, u) = 0 \text{ if and only if } u = 0.$$

EXAMPLES. (1) Let $\{e_1, \cdots, e_n\}$ be a basis for V over R and let

$$(u, v) = \sum_{i=1}^{n} \xi_i \eta_i$$

where $u = \sum \xi_i e_i$, $v = \sum \eta_i e_i$.

(2) Let V be a subspace of the vector space $C[0, 1]$ of continuous functions on the closed interval $[0, 1]$, and define

$$(f, g) = \int_0^1 f(t)g(t) \, dt, \qquad f, g \in V.$$

In both cases the reader may verify that the functions defined are actually inner products.

In the case of R_2 the inner product defined in Example 1 is known to be connected with the angle between the vectors u and v; indeed, if u and v have length 1, then $(u, v) = \cos \theta$ where θ is the angle between u and v. Thus $|(u, v)| \leq 1$ if both u and v have length 1. Our next task is to verify that this same inequality holds in general.

(15.2) Definition. Let (u, v) be a fixed inner product on V. Define the *length* $\|u\|$ of a vector $u \in V$ by

$$\|u\| = \sqrt{(u, u)}.$$

Note that by part (3) of Definition (15.1) we have
$$\|u\| \geq 0, \qquad \|u\| = 0 \text{ if and only if } u = 0.$$
Moreover, we have
$$\|\alpha u\| = |\alpha| \cdot \|u\|$$
where $|\alpha|$ is the absolute value of α in R.

We prove now an important inequality.

(15.3)   Lemma.   *If* $\|u\| = \|v\| = 1$, *then* $|(u, v)| \leq 1$.

Proof.   We have
$$(u - v, u - v) \geq 0.$$
This implies
$$(u, u) + (v, v) - 2(u, v) \geq 0$$
and since $(u, u) = (v, v) = 1$ we obtain
$$(u, v) \leq 1.$$
Similarly, from $(u + v, u + v) \geq 0$ we have
$$-(u, v) \leq 1.$$
Combining these inequalities we have $|(u, v)| \leq 1$.

(15.4)   Theorem (Cauchy-Schwarz Inequality).   *For arbitrary vectors,* $u, v \in V$ *we have*

(15.5)
$$|(u, v)| \leq \|u\| \cdot \|v\|.$$

Proof.   The result is trivial if either $\|u\|$ or $\|v\|$ is zero. Therefore, assume that $\|u\| \neq 0$, $\|v\| \neq 0$. Then
$$\frac{u}{\|u\|}, \qquad \frac{v}{\|v\|}$$
are vectors of length 1, and by Lemma (15.3) we have
$$\left| \left(\frac{u}{\|u\|}, \qquad \frac{v}{\|v\|} \right) \right| \leq 1.$$
It follows that $|(u, v)| \leq \|u\| \cdot \|v\|$, and (15.5) is proved.

As a corollary we obtain the triangle inequality, which is a generalization of an inequality for real numbers (Exercise 2f, Section 2).

(15.6)   Corollary (Triangle Inequality).   *For all vectors* $u, v \in V$ *we have*

$$\|u + v\| \leq \|u\| + \|v\|.$$

Proof.   By the Cauchy-Schwarz inequality and by the triangle inequality for R_1 we have

$$\begin{aligned}
\|u + v\|^2 &= |(u + v, u + v)| = |(u, u) + (v, v) + 2(u, v)| \\
&\leq |(u, u)| + |(v, v)| + 2|(u, v)| \\
&\leq \|u\|^2 + \|v\|^2 + 2\|u\| \cdot \|v\| = (\|u\| + \|v\|)^2.
\end{aligned}$$

Therefore, by Exercise 4 of Section 2,

$$\|u + v\| \leq \|u\| + \|v\|,$$

as required.

(15.7)   Definition.   Let $u, v \in V$. Define the *angle* θ between u and v as the angle, for $0 \leq \theta \leq \pi$, such that

$$\cos \theta = \frac{(u, v)}{\|u\| \ \|v\|}.$$

[Note that $|\cos \theta| \leq 1$ by (15.5).] The vectors u and v are defined *orthogonal* if $(u, v) = 0$ or, in other words, if the cosine of the angle between them is zero. A basis $\{u_1, \cdots, u_n\}$ for a finite-dimensional space V with an inner product is called an *orthonormal basis* if:

(1) $\|u_i\| = 1, \quad 1 \leq i \leq n.$
(2) $(u_i, u_j) = 0, \quad i \neq j.$

An *orthonormal set of vectors* is any set of vectors $\{u_1, \cdots, u_k\}$ satisfying conditions (1) and (2).

(15.8)   Lemma.   *Every orthonormal set of vectors is a linearly independent set.*

Proof.   Let $\{u_1, \cdots, u_k\}$ be an orthonormal set, and suppose

$$\lambda_1 u_1 + \cdots + \lambda_k u_k = 0, \quad \text{for } \lambda_i \in R.$$

Taking the inner product of both sides with u_1 and using the bilinear properties of the inner product we obtain

$$\lambda_1 (u_1, u_1) + \cdots + \lambda_k (u_k, u_1) = 0.$$

By conditions (1) and (2) we have $\lambda_1 = 0$. Taking the inner product with $u_2, \cdots, u_k$ in turn, we have $\lambda_2 = \cdots = \lambda_k = 0$, and we have proved that $\{u_1, \cdots, u_k\}$ are linearly independent.

The next theorem gives an inductive procedure for constructing an orthonormal basis from a given set of basis vectors.

(15.9) **Theorem (Gram-Schmidt Orthogonalization Process).** *Let V be a finite-dimensional vector space with an inner product (u, v), and let $\{w_1, \cdots, w_n\}$ be a basis. Suppose $\{u_1, \cdots, u_r\}$ is an orthonormal basis for the subspace $S(w_1, \cdots, w_r)$. Define*

$$u_{r+1} = \frac{w}{\|w\|}$$

where

$$w = w_{r+1} - \sum_{i=1}^{r} (w_{r+1}, u_i)u_i.$$

Then $\{u_1, \cdots, u_{r+1}\}$ is an orthonormal basis for $S(w_1, \cdots, w_{r+1})$.

Proof. We have three statements to prove: first, that u_{r+1} has length 1; second, that $(u_{r+1}, u_i) = 0$ for $1 \leq i \leq r$; and third, that $S(w_1, \cdots, w_{r+1}) = S(u_1, \cdots, u_{r+1})$ (it follows from the last statement that $\{u_1, \cdots, u_{r+1}\}$ is a linearly independent set). Since $S(u_1, \cdots, u_r) = S(w_1, \cdots, w_r)$, it is clear that $w = w_{r+1} - \sum_1^r (w_{r+1}, u_i)u_i$ is different from zero. Then $u_{r+1} = w/\|w\|$ has length 1. To prove that $(u_{r+1}, u_j) = 0$ for $1 \leq j \leq r$ it is sufficient to prove that $(w, u_j) = 0$. We have

$$(w, u_j) = \left(w_{r+1} - \sum_{i=1}^{r} (w_{r+1}, u_i)u_i, u_j \right)$$

$$= (w_{r+1}, u_j) - \sum_{i=1}^{r} (w_{r+1}, u_i)(u_i, u_j)$$

$$= (w_{r+1}, u_j) - (w_{r+1}, u_j) = 0.$$

Finally, it is clear that $u_{r+1} \in S(w_1, \cdots, w_{r+1})$ and that $w_{r+1} \in S(u_1, \cdots, u_{r+1})$. Since $S(w_1, \cdots, w_r) = S(u_1, \cdots, u_r)$ by assumption, we have $S(u_1, \cdots, u_{r+1}) = S(w_1, \cdots, w_{r+1})$, as required. This completes the proof.

Corollary. *Every finite dimensional vector space V with an inner product has an orthonormal basis.*

Proof. Let $\{v_1, \cdots, v_n\}$ be a basis for V. The Gram-Schmidt process shows that, by mathematical induction, each subspace $S(v_1, v_2, \cdots, v_r)$ $r \leq n$, of V has an orthonormal basis. In particular, $S(v_1, \cdots, v_n) = V$ has such a basis.

We turn now to the concept of length-preserving transformations on a general vector space with an inner product. Some examples of these transformations have already been discussed in the preceding section.

(15.10)   Definition.   Let V be a vector space with an inner product (u, v). A linear transformation $T \in L(V, V)$ is called an *orthogonal transformation*, provided that T preserves length, that is, that $\|T(u)\| = \|u\|$ for all $u \in V.$*

(15.11)   Theorem.   *The following statements concerning a linear transformation $T \in L(V, V)$, where V is finite-dimensional, are equivalent.*

(1) *T is an orthogonal transformation.*
(2) *$(T(u), T(v)) = (u, v)$ for all $u, v \in V$.*
(3) *For some orthonormal basis $\{u_1, \cdots, u_n\}$ of V, the vectors $\{T(u_1), \cdots, T(u_n)\}$ also form an orthonormal set.*
(4) *The matrix $\mathbf{A}$ of T with respect to an orthonormal basis satisfies the condition $^t\mathbf{A} \cdot \mathbf{A} = \mathbf{I}$ where $^t\mathbf{A}$ is the matrix obtained from $\mathbf{A}$ by interchanging rows and columns (called the transpose of $\mathbf{A}$).*

Proof.   Statement (1) implies statement (2). We are given that $\|T(u)\| = \|u\|$ for *all* vectors $u \in V$. This implies that $(T(u), T(u)) = (u, u)$ for all vectors u. Replacing u by $u + v$ we obtain

$$(T(u + v), T(u + v)) = (u + v, u + v).$$

Now expand, using the bilinear and symmetric properties of the inner product, to obtain

$$(T(u), T(u)) + 2(T(u), T(v)) + (T(v), T(v))$$
$$= (u, u) + 2(u, v) + (v, v).$$

Since $(T(u), T(u)) = (u, u)$ and $(T(v), T(v)) = (v, v)$, the last equation implies that $(T(u), T(v)) - (u, v)$ for all u and v.

Statement (2) implies statement (3). Let $\{u_1, \cdots, u_n\}$ be an orthonormal basis of V; then:

$$(u_i, u_i) = 1, \qquad (u_i, u_j) = 0, \qquad i \neq j.$$

By statement (2) we have

$$(T(u_i), T(u_i)) = 1, \qquad (T(u_i), T(u_j)) = 0, \qquad i \neq j,$$

and $\{T(u_1), \cdots, T(u_n)\}$ is an orthonormal set.

Statement (3) implies statement (1). Suppose that for some

---

* In connection with this definition, see Exercise 10 at the end of this section.

orthonormal basis $\{u_1, \cdots, u_n\}$ of V the image vectors $\{T(u_1), \cdots,$ $T(u_n)\}$ form an orthonormal set. Let

$$v = \xi_1 u_1 + \cdots + \xi_n u_n$$

be an arbitrary vector in V. Then

$$\|v\|^2 = (v, v) = (\xi_1 u_1 + \cdots + \xi_n u_n, \xi_1 u_1 + \cdots + \xi_n u_n) = \sum_1^n \xi_i^2$$

since $\{u_1, \cdots, u_n\}$ is an orthonormal set. Similarly, we have

$$\|T(v)\|^2 = (T(v), T(v)) = \left(\sum_1^n \xi_i T(u_i), \sum_1^n \xi_i T(u_i) \right) = \sum_1^n \xi_i^2.$$

Thus statement (1) is proved and we have shown the equivalence of all three statements.

Finally, we prove that statements (3) and (4) are equivalent. Suppose that statement (3) holds and let $\{u_1, \cdots, u_n\}$ be an orthonormal basis for V. Let

$$T(u_i) = \sum_{j=1}^n \alpha_{ji} u_j.$$

Since $\{T(u_1), \cdots, T(u_n)\}$ is an orthonormal set, we have

$$(T(u_i), T(u_i)) = \left(\sum_{j=1}^n \alpha_{ji} u_j, \sum_{j=1}^n \alpha_{ji} u_j \right) = \sum_{j=1}^n \alpha_{ji}^2 = 1$$

and, if $i \neq j$,

$$(T(u_i), T(u_j)) = \left(\sum_{k=1}^n \alpha_{ki} u_k, \sum_{k=1}^n \alpha_{kj} u_k \right) = \sum_{k=1}^n \alpha_{ki} \alpha_{kj} = 0.$$

These equations imply that ${}^t\mathbf{A}\mathbf{A} = \mathbf{I}$, since the (i, k)th entry of ${}^t\mathbf{A}$ is α_{ki}. Conversely, ${}^t\mathbf{A}\mathbf{A} = \mathbf{I}$ implies that the equations above are satisfied and hence that $\{T(u_1), \cdots, T(u_n)\}$ is an orthonormal set. This completes the proof of the theorem.

(15.12) Definition. A matrix $\mathbf{A} \in M_n(R)$ is called an *orthogonal matrix* if ${}^t\mathbf{A} \cdot \mathbf{A} = \mathbf{I}$; then $\mathbf{A}$ is simply the matrix of an orthogonal transformation with respect to an orthonormal basis of V.

EXERCISES

Throughout these exercises, V denotes a finite-dimensional vector space over R with an inner product.

1. Find orthonormal bases, using the Gram-Schmidt process or otherwise, for the subspaces of R_4 generated by the following sets of vectors. It is understood that the usual inner product in R_4 is in use:

$$(\langle \alpha_1, \alpha_2, \alpha_3, \alpha_4 \rangle, \langle \beta_1, \beta_2, \beta_3, \beta_4 \rangle) = \sum_{i=1}^{4} \alpha_i \beta_i.$$

a. $\langle 1, 1, 1, 0 \rangle$, $\langle -1, 1, 2, 1 \rangle$.
b. $\langle 1, 1, 0, 0 \rangle$, $\langle 0, 1, 1, 0 \rangle$, $\langle 0, 0, 1, 1 \rangle$.
c. $\langle -1, 1, 1, 1 \rangle$, $\langle 1, -1, 1, 1 \rangle$, $\langle 1, 1, -1, 1 \rangle$.

2. Find an orthonormal basis for the subspace of $C[0, 1]$ generated by the functions $\{1, x, x^2\}$ with respect to the inner product $(f, g) = \int_0^1 f(t)g(t)\, dt$.

3. Let $\{u_1, u_2, \cdots, u_n\}$ be an orthonormal basis for V.
   a. Show that if $v = \sum \xi_i u_i$, $w = \sum \eta_i u_i$, then

   $$(v, w) = \sum \xi_i \eta_i.$$

   b. Show that every vector $v \in V$ can be expressed uniquely in the form

   $$v = \sum_{i=1}^{n} (v, u_i) u_i.$$

4. Prove that if v_1 and v_2 are characteristic vectors belonging to distinct real characteristic roots of an orthogonal transformation then $(v_1, v_2) = 0$.

5. Let $O(V)$ be the set of all orthogonal transformations on V. Prove $O(V)$ is a group with respect to the operation of multiplication.

6. Two vector spaces V and W with inner products (v_1, v_2) and $[w_1, w_2]$ respectively, are said to be *isometric* if there exists a one-to-one linear transformation T of V onto W such that $[Tv_1, Tv_2] = (v_1, v_2)$ for all $v_1, v_2 \in V$. Such a linear transformation T is called an *isometry*. Let V be a finite-dimensional space with an inner product (u, v), and let $\{v_1, \cdots, v_n\}$ be an orthonormal basis. Prove that the mapping

$$T: \sum_{i=1}^{n} \xi_i v_i \rightarrow \langle \xi_1, \xi_2, \cdots, \xi_n \rangle$$

is an isometry of V onto R_n, where R_n is equipped with the usual inner product given in Example (1) at the beginning of the section.

7. Let V be a finite-dimensional vector space with an inner product, and let W be a subspace of V. Let $W^\perp$ be the set of all vectors $v \in V$ such that $(v, w) = 0$ for all $w \in W$. Prove that $\dim (W) + \dim (W^\perp) = \dim V$.

8. Prove that, if W_1 and W_2 are subspaces of V such that $\dim W_1 = \dim W_2$, then there exists an orthogonal transformation T such that $T(W_1) = W_2$.

9. The vectors mentioned in this problem all belong to R_3, equipped with the usual inner product. A *plane* is a set P of vectors of the form $p + w$, $w \in W$, for some two-dimensional subspace W. From Chapter 2, we know that a set of vectors is a plane in R_3 if and only if it consists of all solutions of a linear equation

$$\alpha_1 x_1 + \alpha_2 x_2 + \alpha_3 x_3 + \alpha_4 = 0, \qquad \alpha_i \in R.$$

where not all of α_1, α_2, α_3 are zero. The two-dimensional subspace W associated with the plane is the set of solutions of the homogeneous equation

$$\alpha_1 x_1 + \alpha_2 x_2 + \alpha_3 x_3 = 0.$$

Note that if $n = \langle \alpha_1, \alpha_2, \alpha_3 \rangle$, then $(n, w) = 0$ for all $w \in W$, and (n, p) is a constant for all $p \in P$. The vector n is called a *normal* vector to the plane.

a. Let n be a nonzero vector in R_3, and α a fixed real number. Show that the set of all vectors p such that

$$(p, n) = \alpha$$

is a plane with a normal vector n, and two-dimensional subspace $S(n)^\perp$.

b. Find a normal vector n and a basis for $S(n)^\perp$ for the plane

$$3x_1 - x_2 + x_3 - 1 = 0.$$

c. Find the equation of the plane with normal vector $n = \langle 1, -1, 2 \rangle$, and containing $p = \langle -1, 1, 0 \rangle$. State the equation both in the form

$$\alpha_1 x_1 + \alpha_2 x_2 + \alpha_3 x_3 = \beta$$

and

$$(n, p) = \alpha.$$

d. Show that a vector x lies on the plane with normal vector n, passing through p, if and only if

$$(x - p, n) = 0.$$

e. Let $a = \langle 2, 0, 1 \rangle$, $b = \langle 1, 1, 0 \rangle$. Find a vector $c \neq 0$ such that $(c, a) = (c, b) = 0$. (*Hint:* show that c is a solution of a certain system of homogeneous equations.)

f. Find the equation of the plane passing through the points $\langle 2, 0, -1 \rangle$, $\langle 1, 1, 1 \rangle$, $\langle 0, 0, 1 \rangle$. (*Hint:* use the result of part **e** to find a normal vector.)

g. Let P be a plane, and let u be a vector not on P. Show that there is a unique vector p_0 on P such that for all $x \in P$,

$$(p_0 - x, p_0 - u) = 0.$$

(*Hint:* Suppose the equation of P is

$$(x - p, n) = 0,$$

where $p \in P$ and n is a normal vector. Then p_0 satisfies the equations

$$(p_0 - p, n) = 0$$
$$p_0 - u = \lambda n$$

for some $\lambda \in R$. Then it is necessary to solve for λ.)

h. Find the perpendicular distance from the vector $\langle 1, 1, 2 \rangle$ to the plane $x_1 + x_2 - x_3 + 1 = 0$, using the result of part **g**.

10. Orthogonal transformations of a finite-dimensional vector space V over R with an inner product are defined by reference to length, not orthogonality. Let T be a linear transformation which preserves orthogonality, in the sense that $(Tv, Tw) = 0$ whenever $(v, w) = 0$. Prove that T is a scalar multiple of an orthogonal transformation.

CHAPTER 5

DETERMINANTS

In calculus, we can learn something about the behavior of a function $f: R \to R$ at a point x by computing the derivative $f'(x)$. For example, if f' is positive on an interval $[a, b]$, the function f is one-to-one on the interval, etc. The determinant plays a similar role in linear algebra. The determinant is a rule which assigns to each linear transformation $T: V \to V$ a number which tells something about the behavior of T (see Section 18). We approach the subject by thinking of the determinant as a function of the row vectors of a matrix of T with respect to some basis. If the matrix of T has real coefficients, the determinant is (up to a sign ± 1) the volume of the parallelopiped whose edges are the rows of the matrix.

16. DEFINITION OF DETERMINANTS

Let us begin with a study of the function $A(a_1, a_2)$ which assigns to each pair of vectors $a_1, a_2 \in R_2$ the area of the parallelogram with edges a_1 and a_2 (Figure 5.1). Instead of working out a formula for

114

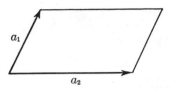

Figure 5.1

this function in terms of the components of a_1 and a_2, let us see what are some of the general properties of the function A. We have, first of all,

(16.1) $A(e_1, e_2) = 1,$ if $e_1 = \langle 1, 0 \rangle$, $e_2 = \langle 0, 1 \rangle$.

Second, if we multiply one of the vectors by a positive real number λ, we multiply A by λ, since the area of a parallelogram is the product of the lengths of the base and height (see Figure 5.2) and the length of λa_1 is λ times the length of a_1.*

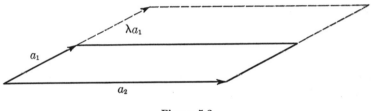

Figure 5.2

In terms of the function A we have:

(16.2) $A(\lambda a_1, a_2) = A(a_1, \lambda a_2) = \lambda A(a_1, a_2),$ for $\lambda > 0$.

Finally, the base and height of the parallelogram with edges a_1, a_2 are the same as those of the parallelogram with edges $a_1 + a_2$ and a_2 (see Figure 5.3), and hence we have:

(16.3) $A(a_1 + a_2, a_2) = A(a_1, a_2) = A(a_1, a_2 + a_1).$

Now stop! One would think that we have not yet described all the essential properties of the area function. We are going to prove,

---

* As in Chapter 4, we define the length of $a = \langle \alpha_1, \alpha_2 \rangle$ as $\sqrt{\alpha_1^2 + \alpha_2^2}$.

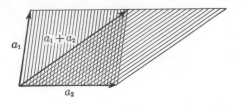

Figure 5.3

however, that there is one and only one function which assigns to each pair of vectors in R_2 a nonnegative real number satisfying conditions (16.1), (16.2), and (16.3). Note also that the function A has a further property:

(16.4) $A(a_1, a_2) \neq 0$ *if and only if a_1 and a_2 are linearly independent.*

It will be convenient to begin by defining a function on sets of vectors from F_n which satisfy Axioms (16.1), (16.2), and (16.3) for arbitrary $\lambda \in F$. We shall derive consequences of these axioms in this section and postpone to the next section the task of proving that such a function really does exist. The reader will note that there is nothing logically wrong with this procedure; it is, for example, what we do in Euclidean geometry, namely, to derive consequences of certain axioms before we have a construction of certain objects that satisfy the axioms. We return to the connection with areas and volumes in Section 19.

(16.5)   Definition.   Let F be an arbitrary field. A *determinant* is a function which assigns to each n-tuple $\{a_1, \cdots, a_n\}$ of vectors in F_n an element of F, $D = D(a_1, \cdots, a_n)$ such that the following conditions are satisfied.

(1) $D(a_1, \cdots, a_{i-1}, a_i + a_j, a_{i+1}, \cdots, a_n) = D(a_1, \cdots, a_n)$,   for $1 \leq i \leq n$ and $j \neq i$.

(2) $D(a_1, \cdots, a_{i-1}, \lambda a_i, a_{i+1}, \cdots, a_n) = \lambda D(a_1, \cdots, a_n)$,   for all $\lambda \in F$.

(3) $D(e_1, \cdots, e_n) = 1$,   if e_i is the ith unit vector

$$\langle 0, \cdots, 0, 1, 0, \cdots, 0 \rangle$$

with a 1 in the ith position and zeros elsewhere.

Now we shall derive some consequences of the definition.

(16.6)   Theorem.   *Let D be a determinant function on F_n; then the following statements are valid.*

(A) $D(a_1, \cdots, a_n)$ *is multiplied by* -1 *if two of the vectors* a_i *and* a_j *are interchanged (where* $i \neq j$*).*

(B) $D(a_1, \cdots, a_n) = 0$ *if two of the vectors* a_i *and* a_j *are equal.*

(C) D *is unchanged if* a_i *is replaced by* $a_i + \sum_{j \neq i} \lambda_j a_j$, *for arbitrary* $\lambda_j \in F$.

(D) $D(a_1, \cdots, a_n) = 0$, *if* $\{a_1, \cdots, a_n\}$ *is linearly dependent.*

(E) $D(a_1, \cdots, a_{i-1}, \lambda a_i + \mu a_i', a_{i+1}, \cdots, a_n)$
$$= \lambda D(a_1, \cdots, a_i, \cdots, a_n) + \mu D(a_1, \cdots, a_i', \cdots, a_n)$$

for $1 \leq i \leq n$, *for arbitrary field elements* λ *and* μ, *and for vectors* a_i *and* $a_i' \in F_n$.

Proof.   (A) We shall use the notation

$$D(\cdots, \underset{i}{a}, \cdots, \underset{i}{b}, \cdots)$$

to indicate that the ith argument of the function D is a and the jth is b, etc. Then we have, for arbitrary i and j,

$$D(\cdots, \underset{i}{a_i}, \cdots, \underset{j}{a_j}, \cdots)$$

$$= -D(\cdots, \underset{i}{-a_i}, \cdots, \underset{j}{a_j}, \cdots) \qquad \text{by property (2)}$$

$$= -D(\cdots, \underset{i}{-a_i}, \cdots, \underset{j}{-a_i + a_j}, \cdots) \quad \text{by property (1)}$$

$$= D(\cdots, \underset{i}{-a_i}, \cdots, \underset{j}{+a_i - a_j}, \cdots) \quad \text{by property (2)}$$

$$= D(\cdots, \underset{i}{-a_j}, \cdots, \underset{j}{a_i - a_j}, \cdots) \qquad \begin{array}{l}\text{by property (1),}\\ \text{since } -a_i \\ \quad + (a_i - a_j) \\ \quad = -a_j\end{array}$$

$$= -D(\cdots, \underset{i}{-a_j}, \cdots, \underset{j}{-a_i + a_j}, \cdots) \quad \text{by property (2)}$$

$$= -D(\cdots, \underset{i}{-a_j}, \cdots, \underset{j}{-a_i}, \cdots) \qquad \begin{array}{l}\text{by properties}\\ \text{(1) and (2).}\end{array}$$

$$= -D(\cdots, \underset{i}{a_j}, \cdots, \underset{j}{a_i}, \cdots)$$

(B) If $a_i = a_j$, $i \neq j$, then by Statement (A) we have

$$D(a_1, \cdots, a_n) = D(\cdots, \underset{i}{a_j}, \cdots, \underset{j}{a_i}, \cdots)$$
$$= D(\cdots, 2a_i, \cdots, a_i, \cdots)$$
$$= -2D(\cdots, -a_i, \cdots, a_i, \cdots)$$
$$= -2D(\cdots, 0, \cdots, a_i, \cdots) = 0,$$

and statement (B) is proved.

(C) Let $j \neq i$, and $\lambda \in F$. We may assume $\lambda \neq 0$. Then

$$D(\cdots, \underset{i}{a_i}, \cdots, \underset{j}{a_j}, \cdots)$$

$$= \lambda^{-1} D(\cdots, \underset{i}{a_i}, \cdots, \underset{j}{\lambda a_j}, \cdots) \qquad \text{by property (2)}$$

$$= \lambda^{-1} D(\cdots, \underset{i}{a_i + \lambda a_j}, \cdots, \underset{j}{\lambda a_j}, \cdots) \quad \text{by property (1)}$$

$$= D(\cdots, a_i + \lambda a_j, \cdots, a_j, \cdots).$$

Repeating this argument, we obtain statement (C).

(D) If $a_1, \cdots, a_n$ are linearly dependent, then some a_i can be expressed as a linear combination of the remaining vectors:

$$a_i = \sum_{j \neq i} \lambda_j a_j.$$

By proposition (C) we have

$$D(a_1, \cdots, a_n) = D\left(\cdots, \underset{i}{a_i - \sum_{j \neq i} \lambda_j a_j}, \cdots \right)$$

$$= D(\cdots, \underset{i}{0}, \cdots)$$

$$= 0 D(\cdots, \underset{i}{0}, \cdots) \qquad \text{by property (2)}$$

$$= 0.$$

(E) Because of property (2) it is sufficient to prove, for example, that

(16.7) $D(a_1 + a_1', a_2, \cdots, a_n)$
$$= D(a_1, a_2, \cdots, a_n) + D(a_1', a_2, \cdots, a_2).$$

We may assume that $\{a_2, \cdots, a_n\}$ are linearly independent [otherwise, by statement (D) both sides of (16.7) are zero and there is nothing to prove]. By (7.15) the set $\{a_2, \cdots, a_n\}$ can be completed to a basis

$$\{\bar{a}_1, a_2, \cdots, a_n\}$$

of R_n. Then by statement (C) and Axiom (2) we have:

(16.8) $D\left(\lambda_1 \bar{a}_1 + \sum_{i>1} \lambda_i a_i, a_2, \cdots, a_n \right) = \lambda_1 D(\bar{a}_1, a_2, \cdots, a_n), \quad \text{for all}$
choices of $\lambda_1, \cdots, \lambda_n$.

Now let

$$a_1 = \lambda_1 \bar{a}_1 + \lambda_2 a_2 + \cdots + \lambda_n a_n,$$
$$a_1' = \mu_1 \bar{a}_1 + \mu_2 a_2 + \cdots + \mu_n a_n.$$

Then
$$a_1 + a_1' = (\lambda_1 + \mu_1)\bar{a}_1 + (\lambda_2 + \mu_2)a_2 + \cdots + (\lambda_n + \mu_n)a_n.$$
By (16.8) we have
$$D(a_1 + a_1', a_2, \cdots, a_n) = (\lambda_1 + \mu_1)D(\bar{a}_1, a_2, \cdots, a_n),$$
$$D(a_1, a_2, \cdots, a_n) = \lambda_1 D(\bar{a}_1, a_2, \cdots, a_n),$$
$$D(a_1', a_2, \cdots, a_n) = \mu_1 D(\bar{a}_1, a_2, \cdots, a_n).$$
By the distributive law in R we obtain (16.7), and the proof of the theorem is completed.

REMARK.   Many authors use statements (E) and (A) instead of Axiom (1) in the definition of determinant. The point of our definition [using Axiom (1)] is that we are assuming much less and can still prove the fundamental rule (E) by using the fairly deep result (7.15) concerning sets of linearly independent vectors in F_n.

EXERCISES

In these exercises D always denotes a fixed determinant function on R_n.

1. Prove that if $a_1 = \langle \xi, \eta \rangle$, $a_2 = \langle \lambda, \mu \rangle$ in R_2, then
$$D(a_1, a_2) = \xi\mu - \eta\lambda.$$
Show that the system of equations
$$\xi x_1 + \lambda x_2 = \beta_1$$
$$\eta x_1 + \mu x_2 = \beta_2$$
has the solutions
$$x_1 = \frac{D(b, a_2)}{D(a_1, a_2)}, \qquad x_2 = \frac{D(a_1, b)}{D(a_1, a_2)},$$
where $b = \langle \beta_1, \beta_2 \rangle$ and $D(a_1, a_2) \neq 0$.

2. Prove that if $a = \langle \alpha_1, \alpha_2, \alpha_3 \rangle$, $b = \langle \beta_1, \beta_2, \beta_3 \rangle$, $c = \langle \gamma_1, \gamma_2, \gamma_3 \rangle$, then
$$D(a, b, c) = \alpha_1(\beta_2\gamma_3 - \gamma_2\beta_3) - \alpha_2(\beta_1\gamma_3 - \beta_3\gamma_1) + \alpha_3(\beta_1\gamma_2 - \beta_2\gamma_1).$$

REMARK.   These problems suggest that Definition (16.5) and Theorem (16.6) can be used to calculate determinants in particular cases, even though we have not as yet proved in general the existence of determinant functions. The next problem gives what is probably the most efficient method of calculating determinants; it is based on the fundamental Theorem (7.22) in Section 7, on reducing sets of vectors to echelon form.

3. **a.** Let $a_1, \cdots, a_n$ be vectors in R_n. Prove either that $a_1, \cdots, a_n$ are linearly dependent [and hence $D(a_1, \cdots, a_n) = 0$] or that

$$D(a_1, \cdots, a_n) = D(b_1, \cdots, b_n),$$

where $b_1, \cdots, b_n$ are in echelon form. [*Hint:* Use Theorem (16.6) and the method of Theorem (7.22); also, see Exercise 4, below.]

   b. Suppose $b_1, \cdots, b_n$ are in echelon form and that $\beta_1, \cdots, \beta_n$ are the first nonzero entries of $b_1, \cdots, b_n$, respectively. Prove that

$$D(b_1, \cdots, b_n) = \beta_1 \cdots \beta_n.$$

   c. Prove that if $a_1, \cdots, a_n$ are linearly independent then $D(a_1, \cdots, a_n) \neq 0$.

4. Calculate the following determinants.

   a. $D(a_1, a_2, a_3, a_4)$, where $a_1 = \langle -1, 0, 1, 1 \rangle$, $a_2 = \langle 2, -1, 0, 2 \rangle$, $a_3 = \langle 1, 2, 1, -1 \rangle$, $a_4 = \langle -1, -1, 1, 0 \rangle$.

   Solution. By Theorem (16.6) we have

$$D(a_1, a_2, a_3, a_4) = D(a_1, a_2', a_3', a_4')$$

where

$$a_2' = a_2 + 2a_1 = \langle 0, -1, 2, 4 \rangle,$$
$$a_3' = a_3 + a_1 = \langle 0, 2, 2, 0 \rangle,$$
$$a_4' = a_4 - a_1 = \langle 0, -1, 0, -1 \rangle.$$

Again by Theorem (16.6), we have

$$D(a_1, a_2', a_3', a_4') = D(a_1, a_2', a_3'', a_4'')$$

where

$$a_3'' = a_3' + 2a_2' = \langle 0, 0, 6, 8 \rangle,$$
$$a_4'' = a_4' - a_2' = \langle 0, 0, -2, -5 \rangle.$$

Finally,

$$D(a_1, a_2, a_3, a_4) = D(a_1, a_2', a_3'', a_4''')$$

where

$$a_4''' = a_4'' + \tfrac{1}{3}a_3'' = \langle 0, 0, 0, -\tfrac{7}{3} \rangle.$$

The vectors a_1, a_2', a_3'', a_4''' are in echelon form, so by part **b** of Exercise 3 we have

$$D(a_1, a_2, a_3, a_4) = (-1)(-1)(6)(-\tfrac{7}{3}) = -14.$$

Note that this whole procedure is easy to check for arithmetical errors.

b. $D(a_1, a_2, a_3)$, where $a_1 = \langle 1, 2, 4 \rangle$, $a_2 = \langle 1, 1, 1 \rangle$, $a_3 = \langle 1, 3, 9 \rangle$.

c. $D(a_1, a_2, a_3, a_4, a_5)$, where $a_1 = \langle 0, 1, 3, 0, 2 \rangle$, $a_2 = \langle 1, -1, 0, 2, 1 \rangle$, $a_3 = \langle 2, 3, -1, 0, 0 \rangle$, $a_4 = \langle 3, 0, 0, -1, 2 \rangle$, $a_5 = \langle 0, -1, 2, 1, 5 \rangle$.

d. $D(a_1, a_2, a_3, a_4)$, where $a_1 = \langle 1, 2, -1, 0 \rangle$, $a_2 = \langle 2, 0, 0, 1 \rangle$, $a_3 = \langle 1, 1, -1, 2 \rangle$, $a_4 = \langle 0, 1, 2, -1 \rangle$.

5. Let $D^*(a_1, \cdots, a_n)$ be a function on vectors $a_1, \cdots, a_n$ in R_n to R such that, for all a_j, a_i', a_i'' in R_n,

(1) $D^*(e_1, \cdots, e_n) = 1$, where the e_i are the unit vectors.

(2) $D^*(a_1, \cdots, \lambda a_i, \cdots, a_n) = \lambda D^*(a_1, \cdots, a_n)$,   for $\lambda \in R$.

(3) $D^*(a_1, \cdots, a_i' + a_i'', \cdots, a_n) = D^*(a_1, \cdots, a_i', \cdots, a_n)$
$$+ D^*(a_1, \cdots, a_i'', \cdots, a_n).$$

(4) $D^*(a_1, \cdots, a_n) = 0$ if $a_i = a_j$ for $i \neq j$.

Prove that D^* is a determinant function on R_n.

17. EXISTENCE AND UNIQUENESS OF DETERMINANTS

It is time to remove all doubts about whether a function D satisfying the conditions of Definition (16.5) exists or not. In this section we shall prove, first, that at most one such function can exist, and then we shall give a construction of such a function. In the course of the discussion we shall obtain some other useful properties of determinants.

(17.1) Theorem. *Let D and D' be two functions satisfying conditions 1, 2, and 3 of Definition* (16.5); *then, for all $a_1, \cdots, a_n$ in F_n,*

$$D(a_1, \cdots, a_n) = D'(a_1, \cdots, a_n).$$

Proof. Consider the function Δ defined by

$$\Delta(a_1, \cdots, a_n) = D(a_1, \cdots, a_n) - D'(a_1, \cdots, a_n).$$

Then, because both the functions D and D' satisfy the conditions of (16.5) as well as of (16.6), Δ has the following properties.

(17.2) $\Delta(e_1, \cdots, e_n) = 0$.

(17.3) $\Delta(a_1, \cdots, a_n)$ changes sign if two of the vectors a_i and a_j are interchanged, and $\Delta(a_1, \cdots, a_n) = 0$,   if $a_i = a_j$ for $i \neq j$.

(17.4) $\Delta(\cdots, \lambda a_i, \cdots) = \lambda \Delta(\cdots, a_i, \cdots)$,   for $\lambda \in F$.

(17.5) $\Delta(\cdots, a_i + a_i', \cdots) = \Delta(\cdots, a_i, \cdots) + \Delta(\cdots, a_i', \cdots).$

Now let $a_1, \cdots, a_n$ be arbitrary vectors in F_n. It is sufficient to prove that $\Delta(a_1, \cdots, a_n) = 0$, and we shall show that this is a consequence of the properties (17.2) to (17.5). Because $e_1, \cdots, e_n$ is a basis of F_n we can express

$$a_i = \lambda_{i1}e_1 + \cdots + \lambda_{in}e_n = \sum_{j=1}^{n} \lambda_{ij}e_j.$$

Using (17.4) and (17.5) applied to the first position, then to the second position, etc., we have

$$\Delta(a_1, \cdots, a_n) = \Delta\left(\sum_{j=1}^{n} \lambda_{1j}e_j, a_2, \cdots, a_n\right)$$

$$= \sum_{j=1}^{n} \lambda_{1j}\Delta(e_j, a_2, \cdots, a_n)$$

$$= \sum_{j_1=1}^{n} \lambda_{1j_1}\Delta\left(e_{j_1}, \sum_{j_2=1}^{n} \lambda_{2j_2}e_{j_2}, a_3, \cdots, a_n\right)$$

$$= \sum_{j_1=1}^{n} \sum_{j_2=1}^{n} \lambda_{1j_1}\lambda_{2j_2}\Delta(e_{j_1}, e_{j_2}, a_3, \cdots, a_n)$$

$$= \cdots = \sum_{j_1=1}^{n} \sum_{j_2=1}^{n} \cdots \sum_{j_n=1}^{n} \lambda_{1j_1}\lambda_{2j_2} \cdots \lambda_{nj_n}\Delta(e_{j_1}, \cdots, e_{j_n})$$

$$= \sum_{j_1, \cdots, j_n=1}^{n} \lambda_{1j_1} \cdots \lambda_{nj_n}\Delta(e_{j_1}, \cdots, e_{j_n})$$

where the last sum consists of n^n terms, and is obtained by letting $j_1, \cdots, j_n$ range independently between 1 and n inclusive. By (17.2) and (17.3) it follows easily by induction* that for all choices of $j_1, \cdots, j_n$, $\Delta(e_{j_1}, \cdots, e_{j_n}) = 0$. Therefore $\Delta(a_1, \cdots, a_n) = 0$, and the uniqueness theorem is proved.

Now we come to the proof of existence of determinants.

(17.6)   Theorem.   *There exists a function $D(a_1, \cdots, a_n)$ satisfying the conditions of Definition (16.5).*

Proof.   We use induction on n. For $n = 1$, the function $D(\alpha) = \alpha$, $\alpha \in F$, satisfies the requirements. Now suppose that D is a function

---

* What has to be proved by induction is that either $\Delta(e_{j_1}, \cdots, e_{j_n}) = 0$ (if two of the j's are equal) or $\Delta(e_{j_1}, \cdots, e_{j_n}) = \pm\Delta(e_1, \cdots, e_n)$ (if the j's are distinct).

on F_{n-1} that satisfies the conditions in Definition (16.5). Fix an index j, $1 \le j \le n$, and let the vectors $a_1, \cdots, a_n$ in F_n be given by

$$a_i = (\alpha_{i1}, \cdots, \alpha_{in}), \qquad \alpha_{ik} \in F, \quad 1 \le i \le n.$$

Then *define:*

(17.7) $D(a_1, \cdots, a_n) = (-1)^{1+j}\alpha_{1j}D_{1j} + \cdots + (-1)^{n+j}\alpha_{nj}D_{nj}$

where, for $1 \le i \le n$, D_{ij} is the determinant of the vectors $a_1^{(i)}, \cdots, a_{n-1}^{(i)}$ in F_{n-1} obtained from the $n-1$ vectors $a_1, \cdots, a_{i-1}, a_{i+1}, \cdots, a_n$ by deleting the jth component in each case.

We shall prove that the function D defined by (17.7) satisfies the axioms for a determinant. By the uniqueness theorem (17.1) it will then follow that all the expansions (17.7) for different j are equal, which is an important result in its own right.

Let us look more closely at (17.7). It says that $D(a_1, \cdots, a_n)$ is obtained by taking the coefficients of the jth column of the matrix $\mathbf{A}$ with rows $a_1, \cdots, a_n$ and multiplying each of them by a power of (-1) times the determinant of certain vectors, which form the rows of a matrix obtained from $\mathbf{A}$, by deleting the jth column and one of the rows.

First let $e_1, \cdots, e_n$ be the unit vectors in F_n; then the matrix $\mathbf{A}$ is given by

$$\mathbf{A} = \begin{pmatrix} 1 & & & 0 \\ & 1 & & \\ & & \cdot & \\ & & & \cdot \\ 0 & & & 1 \end{pmatrix}$$

where zeros fill all the vacant spaces. Then there is only one nonzero entry in the jth column, namely $\alpha_{jj} = 1$. The matrix from whose rows D_{jj} is computed is the $(n-1)$-by-$(n-1)$ matrix

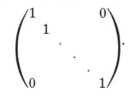

Hence (17.7) becomes

$$D(e_1, \cdots, e_n) = (-1)^{i+j}\alpha_{jj}D_{jj} = 1$$

since $\alpha_{jj} = 1$, and since $D_{jj} = 1$ by the determinant axioms for F_{n-1}.

Next let us consider replacing a_i by λa_i for some $\lambda \in F$. Then the matrix $\mathbf{A}'$ whose rows are $a_1, \cdots, a_{i-1}, \lambda a_i, a_{i+1}, \cdots, a_n$ is

$$\mathbf{A'} = \begin{pmatrix} \alpha_{11} & \cdots & \alpha_{1j} & \cdots & \alpha_{1n} \\ \cdots\cdots\cdots\cdots\cdots\cdots\cdots\cdots\cdots \\ \alpha_{i-1,1} & \cdots & \alpha_{i-1,j} & \cdots & \alpha_{i-1,n} \\ \lambda\alpha_{i1} & \cdots & \lambda\alpha_{ij} & \cdots & \lambda\alpha_{in} \\ \cdots\cdots\cdots\cdots\cdots\cdots\cdots\cdots\cdots \\ \alpha_{n1} & \cdots & \alpha_{nj} & \cdots & \alpha_{nn} \end{pmatrix}.$$

Then (17.7) becomes

(17.8) $\quad D(\cdots, \lambda a_i, \cdots) = (-1)^{1+j}\alpha_{1j}D'_{1j} + \cdots + (-1)^{i+j}\lambda\alpha_{ij}D'_{ij}$
$$+ \cdots + (-1)^{n+j}\alpha_{nj}D'_{nj}$$

where D'_{ij} is defined for $\mathbf{A'}$ as D_{ij} is defined for $\mathbf{A}$. From this definition and the properties of D on F_{n-1} we have $D'_{kj} = \lambda D_{kj}$, for $k \neq i$, and $D'_{ij} = D_{ij}$. Then (17.8) yields the result that

$$D(\cdots, \lambda a_i, \cdots) = \lambda D(a_1, \cdots, a_n).$$

Finally, let $i \neq k$, and consider the determinant of the vectors

$$a_1, \cdots, \underbrace{a_i + a_k}_{i}, \cdots, a_k, \cdots, a_n.$$

Then the matrix $\mathbf{A''}$ whose rows are these vectors is

$$\mathbf{A''} = \begin{matrix} \\ i \\ \\ k \\ \\ \end{matrix} \begin{pmatrix} \alpha_{11} & \cdots & \alpha_{1n} \\ \cdots\cdots\cdots\cdots\cdots\cdots \\ \alpha_{i1} + \alpha_{k1} & \cdots & \alpha_{in} + \alpha_{kn} \\ \cdots\cdots\cdots\cdots\cdots\cdots \\ \alpha_{k1} & \cdots & \alpha_{kn} \\ \cdots\cdots\cdots\cdots\cdots\cdots \\ \alpha_{n1} & \cdots & \alpha_{nn} \end{pmatrix}.$$

Then (17.7) becomes

$$D'' = D(\cdots, \underset{i}{a_i + a_k}, \cdots, \underset{k}{a_k}, \cdots, a_n)$$

(17.9) $\qquad = (-1)^{1+j}\alpha_{1j}D''_{1j} + \cdots + (-1)^{i+j}(\alpha_{ij} + \alpha_{kj})D''_{ij}$
$$+ \cdots + (-1)^{k+j}\alpha_{kj}D''_{kj} + \cdots + (-1)^{n+j}\alpha_{nj}D''_{nj}$$

where the D''_{ij} are defined as in (17.7) from the vectors which constitute the rows of $\mathbf{A''}$. From the induction hypothesis that

$$D(\cdots, \underset{i}{a'_i + a'_s}, \cdots) = D(a'_1, \cdots, a'_{n-1}), \qquad i \neq s \text{ in } F_{n-1}$$

we have now:

(17.10) $\quad D''_{sj} = D_{sj}, \quad \text{for } 1 \leq s \leq n \text{ and } s \neq i, k.$

Inspection of $\mathbf{A}''$ yields also

$$D''_{ij} = D_{ij}.$$

But D''_{kj} is not so easy. The vectors contributing to D''_{kj} are obtained from $\mathbf{A}''$ by deleting the kth row and jth column. Since the ith row of $\mathbf{A}''$ is a sum $a_i + a_j$, we can apply statement (E) of (16.6) to express D''_{kj} as a sum of two determinants, of which the first is D_{kj} and the second $\pm D_{ij}$, where the $\pm$ sign is determined by statement (A) of (16.6) and by an inductive argument is equal to $(-1)^{|k-i|+1}$. Thus we have

$$D''_{kj} = D_{kj} + (-1)^{|k-i|+1}D_{ij}.$$

We shall also need the facts that $(-1)^{|a|} = (-1)^a$ and $(-1)^{a+2b} = (-1)^a$ for all integers a, b. Substituting in (17.9), we obtain

$$
\begin{aligned}
D'' &= (-1)^{1+i}\alpha_{1j}D_{1j} + \cdots + (-1)^{i+i}(\alpha_{ij} + \alpha_{kj})D_{ij} \\
&\quad + \cdots + (-1)^{k+i}\alpha_{kj}[D_{kj} + (-1)^{|k-i|+1}D_{ij}] \\
&\quad + \cdots + (-1)^{n+i}\alpha_{nj}D_{nj} \\
&= D(a_1, \cdots, a_n) + [(-1)^{i+i} + (-1)^{k+j+|k-i|+1}]\alpha_{kj}D_{ij}.
\end{aligned}
$$

We are finished if we can show that the coefficient of $\alpha_{kj}D_{ij}$ is zero. We have

$$
\begin{aligned}
(-1)^{i+j} + (-1)^{k+j+|k-i|+1} &= (-1)^{i+j} + (-1)^{k+i}(-1)^{k-i}(-1) \\
&= (-1)^{i+j} + (-1)^{j-i+1} = (-1)^{i+j} + (-1)^{j+i+1} = 0.
\end{aligned}
$$

This completes the proof of the theorem.

In this section we have proved the existence of a determinant function $D(a_1, \cdots, a_n)$ of n vectors $a_1, \cdots, a_n$ in F_n. If these vectors are given by

$$
\begin{aligned}
a_1 &= \alpha_{11}e_1 + \cdots + \alpha_{1n}e_n \\
&\qquad\qquad\qquad\qquad , \\
a_n &= \alpha_{n1}e_1 + \cdots + \alpha_{nn}e_n
\end{aligned}
$$

that is, if we think of them as the rows of the matrix

$$
\mathbf{A} = \begin{pmatrix} \alpha_{11} & \cdots & \alpha_{1n} \\ & \cdots & \\ & \cdots & \\ & \cdots & \\ \alpha_{n1} & \cdots & \alpha_{nn} \end{pmatrix},
$$

then in the proof of Theorem (17.1) we have shown that

(17.11) $\displaystyle D(a_1, \cdots, a_n) = \sum_{j_1=1}^{n} \cdots \sum_{j_n=1}^{n} \alpha_{1j_1} \cdots \alpha_{nj_n}D(e_{j_1}, \cdots, e_{j_n})$

where the sum is taken over the n^n possible choices of $(j_1, \cdots, j_n)$. Since $D(e_{j_1}, \cdots, e_{j_n}) = 0$ when two of the entries are the same, we can rewrite (17.11) in the form

$$(17.12) \quad D(a_1, \cdots, a_n) = \sum_{j_1, \cdots, j_n} \alpha_{1j_1} \cdots \alpha_{nj_n} D(e_{j_1}, \cdots, e_{j_n})$$

where it is understood that the sum is taken over the $n! = n(n-1)(n-2) \cdots 3 \cdot 2 \cdot 1$ possible choices of $\{j_1, \cdots, j_n\}$ in which all the j_i's are distinct. The formula (17.12) is called the *complete expansion* of the determinant. If we view the determinant $D(a_1, \cdots, a_n)$ as a function $D(\mathbf{A})$ of the matrix whose rows are $a_1, \cdots, a_n$, then the complete expansion shows that, since the $D(e_{j_1}, \cdots, e_{j_n})$ are ± 1, the determinant is a sum (with coefficients ± 1) of products of the coefficients of the matrix $\mathbf{A}$. If the matrix $\mathbf{A}$ has real coefficients, and is viewed as a point in the n^2-dimensional space, then (17.12) shows that $D(\mathbf{A})$ is a continuous function of $\mathbf{A}$.

The idea of viewing the determinant $D(a_1, \cdots, a_n)$ as a function of a matrix $\mathbf{A}$ with rows $a_1, \cdots, a_n$ at once raises another problem. Let $c_1, \cdots, c_n$ be the columns of $\mathbf{A}$. Then we can form $D(c_1, \cdots, c_n)$ and ask what is the relation of this function to $D(a_1, \cdots, a_n)$.

(17.13)   Theorem.   *Let $\mathbf{A}$ be an n-by-n matrix with rows $a_1, \cdots, a_n$ and columns $c_1, \cdots, c_n$; then $D(a_1, \cdots, a_n) = D(c_1, \cdots, c_n)$.*

Proof.   Let us use the complete expansion (17.12) and view (17.12) as defining a new function:

$$(17.14) \quad D^*(c_1, \cdots, c_n) = \sum_{j_1, \cdots, j_n} \alpha_{1j_1} \cdots \alpha_{nj_n} D(e_{j_1}, \cdots, e_{j_n})$$
$$= D(a_1, \cdots, a_n).$$

We shall prove that $D^*(c_1, \cdots, c_n)$ satisfies the axioms for a determinant function; then Theorem (17.1) will imply that $D^*(c_1, \cdots, c_n) = D(c_1, \cdots, c_n)$.

First suppose that $c_1, \cdots, c_n$ are the unit vectors $e_1, \cdots, e_n$. Then the row vectors $a_1, \cdots, a_n$ are also the unit vectors and we have

$$D^*(e_1, \cdots, e_n) = D(e_1, \cdots, e_n) = 1.$$

From (17.14) it is clear, since each term in the sum has exactly one entry from a given column, that

$$D^*(\cdots, \lambda c_i, \cdots) = \lambda D^*(\cdots, c_i, \cdots).$$

Finally, let us consider

$$D^*(\cdots, \underset{i}{c_i + c_k}, \cdots), \qquad k \neq i.$$

That means that, for $1 \leq r \leq n$, α_{ri} is replaced by $\alpha_{ri} + \alpha_{rk}$. Making this substitution in (17.14), we can split up $D^*(\cdots, c_i + c_k, \cdots)$ as a sum $D^*(\cdots, \underset{i}{c_i + c_k}, \cdots) = D^*(\cdots, \underset{i}{c_i}, \cdots) + D^*(\cdots, \underset{i}{c_k}, \cdots)$, and we shall be finished if we can show that $D^*(c_1, \cdots, c_n) = 0$ if two of the vectors, c_r and c_s, are equal, for $r \neq s$. In (17.14), consider a term

$$\alpha_{1j_1} \cdots \alpha_{kj_k} \cdots \alpha_{lj_l} \cdots \alpha_{nj_n} D(e_{j_1}, \cdots, e_{j_k}, \cdots, e_{j_l}, \cdots, e_{j_n})$$

such that $j_k = r$, $j_l = s$. There will also be a term in (17.14) of the form

$$\alpha_{1j_1} \cdots \alpha_{kj_l} \cdots \alpha_{lj_k} \cdots \alpha_{nj_n} D(e_{j_1}, \cdots, e_{j_l}, \cdots, e_{j_k}, \cdots, e_{j_n})$$

and the sum of these two terms will be zero, since $c_r = c_s$ and

$$D(\cdots, e_{j_k}, \cdots, e_{j_l}, \cdots) = -D(\cdots, e_{j_l}, \cdots, e_{j_k}, \cdots).$$

Thus each term of $D^*(c_1, \cdots, c_n)$ is canceled by another, and we have shown that $D^*(c_1, \cdots, c_n) = 0$ if $c_r = c_s$, for $r \neq s$. We have proved that D^* satisfies the axioms for a determinant function. By Theorem (17.1) we conclude that $D(a_1, \cdots, a_n) = D(c_1, \cdots, c_n)$, and Theorem (17.13) is proved.

We can now speak unambiguously of $D(\mathbf{A})$ for any n-by-n matrix $\mathbf{A}$ and know that $D(\mathbf{A})$ satisfies the axioms of a determinant function when viewed as a function either of rows or of columns. When

$$\mathbf{A} = \begin{pmatrix} \alpha_{11} & \cdots & \alpha_{1n} \\ & \cdots & \\ & \cdots & \\ & \cdots & \\ \alpha_{n1} & \cdots & \alpha_{nn} \end{pmatrix}$$

we shall frequently use the notation

$$D(\mathbf{A}) = \begin{vmatrix} \alpha_{11} & \cdots & \alpha_{1n} \\ & \cdots & \\ & \cdots & \\ & \cdots & \\ \alpha_{n1} & \cdots & \alpha_{nn} \end{vmatrix}.$$

Theorem (17.13) can be restated in the form

(17.15) $$D(\mathbf{A}) = D({}^t\mathbf{A}),$$

where ${}^t\mathbf{A}$ is called the *transpose* of $\mathbf{A}$ and is obtained from $\mathbf{A}$ by interchanging rows and columns. Thus, if α_{ij} is the (i, j) entry of $\mathbf{A}$, α_{ji} is the (i, j) entry of $\mathbf{{}^t A}$.

18. THE MULTIPLICATION THEOREM FOR DETERMINANTS

We consider next what is perhaps the most important property of determinants and one that we shall use frequently in the later parts of the book. The definition we have given for determinants was chosen partly because it leads to a simple proof of this theorem.

A natural question to ask is the following. Suppose that $\mathbf{A} = (\alpha_{ij})$ and $\mathbf{B} = (\beta_{ij})$ are n-by-n matrices; then $\mathbf{AB}$ is an n-by-n matrix. Is there any relation between $D(\mathbf{AB})$ and $D(\mathbf{A})$ and $D(\mathbf{B})$? (For 2-by-2 matrices we have already settled this question in Exercise 4 of Section 14.)

The first step is the following preliminary result.*

(18.1) Lemma. *Let $f(a_1, \cdots, a_n)$ be a function of n-tuples of vectors $a_i \in F_n$ to the field F which satisfies Axioms (1) and (2) in the definition (16.5) of the determinant function; then for all $a_1, \cdots, a_n$ in F_n we have*

$$f(a_1, \cdots, a_n) = D(a_1, \cdots, a_n)f(e_1, \cdots, e_n)$$

where the e_i are the unit vectors and D is the determinant function on F_n.

Proof. If $f(e_1, \cdots, e_n) = 1$, then $f = D$ by Theorem (17.1), and the lemma is proved.

Now suppose $f(e_1, \cdots, e_n) \neq 1$ and consider the function

$$\textbf{(18.2)}\quad D'(a_1, \cdots, a_n) = \frac{D(a_1, \cdots, a_n) - f(a_1, \cdots, a_n)}{1 - f(e_1, \cdots, e_n)}.$$

It is clear that D' satisfies the Axioms (1), (2), and (3) of (16.5). Hence, by Theorem (17.1), $D' = D$, and solving for $f(a_1, \cdots, a_n)$ in (18.2) we obtain the conclusion of the lemma.

Before giving the proof of the main theorem, we have to recall a fact about linear transformations on F_n. In Section 12, Example e, we showed that each n-by-n matrix $\mathbf{A}$ defined a linear transformation U of F_n into F_n, where the action of U on a vector $x = \langle \xi_1, \cdots, \xi_n \rangle$

---

* The idea of using this lemma as a key to the multiplication theorem comes from Schreier and Sperner (see the Bibliography).

is given by matrix multiplication of $\mathbf{A}$ with x regarded as a column vector:

$$x \rightarrow U(x) = \mathbf{A} \begin{pmatrix} \xi_1 \\ \cdot \\ \cdot \\ \cdot \\ \xi_n \end{pmatrix}.$$

In the course of the proof of the next theorem, a matrix $\mathbf{A}$ is used to define a linear transformation of F_n according to this definition.

We can now state the main result of this section:

(18.3) Theorem. *Let $\mathbf{A}$ and $\mathbf{B}$ be n-by-n matrices; then $D(\mathbf{AB}) = D(\mathbf{A})D(\mathbf{B})$.*

Proof. Let $\mathbf{A} = (\alpha_{ij})$, $\mathbf{B} = (\beta_{ij})$ and let U be the linear transformation whose matrix is (β_{ij}), that is, $U(a)\mathbf{Ba}$ where $\mathbf{a}$ is the n-by-1 matrix with the same entries as a. Define a function f by

$$f(a_1, \cdots, a_n) = D[U(a_1), \cdots, U(a_n)], \qquad a_i \in F_n.$$

By Axioms (1) and (2) of (16.5) for D it is clear that f satisfies Axioms (1) and (2). By Lemma (18.1) we have $f(a_1, \cdots, a_n) = D(a_1, \cdots, a_n)f(e_1, \cdots, e_n)$ and, hence,

(18.4) $D[U(a_1), \cdots, U(a_n)] = D(a_1, \cdots, a_n)D[U(e_1), \cdots, U(e_n)].$

Now let $a_1, \cdots, a_n$ be the columns of the matrix $\mathbf{A}$. Then for $1 \leq i \leq n$ we compute $U(a_i)$.

Since $a_i = \langle \alpha_{1i}, \cdots, \alpha_{ni} \rangle$, $U(a_i)$ is the vector

$$\left\langle \sum_{k=1}^{n} \beta_{1k}\alpha_{ki}, \cdots, \sum_{k=1}^{n} \beta_{nk}\alpha_{ki} \right\rangle$$

which is the ith column of the matrix $\mathbf{BA}$. Similarly,

$$U(e_i) = \langle \beta_{1i}, \beta_{2i}, \cdots, \beta_{ni} \rangle$$

which is the ith column of the matrix $\mathbf{B}$. Then Equation (18.4) yields

$$D(\mathbf{BA}) = D(\mathbf{A})D(\mathbf{B})$$

and, since $D(\mathbf{A})D(\mathbf{B}) = D(\mathbf{B})D(\mathbf{A})$, the theorem is proved.

As a first application of the multiplication theorem, we prove:

(18.5) Theorem. *Let $\mathbf{A}$ be an n-by-n matrix; then $\mathbf{A}$ has rank n if and only if $D(\mathbf{A}) \neq 0$.*

Proof. Part (D) of Theorem (16.6) shows that if $\mathbf{A}$ has rank less than n then $D(\mathbf{A}) = 0$. It remains to prove that if $\mathbf{A}$ has rank n then $D(\mathbf{A}) \neq 0$. (For another proof see Exercise 3 of Section 16.) Let $\{a_1, \cdots, a_n\}$ be the row vectors of $\mathbf{A}$. Since $\mathbf{A}$ has rank n, $\{a_1, \cdots, a_n\}$ is a basis for F_n; therefore for each i, $1 \leq i \leq n$, we can express the ith unit vector e_i as a linear combination of $\{a_1, \cdots, a_n\}$:

(18.6) $$e_i = \beta_{i1}a_1 + \cdots + \beta_{in}a_n.$$

Let $\mathbf{B}$ be the matrix (β_{ij}); then (18.6) implies that the matrix whose rows are $\{e_1, \cdots, e_n\}$ is the product matrix $\mathbf{BA}$. Since $D(e_1, \cdots, e_n) = 1$, we have by Theorem (18.3),

$$1 = D(\mathbf{BA}) = D(\mathbf{B})D(\mathbf{A})$$

and $D(\mathbf{A}) \neq 0$ as required.

We can now make the following important definition.

(18.7)   Definition.   Let T be a linear transformation of a finite-dimensional vector space over an arbitrary field. Then the *determinant of T*, $D(T)$, is defined to be $D(\mathbf{A})$, when $\mathbf{A}$ is the matrix of T with respect to some basis of the vector space. It is necessary to check that if $\mathbf{A}'$ is the matrix of T with respect to some other basis, then $D(\mathbf{A}) = D(\mathbf{A}')$. By Theorem (13.6) there exists an invertible matrix $\mathbf{X}$ such that

$$\mathbf{A}' = \mathbf{XAX}^{-1}.$$

Then by Theorem (18.3),

$$\begin{aligned}
D(\mathbf{A}') &= D(\mathbf{X})D(\mathbf{A})D(\mathbf{X}^{-1}) \\
&= D(\mathbf{X})D(\mathbf{X}^{-1})D(\mathbf{A}) \\
&= D(\mathbf{XX}^{-1})D(\mathbf{A}) \\
&= D(\mathbf{I})D(\mathbf{A}) \\
&= D(\mathbf{A}),
\end{aligned}$$

where $\mathbf{I}$ is the n-by-n identity matrix.

We can now state the following improvement of Theorem (13.10).

(18.8)   Theorem.   *Let $T \in L(V, V)$, where V is a finite-dimensional vector space over F. Then the following statements are equivalent.*

(1) *T is invertible;*
(2) *T is one-to-one;*

(3) T *is onto;*
(4) $D(T) \neq 0$.

Proof.   The equivalence of (1), (2), and (3) was already proved. By Exercise 8 of Section 13,

$$\dim T(V) = \text{rank } (A),$$

where A is the matrix of T with respect to some basis. If $n = \dim V$, then $T(V) = V$ if and only if the rank of A is n. By Theorem (18.5), the rank of A is n if and only if $D(A) \neq 0$. Combining these statements, we see that (3) and (4) are equivalent, and the theorem is proved.

EXERCISES

1. Compute $D(AB)$ by multiplying out the matrices and also by Theorem (18.3) where

$$A = \begin{pmatrix} 1 & 1 & -2 & 1 \\ 0 & -1 & 2 & 1 \\ 0 & 0 & 3 & 2 \\ 0 & 0 & 0 & -2 \end{pmatrix}, \quad B = \begin{pmatrix} 3 & 0 & 0 & 0 \\ -1 & 1 & 0 & 0 \\ 0 & 1 & -2 & 0 \\ 3 & 2 & 1 & 1 \end{pmatrix}.$$

2. Show that if A, B, C are n-by-n matrices such that $AB = C$, where $D(C) \neq 0$, then $D(A) \neq 0$.

3. Let T be an orthogonal transformation on a finite-dimensional vector space V over the real numbers with an inner product. Show that $D(T) = \pm 1$.

4. Let T be a linear transformation on a finite-dimensional vector space V over F, and let $\alpha \in F$. Prove that α is a characteristic root of T if and only if $D(T - \alpha 1) = 0$, where 1 is the identity transformation on V.

5. This problem shows how the multiplication theorem can be used to derive some important facts about permutations.

   Definitions.   Let $X = \{1, 2, \cdots, n\}$. A *permutation* of X is a one-to-one mapping σ of X onto X. The set of all permutations of X will be denoted by $P(X)$. A permutation σ can be described by the notation

$$\sigma = \begin{pmatrix} 1 & 2 & \cdots & n \\ j_1 & j_2 & \cdots & j_n \end{pmatrix}$$

where $\sigma(1) = j_1$, $\sigma(2) = j_2$, $\cdots$, $\sigma(n) = j_n$. If $\sigma, \tau \in P(X)$, define their product $\sigma\tau$ by the rule

$$(\sigma\tau)(x) = \sigma[\tau(x)], \qquad x \in X.$$

Prove that $\sigma\tau \in P(X)$. For example,

$$\begin{pmatrix} 1 & 2 & 3 & 4 \\ 2 & 3 & 1 & 4 \end{pmatrix} \begin{pmatrix} 1 & 2 & 3 & 4 \\ 1 & 3 & 4 & 2 \end{pmatrix} = \begin{pmatrix} 1 & 2 & 3 & 4 \\ 2 & 1 & 4 & 3 \end{pmatrix}.$$

It can be shown that $P(X)$ is a group.

a. Let V be a vector space over R with a basis of n vectors, $\{v_1, \cdots, v_n\}$. For each permutation σ define a linear transformation $T_\sigma \in L(V, V)$ by the rule

$$T_\sigma(v_i) = v_{\sigma(i)}, \qquad i = 1, \cdots, n.$$

Prove that

$$T_\sigma T_\tau = T_{\sigma\tau}$$

for all permutations σ and τ.

b. Find the matrices of the linear transformations T_ρ, T_σ, T_τ with respect to the basis $\{v_1, v_2, v_3, v_4\}$, in case

$$\rho = \begin{pmatrix} 1 & 2 & 3 & 4 \\ 2 & 1 & 4 & 3 \end{pmatrix} \qquad \sigma = \begin{pmatrix} 1 & 2 & 3 & 4 \\ 1 & 3 & 2 & 4 \end{pmatrix} \qquad \tau = \begin{pmatrix} 1 & 2 & 3 & 4 \\ 4 & 2 & 3 & 1 \end{pmatrix}$$

compute $\rho\sigma$, $\rho\tau$, ρ^2, σ^2, $\tau\rho$, $\tau\sigma$ both from the definition and by multiplying the matrices.

c. Define the *signature* $\epsilon(\sigma)$ of a permutation of $\{1, 2, \cdots, n\}$ by the formula

$$\epsilon(\sigma) = D(T_\sigma)$$

where T_σ is defined as in part **a.** Prove that $\epsilon(\sigma) \pm 1$, and that

$$\epsilon(\sigma\tau) = \epsilon(\sigma)\epsilon(\tau)$$

for all permutations σ and τ.

d. Define a *transposition* $\sigma = (ij)$ to be a permutation such that $\sigma(i) = j$ and $\sigma(j) = i$ for $i \neq j$ and such that $\sigma(x) = x$ for all x different from i or j. Prove by induction that every permutation $\sigma \in P(X)$ is a product of transpositions.

e. Show that the signature of a transposition is always -1.

f. Define a permutation $\sigma \in P(X)$ as *even* if $\epsilon(\sigma) = 1$ and *odd* if $\epsilon(\sigma) = -1$. Prove that σ is even if and only if σ can be factored in at least one way as a product of an even number of transpositions. Prove that even and odd permutations multiply in the following way:

$$(even)(even) = even$$
$$(even)(odd) = (odd)(even) = odd$$
$$(odd)(odd) = even.$$

g. Prove that the complete expansion of the determinant $D(\mathbf{A})$ of a matrix $\mathbf{A} = (\alpha_{ij})$ (see Section 17) can be given in the form

$$D(\mathbf{A}) = \sum_{\sigma \in P(X)} \epsilon(\sigma)\alpha_{1\sigma(1)} \cdots \alpha_{n\sigma(n)}.$$

[This formula is sometimes used as the definition of $D(\mathbf{A})$.]

6. Prove Hadamard's inequality for determinants: if $u_1, \cdots, u_n \in R_n$, then

$$|D(u_1, \cdots, u_n)| \leq \|u_1\| \cdots \|u_n\|.$$

[*Hint:* Show first that it is sufficient to prove that if $\|u_i\| = 1$ for $1 \leq i \leq n$ then $|D(u_1, \cdots, u_n)| \leq 1$. Assume the result for $n - 1$ vectors of length one in R_{n-1}. Prove that if T is an orthogonal transformation then, by Exercise 3 and the multiplication theorem for determinants,

$$|D(Tu_1, \cdots, Tu_n)| = |D(u_1, \cdots, u_n)|.$$

We may assume that $\{u_1, \cdots, u_n\}$ are linearly independent. Then by Exercise 8 of Section 15, there exists an orthogonal transformation T such that $T(u_i) \in S(e_2, \cdots, e_n)$ for $i = 2, \cdots, n$, so that the matrix whose rows are $Tu_1, \cdots, Tu_n$ has the form

$$\mathbf{X} = \begin{pmatrix} \lambda_{11} & \lambda_{12} & \cdots & \lambda_{1n} \\ 0 & \lambda_{22} & \cdots & \lambda_{2n} \\ \cdots & \cdots & \cdots & \cdots \\ \cdots & \cdots & \cdots & \cdots \\ \cdots & \cdots & \cdots & \cdots \\ 0 & \lambda_{n2} & \cdots & \lambda_{nn} \end{pmatrix}$$

where the sum of the squares of the entries in each row is 1 (Why?). Then

$$|D(\mathbf{X})| = |\lambda_{11}| \begin{vmatrix} \lambda_{22} & \cdots & \lambda_{2n} \\ \cdots & \cdots & \cdots \\ \cdots & \cdots & \cdots \\ \cdots & \cdots & \cdots \\ \lambda_{n2} & \cdots & \lambda_{nn} \end{vmatrix} \leq 1$$

by the induction hypothesis and the fact that $|\lambda_{11}| \leq 1$.]

19. FURTHER PROPERTIES OF DETERMINANTS

In this section we take up a few of the many special topics one can study in the theory of determinants.

ROW AND COLUMN EXPANSIONS, AND INVERTIBLE MATRICES

Let $\mathbf{A} = (\alpha_{ij})$ be an n-by-n matrix. Define the (i, j) *cofactor* A_{ij} as $A_{ij} = (-1)^{i+j}D_{ij}$ where D_{ij} is the determinant of the $n - 1$ by $n - 1$ matrix, obtained by deleting the ith row and jth column of $\mathbf{A}$. Then the formulas (17.7) can be stated in the form

$$(19.1) \qquad D(\mathbf{A}) = \sum_{k=1}^{n} \alpha_{kj}A_{kj}, \qquad j = 1, 2, \cdots, n.$$

We shall refer to this formula as the *expansion of $D(\mathbf{A})$ along the jth column*. A related formula is

$$(19.2) \qquad \sum_{k=1}^{n} \alpha_{kj}A_{kl} = 0, \qquad j \neq l.$$

This is easily obtained from (19.1) as follows. Consider the matrix $\mathbf{A}'$ obtained from $\mathbf{A}$ by replacing the lth column of $\mathbf{A}$ by the jth column, for $j \neq l$; then $\mathbf{A}'$ has two equal columns and hence $D(\mathbf{A}') = 0$, since the determinant function satisfies the conditions (1), (2), and (3) of (16.5) when considered as a function of either the row or the column vectors, according to the proof of Theorem (17.13). Taking the expansion of $D(\mathbf{A}')$ along the lth column, we obtain (19.2).

Let $^t\mathbf{A}$ be the transpose of $\mathbf{A}$; then the column expansions of $D(^t\mathbf{A})$ yield the following *row expansions* of $D(\mathbf{A})$, since $D(\mathbf{A}) = D(^t\mathbf{A})$ by (17.15).

$$(19.3) \qquad \sum_{k=1}^{n} \alpha_{jk}A_{jk} = D(\mathbf{A}), \qquad j = 1, 2, \cdots, n.$$

$$(19.4) \qquad \sum_{k=1}^{n} \alpha_{jk}A_{lk} = 0, \qquad j \neq l.$$

These formulas become especially interesting if we interpret them from the point of view of matrix multiplication. Let $\mathbf{A}^*$ be the matrix with A_{ji} in the (i, j) position, and let $\mathbf{I}$ be the matrix whose ith row is the ith unit vector e_i ($\mathbf{I}$ is the *identity matrix*). For any matrix $\mathbf{A} = (\alpha_{ij})$, $\lambda\mathbf{A}$ is the matrix whose (i, j) entry is $\lambda\alpha_{ij}$. Then the formulas (19.1) and (19.2) become

$$(19.5) \qquad\qquad \mathbf{A}^*\mathbf{A} = D(\mathbf{A})\mathbf{I}$$

while (19.3) and (19.4) become

$$(19.6) \qquad\qquad \mathbf{A}\mathbf{A}^* = D(\mathbf{A})\mathbf{I}.$$

We know that the matrix $\mathbf{I}$ plays the same role as 1 in the real number system:

$$\mathbf{A}\mathbf{I} = \mathbf{I}\mathbf{A} = \mathbf{A}$$

for all matrices $\mathbf{A}$. We consider again the problem of deciding if a matrix $\mathbf{A} \neq 0$ has a multiplicative inverse $\mathbf{A}^{-1}$ such that $\mathbf{A}^{-1}\mathbf{A} = \mathbf{A}\mathbf{A}^{-1} = \mathbf{I}$. Let us recall the following definition (see Exercise 7 of Section 12).

(19.7) Definition. An n-by-n matrix $\mathbf{A}$ is *invertible* if there exists an n-by-n matrix $\mathbf{A}^{-1}$, called an *inverse* of $\mathbf{A}$, such that

$$\mathbf{A}\mathbf{A}^{-1} = \mathbf{A}^{-1}\mathbf{A} = \mathbf{I}.$$

(19.8) Theorem. *An n-by-n matrix $\mathbf{A}$ is invertible if and only if $D(\mathbf{A}) \neq 0$. If $D(\mathbf{A}) \neq 0$, then an inverse $\mathbf{A}^{-1}$ is given by*

$$D(\mathbf{A})^{-1}\mathbf{A}^*$$

where $\mathbf{A}^*$ is the matrix whose (j, i) entry is $A_{ij} = (-1)^{i+j}D_{ij}$.

Proof. If $\mathbf{A}\mathbf{A}^{-1} = \mathbf{I}$, then $D(\mathbf{A}) \neq 0$ by the multiplication theorem. If $D(\mathbf{A}) \neq 0$, then setting $\mathbf{A}^{-1} = D(\mathbf{A})^{-1}\mathbf{A}^*$ we have $\mathbf{A}^{-1}\mathbf{A} = \mathbf{A}\mathbf{A}^{-1} = \mathbf{I}$ by formulas (19.5) and (19.6). This completes the proof.

DETERMINANTS AND SYSTEMS OF EQUATIONS

We shall now combine our results to relate determinants to some of the questions studied in Chapter 2 concerning systems of linear equations and the rank of a matrix. The first relation gives an explicit formula for the solution of a system of n nonhomogeneous equations in n unknowns, one that is useful for theoretical purposes. It is less efficient than the methods developed in Chapter 2 for actually computing a solution of a particular system of equations, and cannot be applied to systems with a nonsquare coefficient matrix.

(19.9)   Theorem (Cramer's Rule).   *A nonhomogeneous system of n linear equations in n unknowns*

$$\alpha_{11}x_1 + \cdots + \alpha_{1n}x_n = \beta_1$$

(19.10)

$$\vdots$$

$$\alpha_{n1}x_1 + \cdots + \alpha_{nn}x_n = \beta_n$$

has a unique solution if and only if the determinant of the coefficient matrix $D(\mathbf{A}) \neq 0$. If $D(\mathbf{A}) \neq 0$, the solution is given by

$$x_i = \frac{D(c_1, \cdots, c_{i-1}, b, c_i, \cdots, c_n)}{D(\mathbf{A})}, \qquad 1 \leq i \leq n$$

where $c_1, \cdots, c_n$ are the columns of $\mathbf{A}$ and $b = \langle \beta_1, \cdots, \beta_n \rangle$.

Proof.   By (18.5), $D(\mathbf{A}) \neq 0$ if and only if the columns $c_1, \cdots, c_n$ are linearly independent, and thus the statement about the existence of a unique solution follows from the theorems in Sections 8 and 9 (Why?). Finally, let $D(\mathbf{A}) \neq 0$, and let $\langle x_1, \cdots, x_n \rangle$ be a solution. As in the first part of this section, let

$$A_{ij} = (-1)^{i+j}D_{ij}, \qquad 1 \leq i, j \leq n.$$

For a fixed i, multiply the kth equation in (19.10) by A_{ki}, obtaining

$$A_{ki}\alpha_{k1}x_1 + \cdots + A_{ki}\alpha_{ki}x_i + \cdots + A_{ki}\alpha_{kn}x_n = A_{ki}\beta_k.$$

Adding these expressions together, we obtain

$$\left(\sum_{k=1}^{n} A_{ki}\alpha_{k1}\right)x_1 + \cdots + \left(\sum_{k=1}^{n} A_{ki}\alpha_{ki}\right)x_i$$

$$+ \cdots + \left(\sum_{k=1}^{n} A_{ki}\alpha_{kn}\right)x_n = \sum_{k=1}^{n} A_{ki}\beta_k.$$

By (19.1) and (19.2) we have

$$D(\mathbf{A})x_i = \sum_{k=1}^{n} A_{ki}\beta_k = D(c_1, \cdots, c_{i-1}, b, c_{i+1}, \cdots, c_n)$$

which is the required formula.

One important consequence of these formulas is that when $D(\mathbf{A}) \neq 0$ the solution $\langle x_1, \cdots, x_n \rangle$ of a system (19.10) with real coefficients depends continuously on the coefficient matrix $\mathbf{A}$.

In Sections 8 and 9 we defined the rank of an m-by-n matrix and proved that the row rank and column rank are the same. In (18.5) we showed that for an n-by-n matrix $\mathbf{A}$, the rank is n if and only if $D(\mathbf{A}) \neq 0$. By using this result it is possible to prove a connection between determinants and rank for arbitrary matrices. We first define an *r-rowed minor determinant* of $\mathbf{A}$ as the determinant of an r-by-r matrix obtained from $\mathbf{A}$ by deleting rows and columns. For example, the two-rowed minors of

$$\begin{pmatrix} 1 & -1 & 0 \\ 2 & 3 & 1 \end{pmatrix}$$

are

$$\begin{vmatrix} 1 & -1 \\ 2 & 3 \end{vmatrix}, \quad \begin{vmatrix} 1 & 0 \\ 2 & 1 \end{vmatrix}, \quad \begin{vmatrix} -1 & 0 \\ 3 & 1 \end{vmatrix}.$$

(19.11) Theorem. *The rank of an m-by-n matrix $\mathbf{A}$ is s if and only if there exists a nonzero s-rowed minor and all $(s + k)$-rowed minors are zero for $k = 1, 2, \cdots$.*

Proof. Let us call the number s defined in the statement of the theorem det rank $\mathbf{A}$. We prove first that rank $\mathbf{A} = r$ implies det rank $\mathbf{A} \geq r$. From Section 9, rank $\mathbf{A} = r$ implies that there exists an r-by-r matrix of rank r obtained by deleting rows and columns from $\mathbf{A}$. Then (18.5) implies det rank $\mathbf{A} \geq r$.

Conversely, det rank $\mathbf{A} = s$ implies that there exist s linearly independent rows of $\mathbf{A}$; hence rank $\mathbf{A} \geq s$. Combining the inequalities, we have det rank $\mathbf{A} =$ rank $\mathbf{A}$, and the theorem is proved.

DETERMINANTS AND VOLUMES

We conclude the chapter with the n-dimensional interpretation of the determinant as a volume function. A *volume function* V in R_n is a function which assigns to each n-tuple of vectors $\{a_1, \cdots, a_n\}$ in R_n a real number $V(a_1, \cdots, a_n)$ such that

$$V(a_1, \cdots, a_n) \geq 0,$$
$$V(\cdots, a_i + a_k, \cdots) = V(a_1, \cdots, a_n), \quad i \neq k,$$
$$V(\cdots, \lambda a_i, \cdots) = |\lambda| V(a_1, \cdots, a_n), \quad \lambda \in R,$$
$$V(e_1, \cdots, e_n) = 1, \quad e_i = \text{unit vectors}.$$

Such a function can be interpreted as the volume of the n-dimensional parallelopiped, with edges $a_1, \cdots, a_n$, which consists of all vectors $x = \sum \lambda_i a_i$, for $0 \le \lambda_i \le 1$. The connection between volume functions and determinants is given in the following theorem.

(19.12) Theorem. *There is one and only one volume function* $V(a_1, \cdots, a_n)$ *on* R_n, *which is given by*

$$V(a_1, \cdots, a_n) = |D(a_1, \cdots, a_n)|.$$

Proof. Clearly, $|D(a_1, \cdots, a_n)|$ is a volume function. Now let V be a volume function, and define

$$V^*(a_1, \cdots, a_n) = \begin{cases} \dfrac{V(a_1, \cdots, a_n)D(a_1, \cdots, a_n)}{|D(a_1, \cdots, a_n)|}, & D \ne 0 \\[2mm] 0, & \text{if } D(a_1, \cdots, a_n) = 0. \end{cases}$$

Then one verifies easily that V^* satisfies the axioms for a determinant function and hence that

$$V^*(a_1, \cdots, a_n) = D(a_1, \cdots, a_n)$$

for all $a_1, \cdots, a_n$ in R_n. It then follows from the definition of V^* that $V(a_1, \cdots, a_n) = |D(a_1, \cdots, a_n)|$, and the theorem is proved.

An inductive definition of the k-dimensional volume of a k-dimensional parallelopiped in R_n, based on the fact that the area of a parallelogram is the product of the base and the height, is given in Section 3, Chapter 10, of Birkoff and MacLane (see the Bibliography). They show, by an interesting argument, that the k-dimensional volume in R_n is given by a certain determinant.

EXERCISES

1. List the methods you know for finding the inverse of a matrix. Test the following matrices to see whether or not they are invertible; if they are invertible, find an inverse.

$$\begin{pmatrix} 2 & -1 \\ -2 & 1 \end{pmatrix}, \quad \begin{pmatrix} 2 & 1 \\ 1 & 1 \end{pmatrix}, \quad \begin{pmatrix} 3 & 1 & 0 \\ 1 & 2 & 1 \\ 0 & -1 & 2 \end{pmatrix}.$$

2. Find a solution of the system

$$\begin{aligned} 3x_1 + x_2 \quad\quad &= 1 \\ x_1 + 2x_2 + x_3 &= 2 \\ - x_2 + 2x_3 &= -1 \end{aligned}$$

both by Cramer's rule and by the methods of Chapter 2.

3. Find the ranks of the following matrices using determinants:

$$\begin{pmatrix} 1 & 2 & 3 & 4 \\ -1 & 2 & 1 & 0 \end{pmatrix}, \qquad \begin{pmatrix} -1 & 0 & 1 & 2 \\ 1 & 1 & 3 & 0 \\ -1 & 2 & 4 & 1 \end{pmatrix}.$$

4. Prove that the equation of the line through the distinct points (α, β), (γ, δ) in the plane is given by

$$\begin{vmatrix} x_1 & x_2 & 1 \\ \alpha & \beta & 1 \\ \gamma & \delta & 1 \end{vmatrix} = 0.$$

5. Prove that the following is the equation of the hyperplane in R_3 containing the distinct vectors $\langle \alpha_1, \alpha_2, \alpha_3 \rangle$, $\langle \beta_1, \beta_2, \beta_3 \rangle$, $\langle \gamma_1, \gamma_2, \gamma_3 \rangle$.

$$\begin{vmatrix} x_1 & x_2 & x_3 & 1 \\ \alpha_1 & \alpha_2 & \alpha_3 & 1 \\ \beta_1 & \beta_2 & \beta_3 & 1 \\ \gamma_1 & \gamma_2 & \gamma_3 & 1 \end{vmatrix} = 0.$$

6. Show that the linear transformation $T: a \to T(a)$ of $R_2 \to R_2$, which takes $a = \langle x_1, x_2 \rangle$ onto $T(a) = \langle y_1, y_2 \rangle$ where

$$\begin{aligned} y_1 &= 3x_1 - x_2 \\ y_2 &= x_1 + 2x_2, \end{aligned}$$

carries the square consisting of all points P such that $\overrightarrow{OP} = \lambda e_1 + \mu e_2$, for $0 \le \lambda$ and $\mu \le 1$, onto a parallelogram. Show that the area of this parallelogram is the absolute value of the determinant of the matrix of the transformation T,

$$\begin{pmatrix} 3 & -1 \\ 1 & 2 \end{pmatrix}.$$

7. Show that the area of the triangle in the plane with the vertices (α_1, α_2), (β_1, β_2), (γ_1, γ_2) is given by the absolute value of

$$\frac{1}{2} \begin{vmatrix} \alpha_1 & \alpha_2 & 1 \\ \beta_1 & \beta_2 & 1 \\ \gamma_1 & \gamma_2 & 1 \end{vmatrix}.$$

8. Show that the volume of the tetrahedron with vertices $(\alpha_1, \alpha_2, \alpha_3)$, $(\beta_1, \beta_2, \beta_3)$, $(\gamma_1, \gamma_2, \gamma_3)$, $(\delta_1, \delta_2, \delta_3)$ is given by the absolute value of

$$\frac{1}{6} \begin{vmatrix} \alpha_1 & \alpha_2 & \alpha_3 & 1 \\ \beta_1 & \beta_2 & \beta_3 & 1 \\ \gamma_1 & \gamma_2 & \gamma_3 & 1 \\ \delta_1 & \delta_2 & \delta_3 & 1 \end{vmatrix}.$$

9. Let $p_1, \cdots, p_n$ be vectors in R_n and let

$$p_i = \langle \alpha_{i1}, \cdots, \alpha_{in} \rangle, \qquad 1 \le i \le n.$$

Prove that $p_1, \cdots, p_n$ lie on a linear manifold of dimension $< n - 1$ if and only if

$$\begin{vmatrix} x_1 & \cdots & x_n & 1 \\ \alpha_{11} & \cdots & \alpha_{1n} & 1 \\ \cdots\cdots\cdots\cdots\cdots \\ \alpha_{n1} & \cdots & \alpha_{nn} & 1 \end{vmatrix} = 0$$

for all $x_1, \cdots, x_n$ in R. Prove that, if $p_1, \cdots, p_n$ do not lie on a linear manifold of dimension of $< n - 1$, then $p_1, \cdots, p_n$ lie on a unique hyperplane whose equation is given by the above formula.

10. Prove the following formula for the *van der Monde determinant:*

$$\begin{vmatrix} 1 & \xi_1 & \xi_1^2 & \cdots & \xi_1^{n-1} \\ 1 & \xi_2 & \xi_2^2 & \cdots & \xi_2^{n-1} \\ \cdots\cdots\cdots\cdots\cdots\cdots \\ 1 & \xi_n & \xi_n^2 & \cdots & \xi_n^{n-1} \end{vmatrix} = \pm \prod_{i > j} (\xi_i - \xi_j).$$

(*Hint:* Let $c_1, c_2, \cdots, c_n$ be the columns of the van der Monde matrix. Show that

$$D(c_1, \cdots, c_n) = D(c_1, c_2 - \xi_1 c_1, \cdots, c_{n-1} - \xi_1 c_{n-2}, c_n - \xi_1 c_{n-1})$$

$$= \begin{vmatrix} 1 & 0 & 0 & \cdots & 0 \\ 1 & \xi_2 - \xi_1 & \xi_2^2 - \xi_1\xi_2 & \cdots & \xi_2^{n-1} - \xi_1\xi_2^{n-2} \\ \cdots\cdots\cdots\cdots\cdots\cdots\cdots\cdots\cdots\cdots\cdots \\ 1 & \xi_n - \xi_1 & \xi_n^2 - \xi_1\xi_n & \cdots & \xi_n^{n-1} - \xi_1\xi_n^{n-2} \end{vmatrix}.$$

Then take the row expansion along the first row, factor out appropriate factors from the result, and use induction.)

CHAPTER 6

POLYNOMIALS

and COMPLEX NUMBERS

A prerequisite for understanding the deeper theorems about linear transformations is a knowledge of factorization of polynomials as products of prime polynomials. This topic is developed from its beginning in this chapter, along with the facts about complex numbers that will be needed in later chapters.

20. POLYNOMIALS

Everyone is familiar with the concept of a polynomial $\alpha_0 + \alpha_1 x + \alpha_2 x^2 + \cdots + \alpha_n x^n$ where the α_i are real numbers. However, there are some questions which should be answered: Is a polynomial a function or, if not, what is it? What is x? Is it a variable, or an indeterminate, or a number?

In this section we give one approach to polynomials which answers these questions, and we prove the basic theorem on prime factorization of polynomials in preparation for the theory of linear transformations to come in the next chapter.

141

We begin with a definition. Let F be an arbitrary field. A *polynomial* with coefficients in F is by definition a sequence

$$f = \{\alpha_0, \alpha_1, \alpha_2, \cdots\}, \qquad \alpha_i \in F,$$

such that for some positive integer M depending on f, $\alpha_M = \alpha_{M+1} = \cdots = 0$. We make the following definitions. If

$$g = \{\beta_0, \beta_1, \beta_2, \cdots\},$$

then $f = g$ if and only if $\alpha_0 = \beta_0$, $\alpha_1 = \beta_1$, $\alpha_2 = \beta_2$, $\cdots$. We define addition as for vectors:

$$f + g = \{\alpha_0 + \beta_0, \alpha_1 + \beta_1, \cdots\}$$

and multiplication by the rule

$$fg = \{\gamma_0, \gamma_1, \gamma_2, \cdots\}$$

where, for each k,

(20.1) $$\gamma_k = \sum_{i+j=k} \alpha_i \beta_j = \alpha_0 \beta_k + \alpha_1 \beta_{k-1} + \cdots + \alpha_k \beta_0.$$

It is clear that both $f + g$ and fg are polynomials; that is, $\alpha_M + \beta_M$ and γ_M are zero for sufficiently large M.

For example, let F be the field of real numbers, and let

$$f = \{0, 1, 0, 0, 0, 0, \cdots\}$$
$$g = \{1, 1, -1, 0, 0, 0, \cdots\}.$$

Then

$$f + g = \{1, 2, -1, 0, 0, 0, \cdots\}$$

and

$$
\begin{aligned}
f \cdot g &= \{0 \cdot 1, \ 0 \cdot 1 + 1 \cdot 1, \ 0 \cdot -1, \ + 1 \cdot 1 + 0 \cdot 1, \ 0 \cdot 0 + 1 \cdot -1 \\
&\quad + 0 \cdot 1 + 0 \cdot 1, \ 0 \cdot 0 + 1 \cdot 0 + 0 \cdot 0 + 0 \cdot -1 + 0 \cdot 0, 0, 0, \cdots\} \\
&= \{0, 1, 1, -1, 0, 0, \cdots\}.
\end{aligned}
$$

Computations using these definitions are cumbersome, and after the next theorem we shall derive a more familiar and convenient expression for polynomials.

(20.2) Theorem. *The polynomials with coefficients in F satisfy all the axioms for a field [Definition (4.1)] except the axiom concerning the existence of α^{-1} for $\alpha \neq 0$ such that $\alpha\alpha^{-1} = 1$.*

Proof. Since addition of polynomials is defined as vector addition, it is clear that all the axioms concerning addition alone are satisfied.

The commutative law for multiplication is clear by (20.1). For the associative law, let

$$h = \{\delta_0,\ \delta_1,\ \delta_2,\ \cdots\}.$$

Then the kth coefficient of $(fg)h$ is

$$\sum_{r+s=k}\left(\sum_{i+j=r}\alpha_i\beta_j\right)\delta_s = \sum_{i+j+s=k}(\alpha_i\beta_j)\delta_s$$

while the kth coefficient of $f(gh)$ is

$$\sum_{i+t=k}\alpha_i\left(\sum_{j+s=t}\beta_j\delta_s\right) = \sum_{i+j+s=k}\alpha_i(\beta_j\delta_s)$$

and both expressions are equal because of the associative law in F. Finally, we check the distributive law for multiplication. The kth coefficient of $f(g+h)$ is

$$\sum_{i+j=k}\alpha_i(\beta_j + \delta_j)$$

while the kth coefficient of $fg + fh$ is

$$\sum_{i+j=k}\alpha_i\beta_j + \sum_{i+j=k}\alpha_i\delta_j$$

and these expressions are equal because of the distributive law in F. This completes the proof.

REMARK.   A system which satisfies the axioms for a field except, possibly, the one concerning the existence of solutions of the equations $\alpha x = 1$ is called a *commutative ring*. Thus, the polynomials form a commutative ring. We shall see that the polynomials do not form a field. Another important example of a commutative ring that is not a field is the system of integers defined in Section 3.

It is clear that the mapping

$$\alpha \to \{\alpha,\ 0,\ 0,\ \cdots\} = \alpha'$$

is a one-to-one mapping of F into the polynomials such that

$$(\alpha + \beta)' = \alpha' + \beta', \qquad (\alpha\beta)' = \alpha'\beta'.$$

If we let F' be the set of all polynomials α' obtained in this way, then F' is a field that is *isomorphic* with F, and we shall identify the elements of F with the polynomials that correspond to them; that is, we shall write

$$\alpha = \{\alpha,\ 0,\ 0,\ \cdots\}.$$

Now let x be the polynomial defined by the sequence

$$x = \{0, 1, 0, \cdots\}.$$

Then

$$x^2 = \{0, 0, 1, 0, \cdots\}$$

and (remembering that we index the coefficients starting from 0), in general,

$$x^i = \{0, 0, \cdots, \underset{i}{1}, \cdots\}.$$

Moreover, it is easily checked that we have

$$\alpha x^i = \{\alpha, 0, \cdots\} \{0, \cdots, \underset{i}{1}, \cdots\} = \{0, \cdots, \underset{i}{\alpha}, \cdots\} = x^i \alpha,$$

$$\alpha \in F, \quad i = 1, 2, \cdots.$$

Therefore an arbitrary polynomial

$$f = \{\alpha_0, \alpha_1, \alpha_2, \cdots\}$$

can be expressed uniquely in the form

(20.3) $$f = \alpha_0 + \alpha_1 x + \alpha_2 x^2 + \cdots + \alpha_r x^r.$$

We shall use the notation $F[x]$ for the set of polynomials with coefficients in F.

Computations with polynomials can now be made with ease. For example in order to multiply

$$(3 - x + x^2)(2 + 2x + x^2 - x^3)$$

we see that x^5 is the highest power of x appearing in the product with a nonzero coefficient. Then we compute the product by leaving spaces for the coefficients of $x^0, x^1, \cdots, x^5$ and filling them in by inspection. Thus the product is

$$(3 \cdot 2) + (3 \cdot 2 - 2 \cdot 1)x + (3 - 2 + 2)x^2 + (-3 - 1 + 2)x^3$$
$$+ (1 + 1)x^4 - x^5 = 6 + 4x + 3x^2 - 2x^3 + 2x^4 - x^5.$$

(20.4) **Definition.** Let $f = \alpha_0 + \alpha_1 x + \alpha_2 x^2 + \cdots$ be a polynomial in $F[x]$. We say that the *degree* of f is r, and write $\deg f = r$, if $\alpha_r \neq 0$ and $\alpha_{r+1} = \alpha_{r+2} = \cdots = 0$. We say that the polynomial $0 = 0 + 0x + 0x^2 + \cdots$ does not have a degree.

(20.5) **Theorem.** *Let f, g be nonzero polynomials in $F[x]$; then:*

$$\deg (f + g) \leq \max \{\deg f, \deg g\}, \quad \textit{if } f + g \neq 0,$$
$$\deg fg = \deg f + \deg g.$$

Proof. Let

$$f = \alpha_0 + \alpha_1 x + \cdots + \alpha_r x^r, \qquad \alpha_r \neq 0,$$
$$g = \beta_0 + \beta_1 x + \cdots + \beta_s x^s, \qquad \beta_s \neq 0.$$

Then

$$f + g = (\alpha_0 + \beta_0) + (\alpha_1 + \beta_1)x + \cdots + (\alpha_t + \beta_t)x^t,$$

where $t = \max \{r, s\}$, proving the first statement. For the second statement of the theorem, we observe that fg has no nonzero terms $\gamma_i x^i$ for $i > r + s$ and that the coefficient of x^{r+s} is exactly $\alpha_r \beta_s$, which is nonzero since the product of two nonzero elements of a field is different from zero (Why?). This completes the proof.

(20.6) Corollary. *If f, $g \in F[x]$, then $fg = 0$ implies that $f = 0$ or $g = 0$. If $fg = hg$, and if $g \neq 0$, then $f = h$.*

Proof. If both $f \neq 0$ and $g \neq 0$ then, by (20.5), $\deg fg \geq 0$ and hence $fg \neq 0$. For the proof of the second part let $fg = hg$. Then $(f - h)g = 0$ and, since $g \neq 0$, $f - h = 0$ by the first part of the proof.

(20.7) Corollary. *Let $f \neq 0$ be a polynomial in $F[x]$; then there exists a polynomial $g \in F[x]$ such that $fg = 1$ if and only if $\deg f = 0$. Consequently, $F[x]$ is definitely not a field.*

Proof. If $\deg f = 0$, then $f = \alpha \in F$ and we have $\alpha \alpha^{-1} = 1$ by the axioms for a field. Conversely, if $fg = 1$ for some $g \in F[x]$, then by (20.5) we have

$$\deg f + \deg g = \deg 1 = 0.$$

Since $\deg f$ is a nonnegative integer, this equation implies that $\deg f = 0$, and (20.7) is proved.

(20.8) Theorem (Division Process). *Let f, g be polynomials in $F[x]$ such that $g \neq 0$; then there exist the uniquely determined polynomials Q, R called the quotient and the remainder, respectively, such that*

$$f = Qg + R$$

where either $R = 0$ or $\deg R < \deg g$.

Proof. If $f = 0$, then we may take $Q = R = 0$. Now let

$$(20.9) \quad \begin{aligned} f &= \alpha_0 + \alpha_1 x + \cdots + \alpha_r x^r, & \alpha_r \neq 0, \quad r \geq 0, \\ g &= \beta_0 + \beta_1 x + \cdots + \beta_s x^s, & \beta_s \neq 0, \quad s \geq 0. \end{aligned}$$

We use induction on r to prove the existence of Q and R. First let $r = 0$. If $s > 0$, then

$$f = 0 \cdot g + f$$

satisfies our requirements while, if $s = 0$, then by (20.7) we have $gg^{-1} = 1$ and can write

$$f = (fg^{-1})g + 0.$$

Now assume that $r > 0$ and that the existence of Q and R has been proved for polynomials of degree $\leq r - 1$. Consider f and g as in (20.9). If $s > r$, then $f = 0 \cdot g + f$ satisfies the requirements and there is nothing to prove. Finally, let $s \leq r$. Then, using the distributive law in $F[x]$, we obtain

$$\alpha_r \beta_s^{-1} x^{r-s} g = \beta_0' + \beta_1' x + \cdots + \alpha_r x^r + 0 x^{r+1} + \cdots$$

with coefficients $\beta_i' \in F$ where $\beta_r' = \alpha_r$. The polynomial

(20.10) $f_1 = f - \alpha_r \beta_s^{-1} x^{r-s} g$

had degree $\leq r - 1$, since the coefficients of x^r are canceled out. By the induction hypothesis there exist polynomials Q and R with either $R = 0$ or deg $R < $ deg g such that

$$f_1 = Qg + R.$$

Substituting (20.10) in this formula, we obtain

$$f = (Q + \alpha_r \beta_s^{-1} x^{r-s})g + R,$$

and the existence part of the theorem is proved.

For the uniqueness, let

$$f = Qg + R = Q'g + R'$$

where both R and R' satisfy the requirements of the theorem. We show first that $R = R'$. Otherwise, $R - R' \neq 0$ and we have

$$R - R' = (Q' - Q)g,$$

where deg $(R - R') < $ deg g by (20.5), while $(Q' - Q)g = $ deg $(Q' - Q) + $ deg $g \geq $ deg g. This is a contradiction, and so we must have $R = R'$. Then we obtain

$$(Q - Q')g = 0, \qquad g \neq 0$$

and by (20.6) we have $Q - Q' = 0$. This completes the proof of the theorem.

To illustrate the division process, let

$$f = 3x^3 + x^2 - x + 1,$$
$$g = x^2 + 2x - 1.$$

Then

$$f - 3xg = -5x^2 + 2x + 1,$$
$$-5x^2 + 2x + 1 + 5g = 12x - 4.$$

Since deg $(-8x + 6) <$ deg g, the division is finished and we have

$$f = (3x - 5)g + 12x - 4.$$

Then

$$Q = 3x - 5, \qquad R = 12x - 4$$

Now we come to the important concept of polynomial function.

(20.11) Definition. Let $f = \sum \alpha_i x^i \in F[x]$ and let $\xi \in F$. We define an element $f(\xi) \in F$ by

$$f(\xi) = \sum \alpha_i \xi^i$$

and call $f(\xi)$ the *value of the polynomial f when ξ is substituted for x.* For a fixed polynomial $f \in F[x]$ the *polynomial function* $f(x)$ is the rule which assigns to each $\xi \in F$ the element $f(\xi) \in F$.* A *zero* of a polynomial f is an element $\xi \in F$ such that $f(\xi) = 0$; a zero of f will also be called a *solution* or *root* of the polynomial equation $f(x) = 0$.

The next two results govern the connection between finding the zeros of a polynomial and factoring the polynomial. First we require an important lemma.

(20.12) Lemma. *Let $f, g \in F[x]$ and let $\xi \in F$; then $(f \pm g)(\xi) = f(\xi) \pm g(\xi)$ and $(fg)(\xi) = f(\xi)g(\xi)$.*

Proof. Let $f = \alpha_0 + \alpha_1 x + \cdots + \alpha_r x^r$ and $g = \beta_0 + \beta_1 x + \cdots + \beta_s x^s$. Then

$$(f + g)(\xi) = (\alpha_0 + \beta_0) + (\alpha_1 + \beta_1)\xi + (\alpha_2 + \beta_2)\xi^2 + \cdots$$
$$= (\alpha_0 + \alpha_1\xi + \alpha_2\xi^2 + \cdots) + (\beta_0 + \beta_1\xi + \beta_2\xi^2 + \cdots)$$
$$= f(\xi) + g(\xi).$$

---

* The notation $f(x)$ is sometimes used for a polynomial f; this notation suppresses the distinction between polynomials (which are sequences) and polynomial functions. The need for the distinction arises from the fact that for finite fields F, two different polynomials in $F[x]$ may correspond to the same polynomial function. For example, let F be the field of two elements (see Exercise 1c of Section 4). Then $x^2 - x$ and 0 are distinct polynomials which define the same polynomial function.

Similarly, $(f - g)(\xi) = f(\xi) - g(\xi)$. Next we have

$$
\begin{aligned}
(fg)(\xi) &= \alpha_0\beta_0 + (\alpha_0\beta_1 + \alpha_1\beta_0)\xi + (\alpha_0\beta_2 + \alpha_1\beta_1 + \alpha_2\beta_0)\xi^2 + \cdots \\
&= (\alpha_0 + \alpha_1\xi + \alpha_2\xi^2 + \cdots)(\beta_0 + \beta_1\xi + \beta_2\xi^2 + \cdots) \\
&= f(\xi)g(\xi).
\end{aligned}
$$

This completes the proof of the lemma.

(20.13)   Remainder Theorem.   *Let $f \in F[x]$ and let $\xi \in F$; then the remainder obtained upon dividing f by $x - \xi$ is equal to $f(\xi)$:*

$$
f = Q(x - \xi) + f(\xi).
$$

Proof.   By the division process we have

$$
f = Q(x - \xi) + r
$$

where r is either 0 or an element of F. Substituting ξ for x, we obtain by (20.12) the desired result: $r = f(\xi)$.

(20.14)   Factor Theorem.   *Let $f \in F[x]$ and let $\xi \in F$; then*

$$
f = (x - \xi)Q
$$

for some $Q \in F[x]$ if and only if $f(\xi) = 0$.

The proof is immediate by the remainder theorem.

Now let A be a commutative ring (actually, we have in mind the particular ring $A = F[x]$). If $r, s \in A$, then we say that $r \mid s$ (read "r *divides* s" or "r is a *factor* of s" or "s is a *multiple* of r") if $s = rt$ for some $t \in A$. An element u of A is called a *unit* if $u \mid 1$. An element is, clearly, a unit if and only if it is a factor of every element of A and hence is uninteresting from the point of view of factorization. Since every nonzero element of a field is a unit, it is of no interest to study questions of factorization in a field. An element $p \in A$ is called a *prime** when p is neither 0 nor a unit and when $p = ab$ implies that either a or b is a unit. Two distinct elements are *relatively prime* if their only common divisors are units. An element $d \in A$ is called a *greatest common divisor* of $r_1, r_2, \cdots, r_k \in A$ if $d \mid r_i$, for $1 \leq i \leq k$, and if d' is such that $d' \mid r_i$, $1 \leq i \leq k$, then $d' \mid d$.

We are now going to study these concepts for the ring of polynomials $F[x]$. An almost identical discussion holds for the ring of integers Z, and the reader will find it worthwhile to write out this application for himself.

---

* The primes in $F[x]$, where F is a field, are sometimes called *irreducible polynomials*.

We note first that the set of units in $F[x]$ coincides with the "constant" polynomials $\alpha \in F$ where $\alpha \neq 0$, that is, the polynomials of degree zero.

(20.15) **Theorem.** *Let $f_1, \cdots, f_k$ be arbitrary nonzero polynomials in $F[x]$; then:*

(1) *The elements $f_1, \cdots, f_k$ possess at least one greatest common divisor d.*

(2) *The greatest common divisor d is uniquely determined up to a unit factor and can be expressed in the form*

$$d = h_1 f_1 + \cdots + h_k f_k$$

for some polynomials $\{h_i\}$ in $F[x]$.

Proof. Consider the set S of all polynomials of the form

$$\sum_{i=1}^{k} g_i f_i,$$

where the $\{g_i\}$ are arbitrary polynomials. Then S contains the set of polynomials $\{f_1, \cdots, f_k\}$ and has the property that, if $p \in S$ and $h \in F[x]$, then $ph \in S$. Since the degrees of nonzero elements of S are in $N \cup \{0\}$, by the well-ordering principle (3.2) we can find a nonzero polynomial

$$d = h_1 f_1 + \cdots + h_k f_k \in S$$

such that $\deg d \leq \deg d'$ for all nonzero $d' \in S$.

We prove first that $d \mid f_i$ for $1 \leq i \leq k$. By the division process we have, for $1 \leq i \leq k$,

$$f_i = d q_i + r_i$$

where either $r_i = 0$, or $\deg r_i < \deg d$ and

$$r_i = f_i - d q_i \in S.$$

Because of the choice of d as a polynomial of least degree in S we have $r_i = 0$ and, hence, d divides each f_i for $1 \leq i \leq k$.

Now let d' be another common divisor of $f_1, \cdots, f_k$. Then there are polynomials g_i such that $f_i = d' g_i$, $1 \leq i \leq k$, and

$$d = \sum h_i f_i = \sum h_i d' g_i = d' \left(\sum h_i g_i \right).$$

Therefore $d' \mid d$, and d is a greatest common divisor of $\{f_1, \cdots, f_k\}$.

Finally, let e be another greatest common divisor of $\{f_1, \cdots, f_k\}$. Then $d \mid e$ and $e \mid d$. Therefore there exist polynomials u and v such that $e = du$, $d = ev$. Then $e = euv$ and $e(1 - uv) = 0$. By (20.6) we have $1 - uv = 0$, so that u and v are units. This completes the proof of the theorem.

(20.16) Corollary. *Let* $r_1, \cdots, r_k$ *be elements of* $F[x]$ *that have no common factors other than units; then there exist elements* $x_1, \cdots, x_k$ *in* $F[x]$ *such that*

$$x_1 r_1 + \cdots + x_k r_k = 1.$$

(20.17) Corollary. *Let* p *be a prime in* $F[x]$ *and let* $p \mid ab$; *then either* $p \mid a$ *or* $p \mid b$.

Proof. Suppose p does not divide a. Then a and p are relatively prime, and by (20.15) we have

$$au + pv = 1$$

for some $u, v \in F[x]$. Then

$$abu + pvb = b$$

and, since $p \mid ab$, we have $p \mid b$ by the distributive law in $F[x]$.

(20.18) Unique Factorization Theorem. *Let* $a \neq 0$ *be an element of* $F[x]$; *then either* a *is a unit or*

$$a = p_1 \cdots p_s, \qquad s \geq 1,$$

where $p_1, \cdots, p_s$ *are primes. Moreover,*

(20.19)
$$p_1 \cdots p_s = q_1 \cdots q_t,$$

where the $\{p_i\}$ *and* $\{q_j\}$ *are primes, implies that* $s = t$, *and for a suitable indexing of the* p's *and* q's *we have*

$$p_1 = \epsilon_1 q_1, \cdots, p_s = \epsilon_t q_t$$

where the ϵ_i *are units.*

Proof. The existence of at least one factorization of a into primes is clear by induction on deg a.

For the uniqueness assertion, we use induction on s, the result being clear if $s = 1$. Given (20.19) we apply (20.17) to conclude that p_1 divides some q_j, and we may assume that $j = 1$. Then $q_1 = p_1 \epsilon_1$ for some unit ϵ_1. Then (20.19) becomes

$$p_1 \cdots p_s = \epsilon_1 p_1 q_2 \cdots q_t.$$

By the cancellation law we have

$$p_2 \cdots p_s = \epsilon_1 q_2 \cdots q_t = q_2' q_3 \cdots q_t$$

where $q_2' = \epsilon_1 q_2$. The result now follows, by the induction hypothesis.

We have followed the approach to the unique factorization theorem via the theory of the greatest common divisor because the greatest common divisor will be used in Chapter 7. It is interesting that the uniqueness of factorization can be proved by using nothing but the well-ordering principle for sets of natural numbers and the simplest facts concerning degrees of polynomials. Neither the division process nor the theory of the greatest common divisor is needed.

The following proof was discovered in 1960 by Charles Giffen while he was an undergraduate at the University of Wisconsin.

Suppose the uniqueness of factorization is false in $F[x]$. Then by the well-ordering principle there will be a polynomial of least degree

(20.20) $$f = p_1 \cdots p_r = q_1 \cdots q_s,$$

where the $\{p_i\}$ and $\{q_j\}$ are primes, which has two essentially different factorizations. We may assume that $r > 1$ and $s > 1$ and that no p_i coincides with a q_j, for otherwise we could cancel p_i and q_j and obtain a polynomial of lower degree than that of f with two essentially different factorizations. We may assume also that each p_i and q_j has leading coefficient (that is, the coefficient of the highest power of x) equal to 1. By interchanging the p's and q's, if necessary, we may arrange matters so that deg $p_r \leq$ deg q_s. Then for a suitable power x^i of x the coefficient of $x^{\deg q_s}$ in the polynomial $q_s - x^i p_r$ will cancel and we will have $0 \leq$ deg $(q_s - x^i p_r) <$ deg q_s. Now form the polynomial

$$f_1 = f - q_1 \cdots q_{s-1}(x^i p_r).$$

By (20.20) we have

(20.21) $$f_1 = q_1 \cdots q_{s-1}(q_s - x^i p_r)$$

and so, by what has been said, $f_1 \neq 0$ and deg $f_1 <$ deg f. But from the form of f_1 we see that $p_r \mid f_1$ and, since prime factorization is unique for polynomials of degree $<$ deg f, we conclude from (20.21) that $p_r \mid (q_s - x^i p_r)$, since p_r is distinct from all the primes $q_1, \cdots, q_{s-1}$. Then

$$q_s - x^i p_r = h p_r$$

and

$$q_s = p_r(h + x^i)$$

which is a contradiction. This completes the proof of unique factorization.*

___
* Note that the same argument establishes the uniqueness of factorization in the ring of integers Z. In more detail, if uniqueness of factorization does not hold

We conclude this section with the observation familiar to us from high school algebra that, although $F[x]$ is not a field, $F[x]$ can be embedded in a field, and in exactly the way that the integers can be embedded in the field of rational numbers. Some of the details will be omitted.

Consider all pairs (f, g), for f and $g \in F[x]$, where $g \neq 0$. Define two such pairs (f, g) and (h, k) as *equivalent* if $fk = gh$; in this case we write $(f, g) \sim (h, k)$. Then the relation $\sim$ has the properties:

(1) $(f, g) \sim (f, g)$.
(2) $(f, g) \sim (h, k)$ implies $(h, k) \sim (f, g)$.
(3) $(f, g) \sim (h, k)$, $(h, k) \sim (p, q)$ imply $(f, g) \sim (p, q)$.

[For the proof of property 3 the cancellation law (20.6) is required.] Now define a fraction f/g, with $g \neq 0$, to be the set of all pairs (h, k), $k \neq 0$, such that $(h, k) \sim (f, g)$. Then we can state:

(4) Every pair (f, g) belongs to one and only one fraction f/g.
(5) Two fractions f/g and r/s coincide if and only if $fs = gr$.

Now we define:

(6) $f/g + r/s = (fs + gr)/gs$.
(7) $(f/g)(r/s) = fr/gs$.

It can be proved first of all that the operations of addition and multiplication of fractions are defined independently of the representatives of the fractions. In other words, one has to show that if $f/g = f_1/g_1$ and $r/s = r_1/s_1$ then

$$\frac{fs + gr}{gs} = \frac{f_1 s_1 + g_1 r_1}{g_1 s_1}$$

and that a similar statement holds for multiplication.

Now we shall state a result. The proof offers no difficulties, and will be omitted.

(20.22)   Theorem.   *The set of fractions f/g, $g \neq 0$, with respect to the operations of addition and multiplication previously defined, forms a field $F(x)$. The mapping $f \to fg/g = \varphi(f)$, where $f \in F[x]$, is a one-*

---

in Z, there exists a smallest positive integer $m = p_1 \cdots p_r = q_1 \cdots q_s$ which has two essentially different factorizations. Then we may assume that no p_i coincides with a q_j and that r and s are greater than 1. We may also assume that $p_r < q_s$ and form $m_1 = m - q_1 \cdots q_{s-1} p_r$. Then $m_1 < m$, and $p_r \mid m_1$. Since $m_1 = q_1 \cdots q_{s-1}(q_s - p_r)$, it follows that $p_r \mid (q_s - p_r)$, which is a contradiction. This argument first came to the attention of the author in Courant and Robbins (see the Bibliography).

to-one mapping of $F[x]$ into $F(x)$ such that $\varphi(f + h) = \varphi(f) + \varphi(h)$ and $\varphi(fh) = \varphi(f)\varphi(h)$ for f, $h \in F[x]$.

The field $F(x)$ we have constructed is called the *field of rational functions* in one variable with coefficients in F; it is also called the *quotient field* of the polynomial ring $F[x]$. If we identify the polynomial $f \in F[x]$ with the rational function $\varphi(f) = fg/g$, $g \neq 0$, then we may say that the field $F(x)$ contains the polynomial ring $F[x]$.

EXERCISES

1. Use the method of proof of Theorem (20.8) to find the quotient Q and the remainder R such that
$$f = Qg + R$$
where
$$f = 2x^4 - x^3 + x - 1,$$
$$g = 3x^3 - x^2 + 3.$$

2. Prove that a polynomial $f \in F[x]$ has at most $\deg f$ distinct zeros in F, where F is any field.

3. Let $f = ax^2 + bx + c$, for a, b, c real numbers and $a \neq 0$. Prove that f is a prime in $R[x]$ if and only if $b^2 - 4ac < 0$. Prove that if $b^2 - 4ac = D \geq 0$ then
$$f = a\left(x - \frac{-b + \sqrt{D}}{2a}\right)\left(x - \frac{-b - \sqrt{D}}{2a}\right).$$

4. Let F be any field and let $f \in F[x]$ be a polynomial of degree ≤ 3. Prove that f is a prime in $F[x]$ if and only if f either has degree 1 or has no zeros in F. Is the same result valid if $\deg f > 3$?

5. Prove that, if a rational number m/n, for m and n relatively prime integers, is a root of the polynomial equation
$$a_0x^r + a_1x^{r-1} + \cdots + a_r = 0$$
where the $a_i \in Z$, then $n \mid a_0$ and $m \mid a_r$.* Use this result to list the possible rational roots of the equations
$$2x^3 - 6x^2 + 9 = 0,$$
$$x^3 - 8x^2 + 12 = 0.$$

---

* This argument uses the fact that the law of unique factorization holds for the integers Z, as we pointed out in the footnote to Giffen's proof of unique factorization in $F[x]$.

6. Prove that if m is a positive integer which is not a square in Z then $\sqrt{m}$ is irrational (use Exercise 5).

7. Factor the following polynomials into their prime factors in $Q[x]$ and $R[x]$.
    a. $2x^3 - x^2 + x + 1$.
    b. $3x^3 + 2x^2 - 4x + 1$.
    c. $x^6 + 1$.
    d. $x^4 + 16$.

8. Let A be the ring Z or $F[x]$ and let $a \in A$ and $b \in A$ be expressed in the forms

$$a = p_1^{a_1} \cdots p_r^{a_r},$$
$$b = p_1^{b_1} \cdots p_r^{b_r}, \qquad a_i, b_i \geq 0,$$

where the p_i are distinct primes. Prove that if (a, b) denotes the greatest common divisor of a and b then $(a, b) = p_1^{u_1} \cdots p_r^{u_r}$ for $u_i = \min\{a_i, b_i\}$, $1 \leq i \leq r$. Define the *least common multiple* $[a, b]$ of a, b. Prove that $[a, b]$ exists and is expressible as

$$[a, b] = p_1^{m_1} \cdots p_r^{m_r}, \qquad m_i = \max\{a_i, b_i\}.$$

Prove that $(a, b)[a, b]$ differs from ab by a unit factor.

9. Let $a, b \in F[x]$ for $a, b \neq 0$. Apply the division process to obtain

$$a = bq_0 + r_0$$
$$b = r_0q_1 + r_1, \qquad \deg r_1 < \deg r_0$$
$$r_0 = r_1q_2 + r_2, \qquad \deg r_2 < \deg r_1$$
$$\cdots$$
$$r_i = r_{i+1}q_{i+2} + r_{i+2}, \qquad \deg r_{i+2} < \deg r_{i+1}$$

Show that for some i_0, $r_{i_0} \neq 0$ and $r_{i_0+1} = 0$. Prove that $r_{i_0} = (a, b)$.

10. Find the greatest common divisor of the following pairs of polynomials in the ring $R[x]$.
    a. $4x^3 + 2x^2 - 2x - 1$, $2x^3 - x^2 + x + 1$.
    b. $x^3 - x + 1$, $2x^4 + x^2 + x - 5$.

11. Let F be the field of two elements defined in Exercise 1, part c, of Section 4. Factor the following polynomials into primes in $F[x]$: $x^2 + x + 1$, $x^3 + 1$, $x^4 + x^2 + 1$, $x^4 + 1$.

12. Find the greatest common divisor of $x^5 + x^4 + x^3 + x^2 + x + 1$ and $x^3 + x^2 + x + 1$ in $F[x]$, where F is the field of two elements as in Exercise 11.

21. COMPLEX NUMBERS

The field of real numbers of R has the drawback that not every quadratic equation with real coefficients has a solution in R. This fact was circumvented by mathematicians of the eighteenth and nineteenth centuries by assuming that the equation $x^2 + 1 = 0$ had a solution i, and they investigated the properties of the new system of "imaginary" numbers obtained by considering the real numbers together with the new number i. Although today we do not regard the complex numbers as any more imaginary than real numbers, it was clear that mathematicians such as Euler used the "imaginary" number i with some hesitation, since it was not constructed in a clear way from the real numbers.

Whatever the properties of the new number system, the eighteenth- and nineteenth-century mathematicians insisted upon making the new numbers obey the same rules of algebra as the real numbers. In particular, they reasoned, the new number system had to contain all such expressions as

$$\alpha + \beta i + \gamma i^2 + \cdots$$

where α, β, γ, $\cdots$ were real numbers. Since $i^2 = -1$, $i^3 = -i$, etc., any such expression could be simplified to an expression like

$$\alpha + \beta i, \qquad \alpha, \beta \in R.$$

The rules of combination of these numbers were easily found to be

$$(\alpha + \beta i) + (\gamma + \delta i) = (\alpha + \gamma) + (\beta + \delta)i,$$
$$(\alpha + \beta i)(\gamma + \delta i) = \alpha\gamma + \beta\delta i^2 + \alpha\delta i + \beta i\gamma,$$
$$= (\alpha\gamma - \beta\delta) + (\alpha\delta + \beta\gamma)i.$$

This was the situation when the Irish mathematician W. R. Hamilton became interested in complex numbers in the 1840's. He realized first that the complex numbers would not seem quite so imaginary if there were a rigorous way of constructing them from the real numbers, and we shall give his construction.

(21.1) Definition.   The system of *complex numbers* C is the two-dimensional vector space R_2 over the real numbers R together with two operations, called addition and multiplication, addition being the vector addition defined in R_2 and multiplication being defined by the rule

$$\langle \alpha, \beta \rangle \langle \gamma, \delta \rangle = \langle \alpha\gamma - \beta\delta, \alpha\delta + \beta\gamma \rangle.$$

(21.2)⋆ Theorem. *The complex numbers form a field.*

The mapping $\alpha \rightarrow \langle \alpha, 0 \rangle = \alpha'$ of $R \rightarrow C$ is a one-to-one mapping such that

$$(\alpha + \beta)' = \alpha' + \beta', \qquad (\alpha\beta)' = \alpha'\beta'.$$

In this sense we may say that R is contained in C, and we shall write $\alpha = \langle \alpha, 0 \rangle$.

There is no longer anything mysterious about the equation $x^2 + 1 = 0$. Remembering that $1 = \langle 1, 0 \rangle$, we see that $\pm \langle 0, 1 \rangle$ are the solutions of the equation, so that if we define i by

$$i = \langle 0, 1 \rangle$$

then $i^2 = -1$. For all $\beta = \langle \beta, 0 \rangle \in R$ we have $\beta i = \langle 0, \beta \rangle$, and hence every complex number $z = \langle \alpha, \beta \rangle$ can be expressed as

$$z = \langle \alpha, \beta \rangle = \langle \alpha, 0 \rangle + \langle 0, \beta \rangle = \alpha \cdot 1 + \beta i.$$

We shall call α the *real part* of z and β the *imaginary part*. Moreover, $\alpha + \beta i = \gamma + \delta i$ if and only if $\alpha = \gamma$ and $\beta = \delta$.

Another point that Hamilton emphasized was that not only i but every complex number $z = \alpha + \beta i$ is a root of a quadratic equation with real coefficients. To find the equation, we compare

$$z^2 = (\alpha^2 - \beta^2) + (2\alpha\beta)i$$

with $z = \alpha + \beta i$. We find that

$$z^2 - 2\alpha z = -\alpha^2 - \beta^2$$

so that the equation satisfied by $z = \alpha + \beta i$ is

(21.3) $$z^2 - 2\alpha z + (\alpha^2 + \beta^2) = 0.$$

We know that there is another root of this equation, and we find that it is given by

$$\bar{z} = \alpha - \beta i.$$

Since the constant term of a quadratic polynomial $z^2 + Az + B$ is easily seen by the factor theorem to be the product of the zeros, we see at once that

$$z\bar{z} = \alpha^2 + \beta^2.$$

If we let $|z| = \sqrt{\alpha^2 + \beta^2}$, then $|z|$ is the length of the vector $\langle \alpha, \beta \rangle$, and is called the *absolute value* of z. We have shown that

(21.4) $$z\bar{z} = |z|^2.$$

From this formula we obtain a simple formula for z^{-1}, if $z \neq 0$, namely,

$$(21.5) \qquad z^{-1} = \frac{\bar{z}}{|z|^2}.$$

The complex number $\bar{z}$ is called the *conjugate* of z; it is the other root of the quadratic equation with real coefficients satisfied by z. The operation of taking conjugates has the properties

$$\overline{z_1 + z_2} = \bar{z}_1 + \bar{z}_2, \qquad \overline{z_1 z_2} = \bar{z}_1 \bar{z}_2.$$

Thus $z \to \bar{z}$ is an isomorphism of C onto C, and we say it is an *automorphism* of C. Using this automorphism, we can derive the formula $|z_1 z_2| = |z_1|\, |z_2|$, since

$$|z_1 z_2|^2 = z_1 z_2 \bar{z}_1 \bar{z}_2 = z_1 z_2 \bar{z}_1 \bar{z}_2 = (z_1 \bar{z}_1)(z_2 \bar{z}_2) = |z_1|^2\, |z_2|^2.$$

If $z_1 = \alpha + \beta i$ and $z_2 = \gamma + \delta i$, then this formula gives the remarkable identity for real numbers,

$$(\alpha\gamma - \beta\delta)^2 + (\alpha\delta + \beta\gamma)^2 = (\alpha^2 + \beta^2)(\gamma^2 + \delta^2),$$

which asserts that a product of two sums of two squares can be expressed as a sum of two squares.*

We come next to the important *polar representation* of complex numbers. Let $z = \langle \alpha, \beta \rangle$; then letting $\rho = \sqrt{\alpha^2 + \beta^2} = |z|$, we can write

$$\alpha = \rho \cos \theta, \qquad \beta = \rho \sin \theta,$$

where θ is the angle determined by the rays joining the origin to the points $(1, 0)$ and (α, β). Thus,†

$$z = \alpha + \beta i = \rho\,(\cos \theta + i \sin \theta) = |z|\,(\cos \theta + i \sin \theta)$$

where we note that

$$|z| = |\rho|, \qquad |\cos \theta + i \sin \theta| = 1.$$

If $w = |w|\,(\cos \varphi + i \sin \varphi)$, then we obtain

$$\begin{aligned} zw &= |z|\,|w|(\cos \theta + i \sin \theta)(\cos \varphi + i \sin \varphi) \\ &= |zw|[(\cos \theta \cos \varphi - \sin \theta \sin \varphi) + i(\sin \theta \cos \varphi + \cos \theta \sin \varphi)]. \end{aligned}$$

From the addition theorems for the sine and cosine functions, this formula becomes

---

* For a discussion of this formula and analogous formulas for sums of four and eight squares, see the article by Curtis which appears in the first book listed in the Bibliography. It contains references to the original papers on these questions.

† We write $i \sin \theta$ instead of the more natural $(\sin \theta)i$ in order to keep the number of parentheses down to a minimum.

(21.6) $zw = |z| \, |w| [\cos (\theta + \varphi) + i \sin (\theta + \varphi)]$

which says in geometrical terms that to multiply two complex numbers we must multiply their absolute values and add the angles they make with the "real" axis.

An important application of (21.6) is the following theorem.

(21.7)   De Moivre's Theorem.   *For all positive integers n,*

$$(\cos \theta + i \sin \theta)^n = \cos n\theta + i \sin n\theta.$$

De Moivre's theorem has several important applications. If for a fixed n we expand $(\cos \theta + i \sin \theta)^n$ by using the binomial formula and compare real and imaginary parts on both sides of the equation in (21.7), we then obtain formulas expressing $\cos n\theta$ and $\sin n\theta$ as polynomials in $\sin \theta$ and $\cos \theta$.

Another important application is the construction of the *roots of unity.*

(21.8)★   Theorem.   *For each positive integer n, the equation $x^n = 1$ has exactly n distinct complex roots, $z_1, z_2, \cdots, z_n$, which are given by*

$$z_1 = \cos \frac{2\pi}{n} + i \sin \frac{2\pi}{n}, \cdots, z_k = z_1^k = \cos \frac{2\pi k}{n} + i \sin \frac{2\pi k}{n},$$

$$k = 1, \cdots, n.$$

We come finally to what is perhaps the most important property of the field of complex numbers from the point of view of algebra.

(21.9)   Definition.   A field F is said to be *algebraically closed* if every polynomial $f \in F[x]$ of positive degree has at least one zero in F.

The next theorem is sometimes called "the Fundamental Theorem of Algebra," and although modern algebra no longer extolls it in quite such glowing terms, it is nevertheless a basic result concerning the complex field.

(21.10)   Theorem.   *The field of complex numbers is algebraically closed.*

Many proofs of this theorem have been found, all of which rest on the completeness axiom for the real numbers or on some topological property of the real numbers which is equivalent to the completeness axiom. The reader will find a proof very much in the spirit of this course in Schreier and Sperner's book, and other proofs may be found in Birkhoff and MacLane's book (see the Bibliography for both), or in any book on functions of a complex variable.

(21.11) Theorem. *Let F be an algebraically closed field. Then every prime polynomial in $F[x]$ has (up to a unit factor) the form $x - a$, $a \in F$. Every polynomial $f \in F[x]$ can be factored in the form*

$$\prod_{i=1}^{n} (x - a_i), \qquad a_i \in F.$$

Proof.   Let F be algebraically closed and let $p \in F[x]$ be a prime polynomial. By Definition (21.9) there is an element $a \in F$ such that $p(a) = 0$. By the Factor Theorem (20.14), $x - a$ is a factor of p. Since p is prime, p is a constant multiple of $x - a$, and the first statement is proved. The second statement is immediate from the first.

The disadvantage of this theorem is that, although it asserts the existence of the zeros of a polynomial, it gives no information about how the zeros depend on the coefficients of the polynomial f. This problem belongs to the subject of the Galois theory (Van der Waerden, Vol. I, Chapter 5; see the Bibliography).

We conclude this section with an application of Theorem (21.11) to polynomials with real coefficients.

(21.12) Theorem. *Let $f = \alpha_0 + \alpha_1 x + \cdots + \alpha_n x^n \in R[x]$. If $u \in C$ is a zero of f, then $\bar{u}$ is also a zero of f; if $u \neq \bar{u}$, then*

$$(x - u)(x - \bar{u}) = x^2 - (u + \bar{u})x + u\bar{u}$$

is a factor of f.

Proof.   If u is a zero of f, then

$$\alpha_0 + \alpha_1 u + \cdots + \alpha_n u^n = 0.$$

Taking the conjugate of the left side and using the fact that $u \to \bar{u}$ is an automorphism of C such that $\bar{\alpha} = \alpha$ for $\alpha \in R$, we obtain

$$\alpha_0 + \alpha_1 \bar{u} + \cdots + \alpha_n \bar{u}^n = 0,$$

which is the first assertion of the theorem. The second is immediate by the factor theorem.

An important consequence of the last theorem is its corollary:

(21.13) Corollary. *Every prime polynomial in $R[x]$ has the form (up to a unit factor)*

$$x - \alpha, \quad \text{or} \quad x^2 + \alpha x + \beta, \quad \alpha^2 - 4\beta < 0.$$

Proof. Let $f \in R[x]$ be a prime polynomial; then f has a zero $u \in C$. If $u = \alpha \in R$, then $f = \xi(x - \alpha)$ for some $\xi \in R$. If $u \notin R$, then $\bar{u} \neq u$ and, by (21.12),

$$(x - u)(x - \bar{u}) = x^2 - (u + \bar{u})x + u\bar{u}$$

is a factor of f. Since $u + \bar{u}$ and $u\bar{u}$ belong to R, it follows that f is (up to a unit factor) $x^2 + \alpha x + \beta$. The condition $\alpha^2 - 4\beta < 0$ follows from the fact that f is prime in $R[x]$.

EXERCISES

1. Express in the form $\alpha + \beta i$:

$$(3 + i)(-2 + 4i), \qquad \frac{1}{3 + 2i}, \qquad \frac{2 + i}{2 - i}.$$

2. Derive formulas for $\cos 3\theta$ and $\sin 3\theta$ in terms of $\cos \theta$ and $\sin \theta$.

3. Find all solutions of the equation $x^5 = 2$.

4. Let $a_0 + a_1 x + \cdots + a_{r-1}x^{r-1} + x^r = (x - u_1)(x - u_2) \cdots (x - u_r)$ be a polynomial in $C[x]$ with leading coefficient $a_r = 1$ and with zeros $u_1, \cdots, u_r$ in C. Prove that $a_0 = \pm u_1 u_2, \cdots u_r$ and $a_{r-1} = -(u_1 + u_2 + \cdots + u_r)$.

5. Prove that the field of complex numbers C is isomorphic* with the set of all 2-by-2 matrices with real coefficients of the form

$$\begin{pmatrix} \alpha & -\beta \\ \beta & \alpha \end{pmatrix}, \qquad \alpha, \beta \in R,$$

where the operations are addition and multiplication† of matrices.

6. Prove that the complex numbers of absolute value 1 form a group with respect to the operation of multiplication.

7. Prove that the mapping

$$\begin{pmatrix} \cos \theta & -\sin \theta \\ \sin \theta & \cos \theta \end{pmatrix} \to \cos \theta + i \sin \theta$$

---

*Two fields F and F' are said to be isomorphic if there exists a one-to-one mapping $\alpha \to \alpha'$ of F onto F' such that $(\alpha + \beta)' = \alpha' + \beta'$ and $(\alpha\beta)' = \alpha'\beta'$ for all $\alpha, \beta \in F$.

† For the definitions and properties of addition and multiplication of matrices, see Section 12.

is an isomorphism between the group of rotations in the plane and the multiplicative group of complex numbers of absolute value 1.

8. Let $f(x) = \alpha_0 + \alpha_1 x + \cdots + \alpha_r x^r$ be a polynomial of degree r with coefficients $\alpha_i \in Q$, the field of rational numbers, and let $u \in C$ be a zero of f. Let $Q[u]$ be the set of complex numbers of the form

$$z = \beta_0 + \beta_1 u + \cdots + \beta_{r-1} u^{r-1}, \qquad \beta_i \in Q.$$

Prove that if z, $w \in Q[u]$ then $z \pm w$ and $zw \in Q[u]$. Prove that $Q[u]$ is a field if f is a prime polynomial in $Q[x]$. [*Hint:* In case $f(x)$ is a prime, the main difficulty is proving that if $z = \beta_0 + \beta_1 u + \cdots + \beta_{r-1} u^{r-1} \neq 0$ then there exists $w \in Q[n]$ such that $zw = 1$. Since $z \neq 0$, the polynomial

$$g(x) = \beta_0 + \beta_1 x + \cdots + \beta_{r-1} x^{r-1} \neq 0$$

in $Q[x]$. Since $\deg f(x) = r$, it follows that $f(x)$ and $g(x)$ are relatively prime. Therefore there exist polynomials $a(x)$ and $b(x)$ such that

$$a(x)g(x) + b(x)f(x) = 1.$$

Upon substituting u for x, we obtain

$$a(u)g(u) = 1$$

and, since $g(u) = z$, we have produced an inverse for z.]

CHAPTER 7

THE THEORY of a SINGLE LINEAR TRANSFORMATION

The main topic of this chapter is an introduction to the theory of a single linear transformation on a vector space. We prove the simplest of the theorems on the classification of the invariant subspaces relative to a linear transformation and present several applications of this theorem. Among them is the computation of the exponential function of a matrix and its application to the solution of systems of first-order linear differential equations with constant coefficients.

22. THE MINIMAL POLYNOMIAL

In this section, F denotes an arbitrary field, and V a finite-dimensional space over F. In Section 11 we saw that $L(V, V)$ is a vector space over F. Theorem (13.3) asserts that if we select a basis $\{v_1, \cdots, v_n\}$ of V then the mapping which assigns to $T \in L(V, V)$ its matrix with respect to the basis $\{v_1, \cdots, v_n\}$ is an isomorphism of the vector space $L(V, V)$ onto the vector space $M_n(F)$ of all n-by-n matrices, viewed as a vector space of n^2-tuples. From Section 12,

$M_n(F)$ is an n^2-dimensional vector space. If $\{A_1, \cdots, A_{n^2}\}$ is a basis for $M_n(F)$ over F, then the linear transformations $T_1, \cdots, T_{n^2}$, whose matrices with respect to $\{v_1, \cdots, v_n\}$ are $A_1, \cdots, A_{n^2}$, respectively, form a basis of $L(V, V)$ over F. In particular, the matrices which have a 1 in one position and zeros elsewhere form a basis of $M_n(F)$; therefore the linear transformations $T_{ij} \in L(V, V)$ defined by

$$T_{ij}(v_j) = v_i, \qquad T_{ij}(v_k) = 0, \qquad k \neq j,$$

form a basis of $L(V, V)$ over F. It is instructive to prove directly that the set $\{T_{ij}\}$ forms a basis for $L(V, V)$.

For the rest of this section let T be a fixed linear transformation of V. Since $L(V, V)$ has dimension n^2 over F the $n^2 + 1$ powers of T,

$$1, \quad T, \quad T^2, \quad \cdots, \quad T^{n^2}$$

are linearly dependent. That means that there exist elements of F, $\xi_0, \xi_1, \cdots, \xi_{n^2}$, not all zero, such that

$$\xi_0 1 + \xi_1 T + \xi_2 T^2 + \cdots + \xi_{n^2} T^{n^2} = 0.$$

In other words, there exists a nonzero polynomial

$$f(x) = \xi_0 + \xi_1 x + \cdots + \xi_{n^2} x^{n^2} \in F[x]$$

such that $f(T) = 0$.

As we shall see, the study of these polynomial equations is the key to most of the deeper properties of the transformation T.

Let us make the idea of substituting a linear transformation in a polynomial absolutely precise.

(22.1)   Definition.   Let $f(x) = \lambda_0 + \lambda_1 x + \cdots + \lambda_r x^r \in F[x]$ and let $T \in L(V, V)$; then $f(T)$ denotes the linear transformation

$$f(T) = \lambda_0 \cdot 1 + \lambda_1 T + \cdots + \lambda_r T^r$$

where 1 is the identity transformation on V. Similarly, we may define $f(A)$ where A is an n-by-n matrix over F, with 1 replaced by the identity matrix I.

(22.2)   Lemma.   *Let $T \in L(V, V)$ and let $f, g \in F[x]$; then:*

(1) $f(T)T = Tf(T)$.
(2) $(f \pm g)(T) = f(T) \pm g(T)$.
(3) $(fg)(T) = f(T)g(T)$.

Of course, the same lemma holds for matrices. The proof is similar to the proof of (20.12), and will be omitted.

(22.3)   Theorem.   *Let $T \in L(V, V)$; then* $1, T, T^2, \cdots, T^{n^2}$ *are linearly dependent in* $L(V, V)$. *Therefore there exists a uniquely determined integer* $r \leq n^2$ *such that*

$$1, T, T^2, \cdots, T^{r-1} \qquad \textit{are linearly independent},$$
$$1, T, T^2, \cdots, T^{r-1}, T^r \qquad \textit{are linearly dependent}.$$

Then we have

$$T^r = \xi_0 1 + \xi_1 T + \cdots + \xi_{r-1} T^{r-1}, \qquad \xi_i \in F.$$

Let $m(x) = x^r - \xi_{r-1} x^{r-1} - \cdots - \xi_0 \cdot 1 \in F[x]$. *Then* $m(x)$ *has the following properties:*

(1) $m(x) \neq 0$ *in* $F[x]$ *and* $m(T) = 0$.

(2) *If* $f(x)$ *is any polynomial in* $F[x]$ *such that* $f(T) = 0$, *then* $m(x) \mid f(x)$ *in* $F[x]$.

Proof.   The existence of the polynomial $m(x)$ and the statement (1) concerning it follow from the introductory remarks in this section. Now let $f(x)$ be any polynomial in $F[x]$ such that $f(T) = 0$. Because $1, T, \cdots, T^{r-1}$ are linearly independent, there does not exist a polynomial $R(x) \neq 0$ of degree $< r$ such that $R(T) = 0$. Now apply the division process to $f(x)$ and $m(x)$ and obtain

$$f(x) = m(x)Q(x) + R(x)$$

where either $R(x) = 0$ or $\deg R(x) < r = \deg m(x)$. By Lemma (22.2) we have

$$R(T) = (f - mQ)(T) = f(T) - m(T)Q(T) = 0$$

and by the preceding remark we have $R(x) = 0$ in $F[x]$. This proves that $m(x) \mid f(x)$, and the theorem is proved.

(22.4)   Definition.   Let $T \in L(V, V)$. The polynomial $m(x) \in F[x]$ defined in Theorem (22.3) is called a *minimal polynomial* of T; $m(x)$ is characterized as the nonzero polynomial of least degree such that $m(T) = 0$, and it is uniquely determined up to a constant factor.

The remarks about the uniqueness of $m(x)$ are clear by part (2) of Theorem (22.3). To see this, let $m(x)$ and $m'(x)$ be two nonzero polynomials of degree r such that $m(T) = m'(T) = 0$. Then by the proof of part (2) of Theorem (22.3) we have $m(x) \mid m'(x)$ and $m'(x) \mid m(x)$. It follows from the discussion in Section 20 that $m(x)$ and $m'(x)$ differ by a unit factor in $F[x]$ and, since the units in $F[x]$ are simply the constant polynomials, the uniqueness of $m(x)$ is proved.

We remark that Theorem (22.3) also holds for any matrix $\mathbf{A} \in M_n(F)$. If $T \in L(V, V)$ has the matrix $\mathbf{A}$ with respect to the basis $\{v_1, \cdots, v_n\}$ of V, it follows from Theorem (13.3) that T and $\mathbf{A}$ have the same minimal polynomial. Since we have in Chapter 2 an effective procedure for testing sets of n^2-tuples for linear dependence, the minimal polynomial of $\mathbf{A}$ (and hence the minimal polynomial of T) is—in principle, anyway—capable of being directly calculated by the methods we have developed earlier in the book.

A thorough understanding of the definition and properties of the minimal polynomial will be absolutely essential in the rest of this chapter.

EXERCISES

1. Let $T \in L(V, V)$ and $f, g \in F[x]$. Prove that $f(T)g(T) = g(T)f(T)$.

2. Let V and W be vector spaces over F of dimensions m and n respectively. Find a basis for $L(V, W)$.

3. Let:
$$\mathbf{A} = \begin{pmatrix} \alpha & \beta \\ \gamma & \delta \end{pmatrix}, \qquad \alpha, \beta, \gamma, \delta \in F.$$

Prove that $\mathbf{A}$ satisfies the equation $f(\mathbf{A}) = 0$ where
$$f(x) = x^2 - (\alpha + \delta)x + (\alpha\delta - \beta\gamma).$$
Prove that $\mathbf{A}$ is invertible if and only if $\Delta = \alpha\delta - \beta\gamma \neq 0$ and that, if $\Delta \neq 0$, then
$$\mathbf{A}^{-1} = -\frac{1}{\Delta}[\mathbf{A} - (\alpha + \delta)\mathbf{I}]$$
where $\mathbf{I}$ is the 2-by-2 identity matrix.

4. Prove that if $T \in L(V, V)$ then T is invertible if and only if the constant term of the minimal polynomial of T is different from zero. Describe how to compute T^{-1} from the minimal polynomial. In particular, show that T^{-1} can always be expressed as a polynomial $f(T)$ in T.

5. Find the minimal polynomials of
$$\begin{pmatrix} 2 & 0 \\ 3 & -1 \end{pmatrix}, \quad \begin{pmatrix} 0 & 1 & 0 \\ 0 & 0 & 1 \\ 1 & 0 & 0 \end{pmatrix}, \quad \begin{pmatrix} -1 & 1 \\ 1 & 0 \end{pmatrix}, \quad \begin{pmatrix} 0 & 1 & 3 \\ 0 & 0 & 2 \\ 0 & 0 & 0 \end{pmatrix}.$$

6. **a.** Let $T \in L(V, V)$, and let $\{v_1, \cdots, v_n\}$ be a basis of V consisting

of characteristic vectors for T belonging to characteristic roots $\xi_1, \cdots, \xi_n$ respectively. Then $Tv_i = \xi_i v_i$, $i = 1, \cdots, n$. Prove that $f(T) = 0$, where

$$f(x) = (x - \xi_1)(x - \xi_2) \cdots (x - \xi_n).$$

b. Prove that the minimal polynomial of T is $\Pi(x - \xi_j)$, where the ξ_j are the distinct characteristic roots of T.

23.   INVARIANT SUBSPACES

Let $T \in L(V, V)$. A nonzero vector $v \in V$ is a characteristic vector of T if and only if the one-dimensional subspace $S = S(v)$ is invariant relative to T in the sense that $T(s) \in S$ for all $s \in S$ (see Section 13). The search for invariant subspaces is the key to the deeper properties of a single linear transformation.

For a concrete example, let T be the linear transformation of R_2 such that for some basis $\{v_1, v_2\}$ of R_2,

$$T(v_1) = v_2,$$
$$T(v_2) = v_1.$$

The geometrical behavior of T becomes clear when we find the characteristic vectors of T. These are $w_1 = v_1 + v_2$ and $w_2 = v_1 - v_2$. The matrix of T with respect to the basis $\{w_1, w_2\}$ is

$$\mathbf{A} = \begin{pmatrix} 1 & 0 \\ 0 & -1 \end{pmatrix}.$$

We can see now that T is a reflection with respect to the line through the origin in the direction of the vector w_1; it sends each vector in $S(w_1)$ onto itself and sends w_2 onto its mirror image $-w_2$ with respect

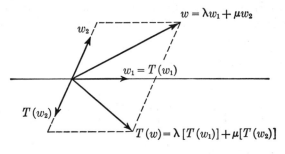

Figure 7.1

to the line $S(w_1)$. Figure 7.1 shows how the image $T(w)$ of an arbitrary vector w can be described geometrically.

The concept illustrated here is the simplest case of the following basic idea.

(23.1) Definition. Let $T \in L(V, V)$. A subspace W of V is called an *invariant subspace relative* to T (or simply a *T-invariant subspace* or *T-subspace*) if $T(w) \in W$ for all $w \in W$. We recall that a generator $v \neq 0$ of a one-dimensional T-invariant subspace is called a *characteristic vector* of T. If $Tv = \xi v$ for $\xi \in F$, then ξ is called a *characteristic root* of T and v is said to *belong to* the *characteristic root* ξ.

The next result shows one way to construct T-invariant subspaces.

(23.2) Lemma. *Let $T \in L(V, V)$ and let $f(x) \in F[x]$; then the set of all vectors $v \in V$ such that $f(T)(v) = 0$ [that is, the null space of $f(T)$] is a T-invariant subspace—notation, $n[f(T)]$.*

Proof. Since $f(T) \in L(V, V)$, the null space $n[f(T)]$ is a subspace of V. We have to prove that if $w \in n[f(T)]$ then $T(w) \in n[f(T)]$. We have

$$f(T)[T(w)] = [f(T)T](w) = [Tf(T)](w) = T[f(T)(w)] = 0,$$

since $f(T)T = Tf(T)$ in $L(V, V)$, and the lemma is proved.

We observe in our example of the reflection that the basis vector w_1 generates the null space of the transformation $T - 1$ and w_2 generates the null space of the transformation $T + 1$. The polynomials $x + 1$ and $x - 1$ are exactly the prime factors of the minimal polynomial $x^2 - 1$ of T. The chief result of this section is a far-reaching generalization of this example.

(23.3) Definition. Let $V_1, \cdots, V_s$ be subspaces of V. The space V is said to be the *direct sum* of $\{V_1, \cdots, V_s\}$ (notation, $V = V_1 \oplus \cdots \oplus V_s$) if, first, every vector $v \in V$ can be expressed as a sum,

(23.4) $v = v_1 + \cdots + v_s, \qquad v_i \in V_i, \quad 1 \leq i \leq s,$

and if, second, the expressions (23.4) are unique, in the sense that if

$$v_1 + \cdots + v_s = v_1' + \cdots + v_s', \qquad v_i, v_i' \in V_i, \quad 1 \leq i \leq s$$

then

$$v_i = v_i', \qquad 1 \leq i \leq s.$$

(23.5) **Lemma.** *Let $V_1, \cdots, V_s$ be subspaces of V; then V is the direct sum $V_1 \oplus \cdots \oplus V_s$ if and only if:*

(1) $V = V_1 + \cdots + V_s$, *that is, every vector $v \in V$ can be expressed in at least one way as a sum*

$$v = v_1 + \cdots + v_s, \qquad v_i \in V_i, \quad 1 \le i \le s.$$

(2) *If $v_i \in V_i$, for $1 \le i \le s$, are vectors such that*

$$v_1 + \cdots + v_s = 0$$

then $v_1 = v_2 = \cdots = v_s = 0$.

Proof. If V is the direct sum $V_1 \oplus \cdots \oplus V_s$, then part (1) is satisfied. If

$$v_1 + \cdots + v_s = 0, \qquad v_i \in V_i,$$

then we have

$$v_1 + \cdots + v_s = 0 + \cdots + 0, \qquad v_i, 0 \in V_i, \quad 1 \le i \le s,$$

and by the second part of Definition (23.3) we have $v_1 = \cdots = v_s = 0$, as required.

Now suppose that conditions (1) and (2) of the lemma are satisfied. To prove that $V = V_1 \oplus \cdots \oplus V_s$ it is sufficient to prove the uniqueness assertion of Definition (23.3). If

$$v_1 + \cdots + v_s = v_1' + \cdots + v_s', \qquad v_i, v_i' \in V_i, \quad 1 \le i \le s,$$

then we can rewrite this equation as

$$(v_1 - v_1') + \cdots + (v_s - v_s') = 0, \qquad v_i - v_i' \in V_i, \quad 1 \le i \le s.$$

By condition (2) we have $v_i - v_i' = 0$ for $1 \le i \le s$ and hence $v_i = v_i'$ for all i. This completes the proof of the lemma.

Finally, we are ready to state our main theorem. It can be stated in the following intuitive way. Let $T \in L(V, V)$ and let $m(x)$ be the minimal polynomial of T. By the theorems of Section 20, $m(x)$ can be factored into primes in $F[x]$, say

$$m(x) = p_1(x)^{e_1} \cdots p_s(x)^{e_s}$$

where the $\{p_i\}$ are distinct primes and the e_i are positive integers. By Lemma (23.2) the null spaces

$$n(p_i(T)^{e_i}), \qquad 1 \le i \le s,$$

are T-subspaces of V. The theorem asserts simply that V is their direct sum. As we shall see, although it is by no means the best theorem that can be proved in this direction, this theorem already goes a long way toward solving the problem of finding a basis of V

such that the matrix of T with respect to this basis is as simple as possible. A formal statement of the theorem follows.

(23.6) Theorem. *Let $T \in L(V, V)$ and let*

$$m(x) = p_1(x)^{e_1} \cdots p_s(x)^{e_s}$$

be the minimal polynomial of T, factored into powers of distinct primes $p_i(x) \in F[x]$; then for each i, where $1 \le i \le s$, the null space of $p_i(T)^{e_i}$, or $n[p_i(T)^{e_i}]$, is a T-subspace of V and we have

$$V = n[p_1(T)^{e_1}] \oplus \cdots \oplus n[p_s(T)^{e_s}].$$

   Proof. Let

$$q_i(x) = \frac{m(x)}{p_i(x)^{e_i}}, \qquad 1 \le i \le s.$$

Then the $\{q_i(x)\}$ are polynomials in $F[x]$ with no common prime factors. Hence by Corollary (20.16) there exist polynomials $a_i(x)$, $1 \le i \le s$, such that

$$1 = q_1(x)a_1(x) + \cdots + q_s(x)a_s(x).$$

Substituting T, we have by Lemma (22.2) the result that

$$1 = q_1(T)a_1(T) + \cdots + q_s(T)a_s(T).$$

Now let $v \in V$; then we have

$$v = q_1(T)a_1(T)v + \cdots + q_s(T)a_s(T)v,$$

and for each i,

$$p_i(T)^{e_i}q_i(T)a_i(T)v = m(T)a_i(T)v = 0.$$

Therefore

$$q_i(T)a_i(T)v \in n[p_i(T)^{e_i}], \qquad 1 \le i \le s,$$

and

$$V = n[p_1(T)^{e_1}] + \cdots + n[p_s(T)^{e_s}].$$

To prove the theorem it is now sufficient to prove that part (2) of Lemma (23.5) is valid. Suppose that

$$v_1 + \cdots + v_s = 0, \qquad v_i \in n[p_i(T)^{e_i}], \quad 1 \le i \le s.$$

Find $a(x), b(x) \in F[x]$ such that, by Corollary (20.16),

$$1 = a(x)p_1(x)^{e_1} + b(x)p_2(x)^{e_2} \cdots p_s(x)^{e_s}.$$

Then we have

$$1 = a(T)p_1(T)^{e_1} + b(T)p_2(T)^{e_2} \cdots p_s(T)^{e_s},$$

and applying this linear transformation to v_1, we have

$$v_1 = 1 \cdot v_1 = a(T)p_1(T)^{e_1}v_1$$
$$+ \, b(T)p_2(T)^{e_2} \cdots p_s(T)^{e_s}(-v_2 - \cdots - v_s) = 0.$$

A similar argument proves that

$$v_2 = \cdots = v_s = 0$$

and the theorem is proved.

As a first application of this theorem, we consider the question of when a basis for V can be chosen that consists of characteristic vectors of T.

(23.7)   Definition.   A linear transformation $T \in L(V, V)$ is called *diagonable* if there exists a basis for V consisting of characteristic vectors of T. A matrix of T with respect to a basis of characteristic vectors is called a *diagonal matrix*; it has the form

$$\begin{pmatrix} \alpha_1 & & 0 \\ & \cdot & \\ & & \cdot \\ 0 & & \alpha_n \end{pmatrix}, \quad \alpha_i \in F,$$

with zeros except in the (i, i) positions, $1 \leq i \leq n$.

(23.8)   Theorem.   *A linear transformation $T \in L(V, V)$ is diagonable if and only if the minimal polynomial of T has the form*

$$m(x) = (x - \xi_1) \cdots (x - \xi_s)$$

with distinct zeros $\xi_1, \cdots, \xi_s$ in F.

Proof.   First suppose that T is diagonable and let $\{v_1, \cdots, v_n\}$ be a basis of T consisting of characteristic vectors belonging to characteristic roots $\xi_1, \cdots, \xi_n$ in F. Suppose the v_i are so numbered that $\xi_1, \cdots, \xi_s$ are distinct and every characteristic root ξ_j coincides with some ξ_i such that $1 \leq i \leq s$. Let

$$m(x) = (x - \xi_1) \cdots (x - \xi_s).$$

Since $T(v_i) = \xi_i v_i$, $1 \leq i \leq s$, we have

$$(T - \xi_i \cdot 1)v_i = 0$$

and hence

$$m(T)v_i = 0, \quad 1 \leq i \leq n.$$

Therefore $m(T) = 0$ and by Lemma (22.3) the minimal polynomial is a factor of $m(x)$. But it is clear that if any prime factor of $m(x)$ is deleted we obtain a polynomial $m^*(x)$ such that $m^*(T) \neq 0$. For example, if $m^*(x) = (x - \xi_1) \cdots (x - \xi_{s-1})$, then

$$m^*(T)v_s = (T - \xi_1) \cdots (T - \xi_{s-1})v_s$$
$$= (\xi_s - \xi_1) \cdots (\xi_s - \xi_{s-1})v_s \neq 0.$$

It follows* that $m(x)$ is the minimal polynomial of T.

Now suppose that the minimal polynomial has the form

$$m(x) = (x - \xi_1) \cdots (x - \xi_s)$$

with distinct $\{\xi_i\}$ in F. By Theorem (23.6) we have

$$V = n(T - \xi_1 \cdot 1) \oplus \cdots \oplus n(T - \xi_s \cdot 1).$$

Let $\{v_{11}, \cdots, v_{1d_1}\}$ be a basis for $n(T - \xi_1 \cdot 1)$, $\{v_{21}, \cdots, v_{2d_2}\}$ a basis for $n(T - \xi_2 \cdot 1)$, etc. Then because V is the direct sum of the subspaces $n(T - \xi_i \cdot 1)$ it follows that

$$\{v_{11}, \cdots, v_{1d_1}, v_{21}, \cdots, v_{2d_2}, \cdots\}$$

is a basis for V. Finally, $w \in n(T - \xi_i \cdot 1)$ implies that $(T - \xi_i \cdot 1)w = 0$ or $T(w) = \xi_i \cdot w$, so that if $w \neq 0$ then w is a characteristic vector of T. Thus all the basis vectors v_{ij} are characteristic vectors of T, and the theorem is proved.

It is worthwhile to translate theorems on linear transformations into theorems on matrices. We have

(23.9) Corollary. *A necessary and sufficient condition for a matrix* $A \in M_n(F)$ *to be similar to a diagonal matrix is that the minimal polynomial of* A *have the form*

$$m(x) = (x - \xi_1) \cdots (x - \xi_s)$$

with distinct $\xi_i \in F$.

EXERCISES

1. Test the following matrices to determine whether or not they are similar to diagonal matrices in $M_2(R)$.

$$\begin{pmatrix} 2 & 1 \\ 0 & -1 \end{pmatrix}, \quad \begin{pmatrix} 1 & -2 \\ 1 & -1 \end{pmatrix}, \quad \begin{pmatrix} 3 & -2 \\ 2 & -1 \end{pmatrix}.$$

2. Show that the matrices

$$\begin{pmatrix} 1 & -2 \\ 1 & -1 \end{pmatrix}, \quad \begin{pmatrix} 0 & 1 \\ -1 & 0 \end{pmatrix}$$

---

* This part of the theorem was already given as Exercise 6 in Section 22.

are similar to diagonal matrices in $M_2(C)$, where C is the complex field, but not in $M_2(R)$. In each case find a basis of C_2 consisting of characteristic vectors for linear transformations defined by the matrices.

3. Let $T \in L(V, V)$ have the minimal polynomial $m(x) \in F[x]$. Let $f(x)$ be an arbitrary polynomial in $F[x]$. Prove that

$$n[f(T)] = n[d(T)],$$

where $d(x)$ is the greatest common divisor of $f(x)$ and $m(x)$.

24. THE TRIANGULAR FORM THEOREM

There are two ways in which a linear transformation T can fail to be diagonable. One is that its minimal polynomial $m(x)$ cannot be factored into linear factors in $F[x]$ (for example, if $m(x) = x^2 + 1$ in $R[x]$ where R is the real field); the other is that $m(x) = (x - \xi_1)^{e_1} \cdots (x - \xi_s)^{e_s}$ with some $e_i > 1$. In the latter case it is desirable to have a theorem that applies to *all* linear transformations and that comes as close to the Diagonal Form Theorem (23.8) as possible.

The main theorem is the following one.

(24.1) Theorem (Triangular Form Theorem). *Let $T \in L(V, V)$, where V is a finite-dimensional vector space over an arbitrary field F, and let the minimal polynomial of T be given by*

$$m(x) = (x - \alpha_1)^{e_1} \cdots (x - \alpha_s)^{e_s}$$

where the $\{e_i\}$ are positive integers and the $\{\alpha_i\}$ are distinct elements of F. Then there exists a basis of V such that the matrix $\mathbf{A}$ of T with respect to this basis has the form

$$\mathbf{A} = \begin{pmatrix} \mathbf{A}_1 & & & 0 \\ & \mathbf{A}_2 & & \\ & & \ddots & \\ 0 & & & \mathbf{A}_s \end{pmatrix}$$

where each $\mathbf{A}_i$ is a d_i-by-d_i block for some integer $d_i \geq e_i$, where $1 \leq i \leq s$, and each $\mathbf{A}_i$ can be expressed in the form

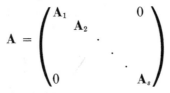

$$\mathbf{A}_i = \begin{pmatrix} \alpha_i & & & * \\ & \ddots & & \\ & & \ddots & \\ 0 & & & \alpha_i \end{pmatrix}$$

where the matrix $\mathbf{A}_i$ *has zeros below the diagonal and, possibly, nonzero entries* (∗) *above. All entries of* $\mathbf{A}$ *not contained in one of the blocks* $\{\mathbf{A}_i\}$ *are zero. To express it all in another way, given a square matrix* $\mathbf{B}$ *whose minimal polynomial is* $m(x)$, *there exists an invertible* $\mathbf{S}$ *such that* $\mathbf{SBS}^{-1} = \mathbf{A}$ *where* $\mathbf{A}$ *has the above-given form.*

REMARK.   A very important observation is that the hypothesis of Theorem (24.1)—that the minimal polynomial of T can be factored into linear factors—is always satisfied if the field F is algebraically closed (see Section 21). The most common example of an algebraically closed field (and the only one we have discussed) is the field of complex numbers.

Proof.   Let V_i be the null space of $(T - \alpha_i \cdot 1)^{e_i}$, for $1 \leq i \leq r$, and let d_i be the dimension of V_i. If we choose bases for the subspaces $V_1, V_2, \cdots, V_s$ separately then, as we pointed out in the proof of Theorem (23.8), the totality of basis elements obtained form a basis of V because V is, by Theorem (23.6), the direct sum of the subspaces $\{V_i\}$. Then let us arrange a basis for V so that the first d_1 elements form a basis for V_1, the next d_2 elements form a basis for V_2, and so on. Since each subspace V_i is invariant relative to T, it is clear that the matrix of T relative to this basis has the form

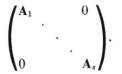

It remains only to prove that the blocks $\mathbf{A}_i$ can be chosen to have the required form and that the inequalities $d_i \geq e_i$ hold, for $1 \leq i \leq s$.

Each space V_i is the null space of $(T - \alpha_i \cdot 1)^{e_i}$. In other words, if we let $N_i = T - \alpha_i \cdot 1$, then $N_i \subset L(V_i, V_i)$ and we have $N_i^{e_i} = 0$. Such a linear transformation is called a *nilpotent linear transformation.*

Thus T, viewed as a linear transformation on V_i, is the sum of a constant times the identity transformation $\alpha_i \cdot 1$ and a nilpotent transformation N_i.

We now state a general result concerning nilpotent transformations, which will settle our problem.

(24.2) Lemma.   *Let N be a nilpotent transformation on a finite-dimensional vector space W; then W has a basis $\{w_1, \cdots, w_t\}$ such that*

$$Nw_1 = 0, \qquad N(w_2) \in S(w_1), \cdots, N(w_i) \in S(w_1, \cdots, w_{i-1})$$

for $2 \leq i \leq t$.

We next present a proof of Lemma (24.2). Notice that the matrix of N with respect to the basis $\{w_1, \cdots, w_t\}$ has the form (illustrated for $t = 4$),

$$\begin{pmatrix} 0 & * & * & * \\ 0 & 0 & * & * \\ 0 & 0 & 0 & * \\ 0 & 0 & 0 & 0 \end{pmatrix}$$

so that the lemma is a special case of the triangular form theorem. The point is that this special case implies the whole theorem. We prove Lemma (24.2) by induction. First find $w_1 \neq 0$ such that $Nw_1 = 0$. Any vector will do for w_1 if $N = 0$ and, if $N^k \neq 0$ and $N^{k+1} = 0$, then let $w_1 = N^k(w) \neq 0$. Then $N(w_1) = N^{k+1}(w) = 0$. Suppose (as an induction hypothesis) that we have found linearly independent vectors $\{w_1, \cdots, w_i\}$ satisfying the conditions of the lemma and let $S = S(w_1, \cdots, w_i)$. If $S = W$ there is nothing more to prove. If $S \neq W$ and $N(W) \subset S$, then any vector not in S can be taken for w_{i+1}. Now suppose $N(W) \not\subset S$. Then there is an integer u such that $N^u(W) \not\subset S$, $N^{u+1}(W) \subset S$. Find $w_{i+1} \in N^u(W)$ such that $w_{i+1} \notin S$. Then $\{w_1, \cdots, w_{i+1}\}$ is a linearly independent set and $N(w_{i+1}) \in S$. This completes the proof of the lemma.

Let us apply Lemma (24.2) to the task of selecting an appropriate basis for the subspace V_i of V. Since $N_i = T - \alpha_1 \cdot 1$ is nilpotent on V_i, the lemma implies that V_i has a basis $\{v_{i,1}, \cdots, v_{i,d_i}\}$ such that

$$N_i(v_{i,1}) = 0, \quad N_i(v_{i,2}) \in S(v_{i,1}), \quad \cdots, \quad N_i(v_{i,k}) \subset S(v_{i,1}, \cdots, v_{i,k-1})$$
$$\text{for } 2 \leq k \leq d_i.$$

Since $N_i = T - \alpha_i \cdot 1$, these equations yield the formulas

$$(T - \alpha_i \cdot 1)v_{i,1} = 0, \quad \cdots, \quad (T - \alpha_i \cdot 1)v_{i,k} \in S(v_{i,1}, \cdots, v_{i,k-1}),$$
$$\text{for } 2 \leq k \leq d_i.$$

These in turn yield

$$\begin{aligned}
\textbf{(24.3)} \qquad & Tv_{i,1} = \alpha_i v_{i,1} \\
& Tv_{i,2} = \alpha_{12} v_{i,1} + \alpha_i v_{i,2} \\
& \cdots \qquad \cdots \\
& Tv_{i,k} = \alpha_{1k} v_{i,1} + \cdots + \alpha_{k-1,k} v_{i,k-1} + \alpha_i v_{i,k}
\end{aligned}$$

and we have shown that, relative to this basis, the matrix of T on the space V_i has the required form.

It remains to prove the inequalities $d_i \geq e_i$, $1 \leq i \leq r$. From Lemma (24.2) it follows that $N_i^{d_i} = 0$, where d_i is the dimension of

V_i. Since $T = \alpha_i \cdot 1 + N_i$ on V_i we have $(T - \alpha_i \cdot 1)^{d_i} = 0$ on V_i, and since V is the direct sum of the subspaces V_i we have

$$(24.4) \qquad (T - \alpha_1 \cdot 1)^{d_1} \cdots (T - \alpha_r \cdot 1)^{d_r} = 0.$$

Therefore, the minimal polynomial $m(x) = \Pi(x - \alpha_i)^{e_i}$ divides the polynomial $\Pi(x - \alpha_i)^{d_i}$ and from the theory of unique factorization in $F[x]$ we have $d_i \geq e_i$. This completes the proof of the theorem.

This result has many important corollaries. The first shows that the minimal polynomial has degree $\leq \dim V$, although from the argument in Section 22 we could have predicted only that its degree is $\leq (\dim V)^2$.

(24.5) Corollary. *Let T be a linear transformation on a finite-dimensional vector space V over an algebraically closed field F; then the minimal polynomial $m(x)$ of T has degree $\leq \dim V$.*

We recall that an element $\alpha \in F$ is called a *characteristic root* of T if there exists a nonzero vector $v \in V$ such that $Tv = \alpha v$ or, in other words, if $(T - \alpha \cdot 1)v = 0$. If $\mathbf{A}$ is a matrix of T with respect to any basis, then $\mathbf{A} - \alpha \cdot 1$ is the matrix of $T - \alpha \cdot 1$ with respect to this basis. The fact that $(T - \alpha \cdot 1)v = 0$ implies that $\mathbf{A} - \alpha \cdot \mathbf{I}$ is not an invertible matrix and, hence, that the determinant $D(\mathbf{A} - \alpha \cdot \mathbf{I}) = 0$. Conversely, if ξ is any element of F such that $D(\mathbf{A} - \xi \cdot \mathbf{I}) = 0$, then $T - \xi \cdot 1$ is not invertible. From the discussion in Section 13 it follows that $n(T - \xi \cdot 1) \neq 0$ and hence that $(T - \xi \cdot 1)v = 0$ for some $v \neq 0$. Then ξ is a characteristic root of T. These considerations lead to the following definition.

(24.6) Definition. Let $T \in L(V, V)$ and let $\mathbf{A}$ be a matrix of T with respect to some basis of V; then the matrix $\mathbf{A} - x \cdot \mathbf{I}$ has coefficients in the quotient field (see Section 20) of the polynomial ring $F[x]$ and its determinant $h(x) = D(\mathbf{A} - x \cdot \mathbf{I})$ is an element of $F[x]$ called the *characteristic polynomial* of T. The characteristic polynomial of T is independent of the choice of the matrix of T. The set of distinct zeros of the characteristic polynomial of T is identical with the set of distinct characteristic roots of T.

Several statements in the definition require proof. First of all, let $\mathbf{A}$ and $\mathbf{B}$ be matrices of T with respect to different bases. Then $\mathbf{B} = \mathbf{SAS}^{-1}$ for an invertible matrix $\mathbf{S}$ and we have

$$\begin{aligned}
D(\mathbf{B} - x \cdot \mathbf{I}) &= D(\mathbf{SAS}^{-1} - x \cdot \mathbf{I}) \\
&= D[\mathbf{S}(\mathbf{A} - x \cdot \mathbf{I})\mathbf{S}^{-1}] \\
&= D(\mathbf{S})D(\mathbf{A} - x \cdot \mathbf{I})D(\mathbf{S})^{-1} \quad \text{[by (18.3)]} \\
&= D(\mathbf{A} - x \cdot \mathbf{I}).
\end{aligned}$$

The statement about the zeros of the characteristic polynomial is clear from the introductory remarks. The fact that $D(\mathbf{A} - x \cdot \mathbf{I}) \in F[x]$ follows from the formula for the complete expansion of $D(\mathbf{A} - x \cdot \mathbf{I})$ given in Section 17.

We now have the following basic corollary of Theorem (24.1).

(24.7) Corollary. *Let V be a vector space over an algebraically closed field F. Let $T \in L(V, V)$, let $m(x)$ be the minimal polynomial of T, and let $h(x)$ be the characteristic polynomial; then:*

(1) $m(x) \mid h(x)$.
(2) *Every zero of $h(x)$ is a zero of $m(x)$.*
(3) $h(T) = 0$.

(The last statement is called the Cayley-Hamilton theorem.)

The proof is immediate if we use the matrix of T given by Theorem (24.1), for then

$$h(x) = \pm \prod (x - \alpha_i)^{d_i},$$

$$m(x) = \prod (x - \alpha_i)^{e_i},$$

and all the statements follow from the fact that $d_i \geq e_i$, as we proved in Theorem (24.1).

We remark that the preceding corollary, and in particular the Cayley-Hamilton theorem, is valid for a linear transformation on a finite-dimensional vector space over an arbitrary field F, even though our proof, based on Theorem (24.1), works only when F is algebraically closed. For a proof in the general case, see Chapter 10, Section 6, of Birkhoff and MacLane's book, listed in the Bibliography.

25. AN EXAMPLE

In this section an example is worked out to indicate the general computational procedure for finding the triangular form of a matrix. Let V be a three-dimensional vector space over the complex field C with basis $\{v_1, v_2, v_3\}$ and let $T \in L(V, V)$ be defined by the equations

$$Tv_1 = -v_1 \qquad\quad + 2v_3$$
$$Tv_2 = 3v_1 + 2v_2 + v_3$$
$$Tv_3 = - v_3.$$

The matrix of T with respect to the basis $\{v_1, v_2, v_3\}$ is given by

$$\mathbf{A} = \begin{pmatrix} -1 & 3 & 0 \\ 0 & 2 & 0 \\ 2 & 1 & -1 \end{pmatrix}.$$

We shall show how to find a new basis for V with respect to which the matrix of T is in the form given in Theorem (24.1).

STEP 1.   Find the distinct characteristic roots of $\mathbf{A}$. This can be done either by finding the prime factors of the characteristic polynomial $h(x)$ or by finding the minimal polynomial $m(x)$ and determining its zeros since, by Corollary (24.7), $m(x)$ and $h(x)$ have the same set of distinct zeros.

The characteristic polynomial $h(x)$ is given by

$$h(x) = D(\mathbf{A} - x \cdot \mathbf{I}) = \begin{vmatrix} -1-x & 3 & 0 \\ 0 & 2-x & 0 \\ 2 & 1 & -1-x \end{vmatrix} = (1+x)^2(2-x).$$

At this point we know from Corollary (24.7) that the distinct characteristic roots of T are $\{-1, 2\}$ and that the minimal polynomial of T is either

$$(1+x)(2-x) \quad \text{or} \quad (1+x)^2(2-x).$$

STEP 2.   Find the null spaces of $T + 1$, $(T + 1)^2$, $T - 2$. If V turns out to be the direct sum of the null spaces of $T + 1$ and $T - 2$, we will know that the minimal polynomial is $(x + 1)(x - 2)$ (Why?) and if not then we will know that the minimal polynomial is $(x + 1)^2(x - 2)$ and will have to find the null space of $(T + 1)^2$.
We have

$$(T + 1)v_1 = 2v_3$$
$$(T + 1)v_2 = 3v_1 + 3v_2 + v_3$$
$$(T + 1)v_3 = 0 \qquad .$$

The rank of $T + 1$ can now be found by determining the maximal number of linearly independent vectors among $\langle 0, 0, 2 \rangle$, $\langle 3, 3, 1 \rangle$, $\langle 0, 0, 0 \rangle$. In this case the number is obviously two and, by Theorem (13.9), the null space of $T + 1$ has dimension $3 - 2 = 1$.

Similarly, we have

$$(T - 2)v_1 = -3v_1 \qquad\quad + 2v_3$$
$$(T - 2)v_2 = \quad\; 3v_1 \qquad + v_3$$
$$(T - 2)v_3 = \qquad\qquad\qquad - 3v_3$$

and we find that rank $(T - 2) = 2$, so that the null space of $T - 2$ has dimension 1.

At this point we have shown that V is not the direct sum of $n(T + 1)$ and $n(T - 2)$. We may conclude that the minimal polynomial is

$$m(x) = (x + 1)^2(x - 2)$$

and that, by Theorem (23.8), it is impossible to find a basis of V with respect to which T has a diagonal matrix.

It remains to find the null spaces of $(T + 1)^2$ and $T - 2$. We have, from the computation of $T + 1$,

$$(T + 1)^2 v_1 = (T + 1)(2v_3) = 0,$$
$$(T + 1)^2 v_2 = (T + 1)(3v_1 + 3v_2 + v_3) = 9v_1 + 9v_2 + 9v_3,$$
$$(T + 1)^2 v_3 = 0.$$

Therefore $\{v_1, v_3\}$ is a basis for the null space of $(T + 1)^2$.

To find the null space of $T - 2$ we may suppose that $v = \xi_1 v_1 + \xi_2 v_2 + \xi_3 v_3 \in n(T - 2)$ and try to find ξ_1, ξ_2, ξ_3. We have

$$(T - 2)v = \xi_1(-3v_1 + 2v_3) + \xi_2(3v_1 + v_3) + \xi_3(-3v_3) = 0$$

and we have the following homogeneous system of equations to be solved for the ξ's:

$$-3\xi_1 + 3\xi_2 \qquad\quad = 0$$
$$2\xi_1 + \;\;\xi_2 - 3\xi_3 = 0.$$

This system has the solution vector $\langle 1, 1, 1 \rangle$. As a matter of fact, it is clear by inspection that $v_1 + v_2 + v_3$ is in $n(T - 2)$ and, since the dimension of $n(T - 2)$ is one, we know that $v_1 + v_2 + v_3$ generates $n(T - 2)$.

STEP 3. Find the matrix of T with respect to the new basis. According to Theorem (24.1), we should find a basis $\{w_1, w_2\}$ for $n[(T + 1)^2]$ such that $(T + 1)w_1 = 0$, $(T + 1)w_2 \in S(w_1)$, and let w_3 be a basis of $n(T - 2)$. We see that we should have

$$w_1 = v_3, \qquad w_2 = v_1, \qquad w_3 = v_1 + v_2 + v_3.$$
$$T(w_1) = -w_1, \qquad T(w_2) = -w_2 + 2w_1, \qquad T(w_3) = 2w_3.$$

The matrix relating these two bases is

$$S = \begin{pmatrix} 0 & 1 & 1 \\ 0 & 0 & 1 \\ 1 & 0 & 1 \end{pmatrix}$$

and the matrix of T with respect to $\{w_1, w_2, w_3\}$ is, by the equations on the preceding page,

$$B = \begin{pmatrix} -1 & 2 & 0 \\ 0 & -1 & 0 \\ 0 & 0 & 2 \end{pmatrix}.$$

We should now recall that either $SB = AS$ or $BS = SA$ (to remember which of the two holds is much too hard!). Checking the multiplications we see that

$$SB = AS$$

or

$$B = S^{-1}AS.$$

EXERCISES

1. Let T be a linear transformation on a vector space over the complex numbers such that

$$T(v_1) = -v_1 - v_2$$
$$T(v_2) = v_1 - 3v_2$$

where $\{v_1, v_2\}$ is a basis for the vector space.
   a. What is the characteristic polynomial of T?
   b. What is the minimal polynomial of T?
   c. What are the characteristic roots of T?
   d. Does there exist a basis for the vector space consisting of characteristic vectors of T? Explain.
   e. Find a characteristic vector of T.
   f. Find a triangular matrix B and an invertible matrix S such that $SB = AS$ where A is the matrix of T with respect to the basis $\{v_1, v_2\}$.

2. Answer the questions in Exercise 1 for the linear transformation $T \in L(C_2, C_2)$ defined by the equations

$$T(v_1) = v_1 + iv_2$$
$$T(v_2) = -iv_1 + v_2,$$

where $\{v_1, v_2\}$ is a basis for C_2.

3. Let V be a two-dimensional vector space over the real numbers R and let $T \in L(V, V)$ be defined by

$$T(v_1) = -\alpha v_2$$
$$T(v_2) = \beta v_1$$

where α and β are positive real numbers. Does there exist a basis of V consisting of characteristic vectors of T? Explain.

Note. In Exercises 4 to 8, V denotes a finite-dimensional vector space over the complex numbers C.

4. Let $T \in L(V, V)$ be a linear transformation whose characteristic roots are all equal to zero. Prove that T is nilpotent: $T^n = 0$ for some n.

5. Let $T \in L(V, V)$ be a linear transformation such that $T^2 = T$. Discuss whether or not there exists a basis of V consisting of characteristic vectors of T.

6. Answer the question of Exercise 5 for the case of a transformation T such that $T^r = 1$ for some positive integer r.

7. Let T be a linear transformation of rank 1, that is, dim $T(V) = 1$. Then $T(V) = S(v_0)$ for some vector $v_0 \neq 0$. In particular, $T(v_0) = \lambda v_0$ for some $\lambda \in C$. Prove that

$$T^2 = \lambda T.$$

Does there exist a basis of V consisting of characteristic vectors of T? Explain.

8. Prove that every linear transformation $T \in L(V, V)$ can be expressed in the form

$$T = D + N$$

where D is a diagonable transformation, N is nilpotent, and $DN = ND$. [*Hint:* This result follows almost at once from Theorem (24.1).]

9. a. Let $\mathbf{A} = (\alpha_{ij})$ be an n-by-n matrix with complex coefficients. Define the *trace* of $\mathbf{A}$ [notation: Tr $(\mathbf{A})$] by the formula

$$\text{Tr } (\mathbf{A}) = \sum_{i=1}^{n} \alpha_{ii}.$$

Prove that if $\mathbf{B}$ is another n-by-n matrix, then

$$\mathrm{Tr}\ (\mathbf{AB}) = \mathrm{Tr}\ (\mathbf{BA}).$$

b. Define the trace of a linear transformation $T \in L(V, V)$ to be the trace of $\mathbf{A}$, when $\mathbf{A}$ is a matrix of T with respect to some basis of T. Prove that the trace of T is defined independently of the choice of a matrix of T.

c. Prove that $\mathrm{Tr}\ (T)$ is the sum of the characteristic roots of T.

d. Let

$$h(x) = D(\mathbf{A} - x\mathbf{I})$$

be the characteristic polynomial of T, where $\mathbf{A}$ is the matrix of T with respect to some basis. Show that if $h(x)$ has degree r, then $\pm \mathrm{Tr}\ (T)$ is the coefficient of x^{r-1} in $h(x)$, while $\pm D(T)$ is the constant term of $h(x)$.

e. Show that the mapping

$$T \to \mathrm{Tr}\ (T)$$

is a linear transformation of $L(V, V) \to C$, and that the linear transformations of trace zero form a subspace of $L(V, V)$ of dimension $n^2 - 1$, where $n = \dim\ (V)$.

26. APPLICATION TO DIFFERENTIAL EQUATIONS*

We consider in this section a system of first-order linear differential equations with constant coefficients in the unknown functions $y_1(t)$, $\cdots$, $y_n(t)$ where t is a real variable and the $y_i(t)$ are real-valued functions. All this means is that we are given differential equations

$$\frac{dy_1}{dt} = \alpha_{11}y_1 + \cdots + \alpha_{1n}y_n$$

(26.1) $\cdots\cdots\cdots\cdots\cdots\cdots\cdots\cdots$

$$\frac{dy_n}{dt} = \alpha_{n1}y_1 + \cdots + \alpha_{nn}y_n$$

where $\mathbf{A} = (\alpha_{ij})$ is a fixed n-by-n matrix with real coefficients. We shall discuss the problem of finding a set of solutions $y_1(t), \cdots, y_n(t)$ which take on a prescribed set of initial conditions $y_1(0), \cdots, y_n(0)$. For example, we are going to show, if t is the time and if $y_1(t), \cdots$,

---

* This section is optional.

$y_n(t)$ describe the motion of some mechanical system, how to solve the equations of motion with the requirement that the functions take on specified values at time $t = 0$.

The simplest case of such a system is the case of one equation

$$\frac{dy}{dt} = \alpha y$$

and in this case we know from elementary calculus that the function

$$y(t) = y(0)\, e^{\alpha t}$$

solves the differential equation and takes on the initial value $y(0)$ when $t = 0$.

We shall show how matrix theory can be used to solve a general system (26.1) in an equally simple way. We should also point out that our discussion includes as a special case the problem of solving an nth-order linear differential equation with constant coefficients.

$$(26.2) \quad \alpha_0 \frac{d^n y}{dt^n} + \alpha_1 \frac{d^{n-1} y}{dt^{n-1}} + \cdots + \alpha_{n-1} \frac{dy}{dt} + \alpha_n y = 0, \qquad \alpha_0 \neq 0,$$

where the α_i are real constants. This equation can be replaced by a system of the form (26.1) if we view $y(t)$ as the unknown function $y_1(t)$ and rename the derivatives as follows:

$$\frac{d^i y}{dt^i} = y_{i+1}(t), \qquad 1 \leq i \leq n - 1.$$

Then the functions $y_i(t)$ satisfy the system

$$\frac{dy_1}{dt} = y_2$$

$$\frac{dy_2}{dt} = y_3$$

(26.3)

$$\vdots$$

$$\frac{dy_n}{dt} = -\frac{\alpha_n}{\alpha_0} y_1 - \frac{\alpha_{n-1}}{\alpha_0} y_2 - \cdots - \frac{\alpha_1}{\alpha_0} y_n$$

and, conversely, any set of solutions of the system (26.3) will also yield a solution $y_1(t) = y(t)$ of the original equation (26.2). The initial conditions in this case amount to specifying the values of $y(t)$ and its first $n - 1$ derivatives at $t = 0$.

Now let us proceed with the discussion. We may represent the functions $y_1(t), \cdots, y_n(t)$ in vector form (or as an n-by-1 matrix):

$$\mathbf{y}(t) = \begin{pmatrix} y_1(t) \\ \cdot \\ \cdot \\ \cdot \\ y_n(t) \end{pmatrix}.$$

We have here a function which, viewed abstractly, assigns to a real number t the vector $\mathbf{y}(t) \in R_n$. We may define limits of such functions as follows:

$$\lim_{t \to t_0} \mathbf{y}(t) = \begin{pmatrix} \lim_{t \to t_0} y_1(t) \\ \cdot \\ \cdot \\ \lim_{t \to t_0} y_n(t) \end{pmatrix}$$

provided all the limits $\lim_{t \to t_0} y_i(t)$ exist.

It will be useful to generalize all this slightly. We may consider functions

$$t \to \mathbf{A}(t) = \begin{pmatrix} a_{11}(t) & \cdots & a_{1r}(t) \\ \cdots\cdots\cdots\cdots \\ \cdots\cdots\cdots\cdots \\ a_{s1}(t) & \cdots & a_{sr}(t) \end{pmatrix}$$

which assign to a real number t an s-by-r matrix $\mathbf{A}(t)$ whose coefficients are complex numbers $a_{ij}(t)$. For a 1-by-1 matrix function we may define

$$\lim_{t \to t_0} a(t) = u$$

for some complex number u, provided that for each $\epsilon > 0$ there exists a $\delta > 0$ such that $0 < |t - t_0| < \delta$ implies $|a(t) - u| < \epsilon$ where $|a(t) - u|$ denotes the distance between the points $a(t)$ and u in the complex plane. By using the fact (proved in Section 15) that

$$|u + v| \leq |u| + |v|$$

for complex numbers u and v, it is easy to show that the usual limit theorems of elementary calculus carry over to complex-valued functions. We may then define, as in the case of a vector function $\mathbf{y}(t)$,

$$\lim_{t \to t_0} \mathbf{A}(t),$$

$$\frac{d\mathbf{A}}{dt} = \lim_{h \to 0} \frac{\mathbf{A}(t+h) - \mathbf{A}(t)}{h} = \begin{pmatrix} \dfrac{da_{11}}{dt} \cdots \dfrac{da_{1r}}{dt} \\ \cdots\cdots\cdots \\ \cdots\cdots\cdots \\ \cdots\cdots\cdots \\ \dfrac{da_{s1}}{dt} \cdots \dfrac{da_{sr}}{dt} \end{pmatrix}$$

and

$$\lim_{n \to \infty} \mathbf{A}_n(t) = \begin{pmatrix} \lim_{n \to \infty} a_{11}^n(t) \cdots \lim_{n \to \infty} a_{1r}^n(t) \\ \cdots\cdots\cdots\cdots\cdots \\ \cdots\cdots\cdots\cdots\cdots \\ \lim_{n \to \infty} a_{s1}^n(t) \cdots \lim_{n \to \infty} a_{sr}^n(t) \end{pmatrix}$$

where $\{\mathbf{A}_n(t)\}$ is a sequence of matrix-valued functions $\mathbf{A}_n(t) = (a_{ij}^{(n)}(t))$.

We can now express our original system of differential equations (26.1) in the more compact form

$$(26.4) \qquad\qquad \frac{d\mathbf{y}}{dt} = \mathbf{A}\mathbf{y}$$

where

$$\mathbf{y}(t) = \begin{pmatrix} y_1(t) \\ \cdot \\ \cdot \\ \cdot \\ y_n(t) \end{pmatrix}$$

is a vector-valued function and $\mathbf{A}\mathbf{y}$ denotes the product of the constant n-by-n matrix $\mathbf{A}$ by the n-by-1 matrix $\mathbf{y}(t)$.

The remarkable thing is that the equation (26.4) can be solved exactly as in the one-dimensional case. Let us begin with the following definition.

(26.5) Definition. Let $\mathbf{B}$ be an n-by-n matrix with complex coefficients (β_{ij}). Define the sequence of matrices

$$\mathbf{E}^{(n)} = \mathbf{I} + \mathbf{B} + \frac{1}{2}\mathbf{B}^2 + \cdots + \frac{1}{n!}\mathbf{B}^n, \qquad n = 0, 1, 2, \cdots.$$

Define the *exponential matrix*

$$e^{\mathbf{B}} = \lim_{n \to \infty} \mathbf{E}^{(n)} = \lim_{n \to \infty} \left(\mathbf{I} + \mathbf{B} + \frac{1}{2}\mathbf{B}^2 + \cdots + \frac{1}{n!}\mathbf{B}^n \right).$$

Of course, it must first be verified that e^B exists, that, in other words, the limit of the sequence $\{\mathbf{E}^{(n)}\}$ exists. Let ρ be some upper bound for the $\{|\beta_{ij}|\}$; then $|\beta_{ij}| \leq \rho$ for all (i, j). Let $\mathbf{B}^n = (\beta_{ij}^{(n)})$. Then the (i, j) entry of $\mathbf{E}^{(n)}$ is

$$\beta_{ij}^{(0)} + \beta_{ij}^{(1)} + \frac{1}{2}\beta_{ij}^{(2)} + \cdots + \frac{1}{n!}\beta_{ij}^{(n)}$$

and we have to show that this sequence tends to a limit. This means that the infinite series

$$\sum_{k=0} \frac{1}{k!}\beta_{ij}^{(k)}$$

converges, and this can be checked by making a simple comparison test as follows. By induction on k we show first that for $k = 1, 2, \cdots,$

$$|\beta_{ij}^{(k)}| \leq n^{k-1}\rho^k, \qquad 1 \leq i, \ j \leq n.$$

Then each term of the series

$$\sum_{k=0}^{\infty} \frac{1}{k!}\beta_{ij}^{(k)}$$

is dominated in absolute value by the corresponding term in the series of positive terms

$$\sum_{k=0}^{\infty} \frac{1}{k!} n^{k-1}\rho^k$$

and this series converges for all ρ by the ratio test. This completes the proof that e^B exists for all matrices $\mathbf{B}$.

We now list some easily verified properties of the function $\mathbf{B} \rightarrow e^B$.

(26.6)★ $e^{A+B} = e^A e^B$ *provided that* $\mathbf{AB} = \mathbf{BA}$.

(26.7)★ $\dfrac{d}{dt} e^{tB} = \mathbf{B}\, e^{tB}$ *for all n-by-n matrices* $\mathbf{B}$.

(26.8)★ $\mathbf{S}^{-1}e^A\mathbf{S} = e^{S^{-1}AS}$ *for an arbitrary invertible matrix* $\mathbf{S}$.

The solution of (26.4) can now be given as follows.

(26.9)   Theorem.   *The vector differential equation*

$$\frac{d\mathbf{y}}{dt} = \mathbf{A}\mathbf{y},$$

where $\mathbf{A}$ *is an arbitrary constant matrix with real coefficients, has the solution*

$$\mathbf{y}(t) = e^{tA} \cdot \mathbf{y}_0,$$

which takes on the initial value $\mathbf{y}_0$ *when* $t = 0$.

Proof. It is clear that $\mathbf{y}(0) = \mathbf{y}_0$, and it remains to check that $\mathbf{y}(t)$ is actually a solution of the differential equation. We note first that, if $\mathbf{A}(t)$ is a matrix function and $\mathbf{B}$ is a constant vector, then

$$\frac{d}{dt}[\mathbf{A}(t)\mathbf{B}] = \frac{d\mathbf{A}}{dt} \cdot \mathbf{B}.$$

Applying this to $\mathbf{y}(t) = e^{tA} \cdot \mathbf{y}_0$ and using (26.7), we have

$$\frac{d\mathbf{y}}{dt} = \left(\frac{d}{dt}e^{tA}\right) \cdot \mathbf{y}_0 = (\mathbf{A}\,e^{tA})\mathbf{y}_0 = \mathbf{A}\mathbf{y}(t).$$

This completes the proof of the theorem.

Theorem (26.9) solves the problem stated at the beginning of the section, but the solution is still not of much practical importance because of the difficulty of computing the matrix e^{tA}. We show now how Theorem (24.1) can be used to give a general method for calculating e^{tA}, provided that the complex roots of the minimal polynomial of the matrix $\mathbf{A}$ are known. Let

$$m(x) = (x - \alpha_1)^{e_1} \cdots (x - \alpha_s)^{e_s}, \qquad e_i > 0,$$

be the minimal polynomial of $\mathbf{A}$. Then there exists an invertible matrix $\mathbf{S}$, possibly with complex coefficients, such that, by Theorem (24.1),

$$\mathbf{S}^{-1}\mathbf{A}\mathbf{S} = \mathbf{D} + \mathbf{N}$$

where

$$
\mathbf{D} = \begin{pmatrix}
\alpha_1 & & 0 & & & \\
 & \cdot & & & 0 & \\
 & & \cdot & & & \\
0 & & \alpha_1 & & & \\
\hline
 & & & \alpha_2 & & 0 \\
0 & & & & \cdot & \\
 & & & & & \cdot \\
 & & & 0 & & \alpha_2 \\
\hline
 & & & & & \\
\end{pmatrix}
$$

is a diagonal matrix, $\mathbf{N}$ is nilpotent, and $\mathbf{DN} = \mathbf{ND}$ (see Exercise 8 of Section 25). Moreover, $\mathbf{S}$, $\mathbf{D}$, and $\mathbf{N}$ can all be calculated by the methods of Sections 24 and 25. Then

$$\mathbf{A} = \mathbf{S}(\mathbf{D} + \mathbf{N})\mathbf{S}^{-1}$$

and, by (26.6) and (26.8), we have

(26.10) $\qquad e^{tA} = e^{t\mathbf{S}(\mathbf{D}+\mathbf{N})\mathbf{S}^{-1}} = \mathbf{S}(e^{t\mathbf{D}+t\mathbf{N}})\mathbf{S}^{-1}$

$$= \mathbf{S}\, e^{t\mathbf{D}}\, e^{t\mathbf{N}}\mathbf{S}^{-1}.$$

The point of all this is that $e^{t\mathbf{D}}$ and $e^{t\mathbf{N}}$ are both easy to compute; $e^{t\mathbf{D}}$ is simply the diagonal matrix

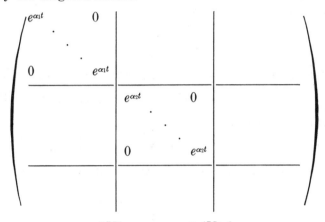

while $e^{t\mathbf{N}} = \mathbf{I} + t\mathbf{N} + \dfrac{t^2\mathbf{N}^2}{2} + \cdots + \dfrac{t^{r-1}\mathbf{N}^{r-1}}{(r-1)!}$ if $\mathbf{N}^r = 0$. The solution vector $\mathbf{y}(t) = \mathbf{S}\, e^{t\mathbf{D}} e^{t\mathbf{N}}\mathbf{S}^{-1}\mathbf{y}_0$.

These remarks, of course, serve only as an introduction to the modern theory of vector differential equations. The point of it for us is to show how the triangular form theorem is used to make enormous simplifications in a seemingly impossible computational problem. For a more thorough (and advanced) treatment, see Coddington and Levinson, listed in the Bibliography.

EXERCISES

1. Let

$$\mathbf{A} = \begin{pmatrix} 0 & 1 \\ 0 & 0 \end{pmatrix}, \qquad \mathbf{B} = \begin{pmatrix} -1 & 0 \\ 0 & 0 \end{pmatrix}.$$

Show that $\mathbf{AB} \neq \mathbf{BA}$. Calculate e^A, e^B, e^{A+B}, and show that $e^{A+B} \neq e^A e^B$. Thus (26.7) does not hold without some hypothesis like $\mathbf{AB} = \mathbf{BA}$.

2. Show that $D(e^A) = e^{\Sigma \alpha_i}$ where the $\{\alpha_i\}$ are the characteristic roots of $\mathbf{A}$. [*Hint:* Use the triangular form theorem (24.1) together with (26.8).]

3. Show that e^A is always invertible and that $(e^A)^{-1} = e^{-A}$ for all $\mathbf{A} \in M_n(C)$.

4. Let $\mathbf{y}(t)$ be any solution of the differential equation $\dfrac{d\mathbf{y}}{dt} = \mathbf{Ay}$ such that $\mathbf{y}(t) = \mathbf{y}_0$. Prove that

$$\frac{d}{dt} (e^{-At}\mathbf{y}) = 0$$

and hence that $\mathbf{y} = e^{At} \cdot \mathbf{y}_0$. Thus the solution of the differential equation $\dfrac{d\mathbf{y}}{dt} = \mathbf{Ay}$ satisfying the given initial condition is uniquely determined.

5. Prove that $^t(e^A) = e^{\,^tA}$, where $^t\mathbf{A}$ is the transpose of $\mathbf{A}$.

6. Define a matrix $\mathbf{A}$ to be skew symmetric if $^t\mathbf{A} = -\mathbf{A}$, for example

$$\mathbf{A} = \begin{pmatrix} 0 & 1 \\ -1 & 0 \end{pmatrix}.$$

Prove that if $\mathbf{A}$ is any real skew-symmetric matrix then e^A is an orthogonal matrix of determinant $+1$.

7. Apply the methods of this section to compute a solution for the differential equation

$$\frac{d^2y}{dt^2} + y = 0$$

such that $y(0) = 0$, $y'(0) = 1$. (Of course, this problem can also be done directly as a check.)

8. Solve the system

$$\begin{cases} \dfrac{dy_1}{dt} = -y_1 + y_2 \\[2mm] \dfrac{dy_2}{dt} = -y_1 - 3y_2 \end{cases} \qquad y_1(0) = 0, \quad y_2(0) = 1.$$

(Note that the matrix

$$\begin{pmatrix} -1 & 1 \\ -1 & -3 \end{pmatrix}$$

is the same as the matrix involved in Exercise 1 of Section 25.)

9. Let $\mathbf{A}$ be the coefficient matrix of the vector differential equation equivalent to

$$\alpha_0 \frac{d^n y}{dt^n} + \alpha_1 \frac{d^{n-1} y}{dt^{n-1}} + \cdots + \alpha_n y = 0.$$

Prove that the characteristic polynomial of $\mathbf{A}$ is

$$\alpha_0 x^n + \alpha_1 x^{n-1} + \cdots + \alpha_n.$$

10. (Optional.) Verify the following derivation of a particular solution of the "nonhomogeneous" vector differential equation

$$\frac{d\mathbf{y}}{dt} = \mathbf{A}\mathbf{y} + \mathbf{f}(t)$$

where $\mathbf{f}(t)$ is a given continuous vector function of t. Attempt to find a solution of the form $\mathbf{y}(t) = e^{At}\mathbf{c}(t)$, where $\mathbf{c}(t)$ is a vector function to be determined. Differentiate to obtain

$$\frac{d\mathbf{y}}{dt} = \mathbf{A}\, e^{At}\mathbf{c}(t) + e^{At}\frac{d\mathbf{c}(t)}{dt} = \mathbf{A}\mathbf{y} + \mathbf{f}(t).$$

Since $\mathbf{A}e^{At}\mathbf{c}(t) = \mathbf{A}\mathbf{y}$, we obtain [since $(e^{At})^{-1} - e^{-At}$]

$$\frac{d\mathbf{c}}{dt} = e^{-At}\mathbf{f}(t).$$

Thus $\mathbf{c}(t)$ is an indefinite integral of $e^{-At}\mathbf{f}(t)$ and can be expressed as

$$\mathbf{c}(t) = \int_{t_0}^{t} e^{-As}\mathbf{f}(s)\, ds.$$

Then $\mathbf{y}(t) = e^{At}\int_{t_0}^{t} e^{-As}\mathbf{f}(s)\, ds = \int_{t_0}^{t} e^{A(t-s)}\mathbf{f}(s)\, ds$. Finally, verify that $\mathbf{y}(t)$ is a solution of the differential equation.

27.   THE JORDAN NORMAL FORM *

Let T be a linear transformation on a finite-dimensional vector space V over an algebraically closed field F. From the triangular

---

* The material in this section is optional, and several steps in the discussion are left as exercises for the reader.

form theorem, it follows that the matrix $\mathbf{A}$ of T is similar to $\mathbf{D} + \mathbf{N}$, where $\mathbf{D}$ is a diagonal matrix, $\mathbf{N}$ is nilpotent, and $\mathbf{DN} = \mathbf{ND}$. The entries along the diagonal of $\mathbf{D}$ are the characteristic roots of T, with each characteristic root α repeated as many times as the linear factor $x - \alpha$ appears in a factorization of the characteristic polynomial of T into primes. Apart from the order in which the characteristic roots appear on the diagonal of $\mathbf{D}$, $\mathbf{D}$ is completely determined by the characteristic polynomial of T. The matrix $\mathbf{N}$, on the other hand, is not uniquely determined and depends on the choice of the bases for the null spaces of $(T - \alpha \cdot 1)^m$ where $(x - \alpha)^m$ is a prime power factor of the minimal polynomial of T. For the applications to differential equations and the computation of e^A, and for other purposes as well, it is desirable to know the simplest possible choice for the nilpotent matrix $\mathbf{N}$. We present a solution of this problem here.

We begin with a close study of a nilpotent linear transformation T on a finite-dimensional space V over an arbitrary field F. Let v be a nonzero vector in V, and consider the set of vectors $\{v, Tv, T^2v, \cdots\}$. These vectors generate a T-subspace of V called the *cyclic subspace generated by* v. An arbitrary T-subspace W of V is called a *cyclic subspace relative to* T (or simply a *cyclic T-subspace*) if there exists a vector $w \in W$ such that W is generated by the vectors w, Tw, T^2w, $\cdots$.

(27.1) Lemma.   *Let W be a cyclic subspace relative to T. Then there exists a vector $w \in W$ and a positive integer k such that $T^kw = 0$, and such that $\{T^{k-1}w, T^{k-2}w, \cdots, Tw, w\}$ is a basis of W. The matrix of the transformation of W determined by T with respect to this basis is*

$$\begin{pmatrix} 0 & 1 & 0 & \cdots & 0 \\ \cdot & 0 & 1 & & \cdot \\ \cdot & \cdot & 0 & & \cdot \\ \cdot & \cdot & \cdot & & 1 \\ 0 & 0 & 0 & \cdots & 0 \end{pmatrix}.$$

Proof.   Since W is cyclic, there exists a vector $w \in W$ such that W is generated by the vectors w, Tw, $\cdots$. Since W is finite-dimensional, there exists a positive integer k such that $\{w, Tw, \cdots, T^{k-1}w\}$ is a linearly independent set, and $T^kw \in S(w, Tw, \cdots, T^{k-1}w)$. It is clear that for all integers $m \geq k$, $T^mw \in S(w, Tw, \cdots, T^{k-1}w)$, and hence $\{w, Tw, \cdots, T^{k-1}w\}$ is a basis for W. Now let T_1 be the linear transformation defined by T on the space W; then $T_1(u) = T(u)$ for all $u \in W$. Since T is nilpotent on V, T_1 is nilpotent on W, and hence the minimal polynomial of T_1 on W has the form x^t, for some $t \leq \dim W$. Since $\dim W = k$, we have $t \leq k$, and hence $T_1^k = T^k = 0$ on W. In particular, $T^k w = 0$. The form of the matrix of T_1 relative to the basis given in the statement of the lemma is clear by the definition of the matrix of a linear transformation. This completes the proof of the lemma.

For the proof of the main result it will be necessary to introduce the important concepts of dual space, dual basis, and transpose of a linear transformation. The idea behind these constructions is that for every vector space V and linear transformation $T \in L(V, V)$, there is a vector space V^*, called the *dual* of V, which is a kind of mirror to V, and a linear transformation T^* of V^* which mirrors the behavior of T. We shall see in the proof of the main result how the interaction between T and T^* can provide new information about T.

(27.2)   **Definition.**   Let V be a finite-dimensional vector space over F. The *dual space* V^* of V is defined to be the vector space $L(V, F)$, where F is identified with the vector space of one-tuples over F. The elements of V^* are simply functions f from V into F such that $f(v_1 + v_2) = f(v_1) + f(v_2)$, $v_1, v_2 \in V$, and $f(\alpha v) = \alpha f(v)$, $\alpha \in F$, $v \in V$. Elements of V^* are called *linear functions* on V.

(27.3)   **Lemma.**   *Let $\{v_1, \cdots, v_n\}$ be a basis for V over F. Then there exist linear functions $\{f_1, \cdots, f_n\}$ such that for each i,*

$$f_i(v_i) = 1, \qquad f_i(v_j) = 0, \qquad j \neq i.$$

The linear functions $\{f_1, \cdots, f_n\}$ form a basis for V^* over F, called the dual basis to $\{v_1, \cdots, v_n\}$.

Proof.   First of all, the linear functions exist because of Theorem (13.1), which allows us to define linear transformations which map basis elements of a vector space onto arbitrary vectors in the image space. We next show that $\{f_1, \cdots, f_n\}$ are linearly independent. Suppose

$$\alpha_1 f_1 + \cdots + \alpha_n f_n = 0, \qquad \alpha_i \in F.$$

Then applying both sides to the vector v_1, and using the definition of the vector space operations in V^*, we have

$$\alpha_1 f_1(v_1) + \alpha_2 f_2(v_1) + \cdots + \alpha_n f_n(v_1) = 0.$$

Therefore $\alpha_1 = 0$ because $f_1(v_1) = 1$ and $f_2(v_1) = \cdots = f_n(v_1) = 0$. Similarly $\alpha_2 = \cdots = \alpha_n = 0$.

Finally we check that $\{f_1, \cdots, f_n\}$ form a set of generators for

V^*. Let $f \in V^*$, and let $f(v_i) = \alpha_i$, $i = 1, 2, \cdots, n$. Then it is easily checked, by applying both sides to the basis elements $\{v_1, \cdots, v_n\}$ in turn, that

$$f = \alpha_1 f_1 + \cdots + \alpha_n f_n.$$

This completes the proof of the lemma.

(27.4)   Definition.   Let $T \in L(V, V)$, where V is finite-dimensional over F. Define $T^* \in L(V^*, V^*)$ as follows. For each linear function $f \in V^*$, T^*f is defined by the rule

$$(T^*f)(x) = f(Tx), \qquad x \in V.$$

The linear transformation T^* is called the *transpose* of T.

We must check that the statements made in the definition are correct. First of all, T^*f is a linear function, because

$$(T^*f)(v_1 + v_2) = f[T(v_1 + v_2)] = f[T(v_1)] + f[T(v_2)]$$
$$= (T^*f)(v_1) + (T^*f)(v_2),$$

for all $v_1, v_2 \in V$ and $f \in V^*$, and

$$(T^*f)(\alpha v) = f[T(\alpha v)] = f[\alpha(Tv)] = \alpha f(Tv)$$
$$= \alpha[T^*f(v)], \qquad v \in V, \alpha \in F.$$

We must then check that $T^* \in L(V^*, V^*)$. For $f_1, f_2 \in V^*$, we have

$$[T^*(f_1 + f_2)](v) = (f_1 + f_2)(Tv) = f_1(Tv) + f_2(Tv)$$
$$= (T^*f_1 + T^*f_2)(v).$$

Moreover,

$$[T^*(\alpha f)](v) = (\alpha f)(Tv) = f[\alpha(Tv)] = f[T(\alpha v)]$$
$$= (T^*f)(\alpha v) = [\alpha(T^*f)](v),$$

for all $v \in V$ and $\alpha \in F$. It is interesting to notice how the linearity of T and f, and the vector space operations in V^*, are used in these verifications.

The main theorem in the appendix can now be stated.

(27.5)   Theorem.   *Let T be a nilpotent linear transformation on a finite-dimensional space V over an arbitrary field F. Then V can be expressed as a direct sum $V = V_1 \oplus \cdots \oplus V_s$, where each V_i is a cyclic T-subspace.*

Proof.   We define a T-subspace W of V to be *indecomposable* if $W \neq 0$ and if it is impossible to express W as a direct sum of two nonzero T-subspaces. We first prove, by induction on dim V, that V

is either indecomposable or a direct sum of indecomposable invariant subspaces. We shall then prove that every indecomposable invariant subspace is cyclic.

If dim $V = 1$, then V is indecomposable. Suppose now that dim $V > 1$ and that every T-subspace $W \neq V$ is either indecomposable or a direct sum of indecomposable subspaces relative to T. If V is indecomposable, there is nothing to prove. If V is not indecomposable, then there exist invariant subspaces V_1 and V_2, both different from zero, such that $V = V_1 \oplus V_2$. Then both V_1 and V_2 have dimensions less than dim V. Upon applying the induction hypothesis to V_1 and V_2, it follows that V is a direct sum of indecomposable invariant subspaces, as required.

In order to prove that if V is indecomposable then V is cyclic, we shall prove instead that if V is not cyclic then V is not indecomposable. Let x^k be the minimal polynomial of T on V. Then there exists a cyclic subspace W of V with a basis $\{w, Tw, \cdots, T^{k-1}w\}$. Otherwise, by Lemma (27.1), $T^{k-1} = 0$ on V, contrary to the assumption that x^k is the minimal polynomial of T. Since by assumption V is not cyclic, $W \neq V$.

Now let V^* be the dual space of V [see Definition (27.2)], and let $W^\perp$ be the set of all linear functions $f \in V^*$ such that $f(W) = 0$. Then $W^\perp$ is a subspace of V^*. Let $\{v_1, \cdots, v_n\}$ be a basis of V such that $\{v_1, \cdots, v_k\}$ is a basis of W, and let $\{f_1, \cdots, f_n\}$ be the corresponding basis of V^* defined in Lemma (27.3). Then the reader can verify that $\{f_{k+1}, \cdots, f_n\}$ is a basis of $W^\perp$, so that dim $W^\perp = n - k$.

Now let T^* be the transpose of T, defined earlier in this section. The reader can show that for all integers $i \geq 1$, $(T^*)^i = (T^i)^*$. Therefore $(T^*)^k = 0$. On the other hand, we shall prove that for some linear function $f \in V^*$, $(T^*)^{k-1}f \notin W^\perp$. Otherwise $(T^*)^{k-1}f \in W^\perp$ for all $f \in V^*$. Then $0 = [(T^*)^{k-1}f](w) = f(T^{k-1}w)$ for all $f \in V^*$. It follows that $T^{k-1}w = 0$ (Why?). But this is contrary to the definition of the vector w. Thus $(T^*)^{k-1}f \notin W^\perp$ for some $f \in V^*$.

We prove next that if

$$\alpha_0 f + \alpha_1(T^*f) + \cdots + \alpha_{k-1}[(T^*)^{k-1}f] \in W^\perp,$$

then $\alpha_0 = \cdots = \alpha_{k-1} = 0$. Suppose we have such a relation, with $\alpha_0 = \cdots = \alpha_{i-1} = 0$, $\alpha_i \neq 0$. Then

$$\alpha_i(T^*)^i f + \cdots + \alpha_{k-1}(T^*)^{k-1}f \in W^\perp,$$

and multiplying by $(T^*)^{k-1-i}$ and using the fact that $(T^*)^k = 0$, we obtain

$$\alpha_i(T^*)^{k-1}f \in W^\perp$$

where $\alpha_i \neq 0$, contrary to our choice of f. It follows that if S is the subspace of V^* generated by f, T^*f, $\cdots$, $(T^*)^{k-1}f$, then $S \cap W^\perp = 0$, and dim $S = k$. Therefore $V^* = W^\perp + S$, by (7.17), and

$$(27.6) \qquad\qquad V^* = W^\perp \oplus S.$$

Moreover, since $(T^*)^k = 0$, S is a T^*-subspace of V^*.

Finally, let $S^\perp$ be the set of vectors v in V such that $g(v) = 0$ for all $g \in S$. Then $S^\perp$ is a T-subspace of V, since S is a T^*-subspace of V^*. We shall complete the argument by showing that

$$V = W \oplus S^\perp$$

and hence that V is not indecomposable.

First of all, let $v \in W \cap S^\perp$. Then, by (27.6), $\varphi(v) = 0$ for all $\varphi \in V^*$, and hence $v = 0$. Thus $W \cap S^\perp = 0$. Now let $\{\varphi_1, \cdots, \varphi_k\}$ be a basis for S. Then the reader can check that

$$\varphi_1(x) = 0, \quad \cdots, \quad \varphi_k(x) = 0$$

is a system of homogeneous equations whose coefficient matrix has rank k, and whose solution space is exactly $S^\perp$. It follows that dim $S^\perp = n - k$. Since dim $W = k$ and $W \cap S^\perp = 0$, we have $V = W \oplus S^\perp$. This completes the proof of the theorem.

(27.7) Corollary. *Let T be a nilpotent transformation on a finite-dimensional space V. Then V has a basis such that the matrix of T relative to this basis has the form*

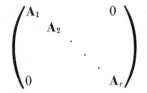

with zeros except in the diagonal blocks, and each diagonal block has the form

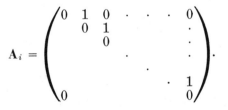

Using the main theorem of Section 23, we obtain the following result:

(27.8) **Corollary.** *Let T be a linear transformation on a finite-dimensional space V over a field F whose minimal polynomial has the form $\prod\limits_{i=1}^{s} (x - \alpha_i)^{d_i}$, where the $\{\alpha_i\}$ are the characteristic roots of T. (This hypothesis is satisfied, for example, if F is an algebraically closed field.) Then there exists a basis of V such that the matrix of T with respect to this basis has the form*

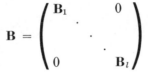

$$\mathbf{B} = \begin{pmatrix} \mathbf{B}_1 & & & 0 \\ & \cdot & & \\ & & \cdot & \\ 0 & & & \mathbf{B}_l \end{pmatrix}$$

with zeros except in the diagonal blocks, and the blocks $\{\mathbf{B}_j\}$ have the form

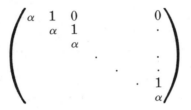

$$\begin{pmatrix} \alpha & 1 & 0 & & & & 0 \\ & \alpha & 1 & & & & \\ & & \alpha & & & & \\ & & & \cdot & & & \\ & & & & \cdot & 1 & \\ & & & & & & \alpha \end{pmatrix}$$

where α is one of the characteristic roots of T.

Proof. By Theorem (23.6), V can be expressed as the direct sum of the null spaces $V_i = n((T - \alpha_i \cdot 1)^{d_i})$. On the space V_i, $T - \alpha_i 1$ is a nilpotent transformation. Apply Corollary (27.7) to $T - \alpha_i \cdot 1$ on the space V_i. There exists a basis of V_i such that the matrix $\mathbf{A}$ of $T - \alpha_i 1$ on V_i has the form

$$\mathbf{A} = \begin{pmatrix} \mathbf{A}_1 & & & 0 \\ & \cdot & & \\ & & \cdot & \\ 0 & & & \mathbf{A}_r \end{pmatrix}$$

where the $\mathbf{A}_i$ are as in Corollary (27.7). If $\mathbf{B}$ is the matrix of T on the space V_i relative to this basis, then $\mathbf{A} = \mathbf{B} - \alpha_i \cdot \mathbf{I}$, and

$$\mathbf{B} = \alpha_i \mathbf{I} + \mathbf{A}.$$

It follows that

$$\mathbf{B} = \begin{pmatrix} \mathbf{B}_1 & & & 0 \\ & \cdot & & \\ & & \cdot & \\ 0 & & & \mathbf{B}_r \end{pmatrix}$$

where each $\mathbf{B}_j$ has the form

$$\begin{pmatrix} \alpha_i & 1 & 0 & \cdot & \cdot & \cdot & 0 \\ & \alpha_i & 1 & & & & \cdot \\ & & \alpha_i & & & & \cdot \\ & & & \cdot & & & \\ & & & & \cdot & & \\ & & & & & \cdot & 1 \\ 0 & & & & & & \alpha_i \end{pmatrix}.$$

Combining these bases for the various spaces $n((T - \alpha_i 1)^{d_i})$, we obtain a basis of V with respect to which the matrix of T has the required form. This completes the proof of the corollary.

It follows from earlier results in this chapter that every n-by-n matrix $\mathbf{A}$ whose minimal polynomial has the form $\Pi(x - \alpha_i)^{d_i}$ is similar to a matrix in the form given in Corollary (27.8). This form is called the *Jordan normal form* of the matrix of T. Our result proves only the existence of the Jordan normal form. It leaves open the questions of how to give an algorithm for putting a matrix in its Jordan normal form, the uniqueness of the blocks in the Jordan normal form, and what can be said for linear transformations over fields which are not necessarily algebraically closed. For a discussion of these questions, the reader may consult one of the more advanced books on linear algebra, such as Jacobson or Schreier and Sperner, listed in the Bibliography.

EXERCISES

1. Let $\{v_1, \cdots, v_n\}$ be a basis for a vector space V over F, and let $\{f_1, \cdots, f_n\}$ be the dual basis of V^*. Let $T \in L(V, V)$ be a linear transformation whose matrix with respect to the basis $\{v_1, \cdots, v_n\}$ is $\mathbf{A}$. Prove that the matrix of T^* with respect to the basis $\{f_1, \cdots, f_n\}$ of V^* is the transpose ${}^t\mathbf{A}$ of $\mathbf{A}$.

2. Let $T_1, T_2 \in L(V, V)$. Show that

$$(T_1 T_2)^* = T_2^* T_1^*.$$

3. Prove that the minimal polynomial of $T \in L(V, V)$ is equal to the minimal polynomial of T^*.

4. Let W be a subspace of V, and let $W^\perp$ be the set of linear functions vanishing on W. Similarly, if Y is a subspace of V^*, let $Y^\perp$ denote the set of all vectors v in V such that $f(v) = 0$ for all $f \in Y$. Prove

(assuming V is finite-dimensional) that for every subspace W of V, $(W^{\perp})^{\perp} = W$.

5. Let T be a linear transformation of a 3-dimensional vector space over the complex numbers defined by

$$T(v_1) = v_1 + v_2 - 2v_3$$
$$T(v_2) = v_2 + v_3$$
$$T(v_3) = v_3.$$

Find a basis of V such that the matrix of T with respect to this basis is in the Jordan normal form. [*Hint:* Show that $(T - 1)^3 = 0$, and find a vector w such that $(T - 1)^3 w = 0$, but $(T - 1)^2 w \neq 0$.]

CHAPTER 8

ORTHOGONAL, UNITARY, and SYMMETRIC TRANSFORMATIONS

In Section 28, the methods of the preceding chapter are used to give a deeper analysis of orthogonal transformations of vector spaces with an inner product. Then quadratic forms and symmetric transformations are investigated. Finally, the finite subgroups of the rotation group in three dimensions are determined.

28. THE STRUCTURE OF ORTHOGONAL TRANSFORMATIONS

In Section 14 we showed that every orthogonal transformation of the plane is either a rotation or a reflection. We wish to find in this section a geometrical description of orthogonal transformations on an n-dimensional real vector space V with an inner product (u, v). From the point of view of Chapter 7, given an orthogonal transformation T we look for an orthonormal basis of V with respect to which the matrix of T is as simple as possible.

The matrix

$$\mathbf{A} = \begin{pmatrix} \cos\dfrac{2\pi}{3} & -\sin\dfrac{2\pi}{3} \\[2mm] \sin\dfrac{2\pi}{3} & \cos\dfrac{2\pi}{3} \end{pmatrix} = \begin{pmatrix} -\dfrac{1}{2} & -\dfrac{\sqrt{3}}{2} \\[2mm] \dfrac{\sqrt{3}}{2} & -\dfrac{1}{2} \end{pmatrix}$$

is an orthogonal matrix such that $\mathbf{A}^3 = \mathbf{I}$. Its minimal polynomial is

$$x^2 + x + 1$$

which is a prime in the polynomial ring $R[x]$. Therefore, by Theorem (23.8), $\mathbf{A}$ cannot be diagonalized over the real field and cannot even be put in triangular form, since a triangular 2-by-2 orthogonal matrix can easily be shown to be diagonal. Thus the methods of Chapter 7 yield little new information, even in this simple case.

The difficulty is that the real field is not algebraically closed. It is here that, as Hermann Weyl remarked, Euclid enters the scene, brandishing his ruler and his compass. The ideas necessary to treat orthogonal transformations on a real vector space will throw additional light on the problems considered in Chapter 7, as well. The existence of an inner product allows us to get information about minimal polynomials, etc., that would have seemed almost impossible from the methods of Chapter 7 alone. We begin with some general definitions and theorems.

(28.1) Definition. Let $T \in L(V, V)$ be a linear transformation on an arbitrary finite-dimensional vector space V over an arbitrary field F. A nonzero invariant subspace $W \subset V$ (relative to T) is called *irreducible* if the only T-invariant subspaces contained in W are $\{0\}$ and W.

(28.2) Theorem. (A) *If V is a vector space over an algebraically closed field F, then every irreducible invariant subspace W relative to $T \in L(V, V)$ has dimension 1. (B) If V is a vector space over the real field R and if W is an irreducible invariant subspace relative to $T \in L(V, V)$, then W has dimension 1 or 2.*

Proof of (A).   Let W be an irreducible invariant subspace relative to T; then T defines a linear transformation T_W of W into itself, where

$$T_W(w) = T(w), \qquad w \in W.$$

From Section 24, W contains a characteristic vector w relative to T; then $S(w)$ is an invariant subspace contained in W, and hence $W = S(w)$ because W is irreducible. This proves part (A).

Proof of (B).   Let W be an irreducible invariant subspace relative to T and let $m(x)$ be the minimal polynomial of T_W. From Theorem (23.6), $m(x) = p(x)^e$ where $p(x)$ is a prime polynomial in $R[x]$; otherwise, W would be the direct sum of subspaces, contrary to the assumption that W is irreducible. If $m(x) = p(x)^e$ is the minimal polynomial of T_W, then $e = 1$; otherwise, the null space of $p(T)^{e-1}$ would be an invariant subspace different from $\{0\}$ and W. Thus we have, by Corollary (21.13), either

$$m(x) = x - \alpha \qquad \text{or} \qquad m(x) = x^2 + \alpha x + \beta, \qquad \alpha^2 - 4\beta < 0.$$

Let w be a nonzero vector of W. Then, if $m(x) = x - \alpha$, w is a characteristic vector of T, and $W = S(w)$ as in part (A). If $m(x) = x^2 + \alpha x + \beta$ for $\alpha^2 - 4\beta < 0$, then $S[w, T(w)]$ is an invariant subspace, and hence $W = S[w, T(w)]$. Therefore W has dimension either 1 or 2, and the theorem is proved.

Now we apply this theorem to orthogonal transformations as follows.

(28.3)   Theorem.   *Let T be an orthogonal transformation on a real vector space V with an inner product and let W be an irreducible invariant subspace relative to T; then either of the two following holds.*

(1)   *dim $W = 1$ and, if $w \neq 0$ in W, then $T(w) = \pm w$.*
(2)   *dim $W = 2$ and there is an orthonormal basis $\{w_1, w_2\}$ for W such that the matrix of T with respect to $\{w_1, w_2\}$ has the form*

$$\begin{pmatrix} \cos \theta & -\sin \theta \\ \sin \theta & \cos \theta \end{pmatrix}.$$

In other words, T_W is a rotation in the two-dimensional space W (see Section 14).

Proof.   By Theorem (28.2), dim W is either 1 or 2. In case 1 of the theorem, $T(w) = \lambda w$ for some $\lambda \in R$, and

$$\|T(w)\| = \|w\|$$

implies $|\lambda| = 1$. Therefore, $\lambda = \pm 1$ and $T(w) = \pm w$.

If dim $W = 2$, then the minimal polynomial of T has the form

$$x^2 + \alpha x + \beta, \qquad \alpha^2 - 4\beta < 0.$$

Let $\{w_1, w_2\}$ be an orthonormal basis for W and let

$$T(w_1) = \lambda w_1 + \mu w_2.$$

Then $\lambda^2 + \mu^2 = 1$ and, since $(T(w_1), T(w_2)) = 0$, $T(w_2)$ is either $-\mu w_1 + \lambda w_2$ or $\mu w_1 - \lambda w_2$. In the first case, the matrix of T is

$$\begin{pmatrix} \lambda & -\mu \\ \mu & \lambda \end{pmatrix}$$

and we can find θ such that $\cos \theta = \lambda$, $\sin \theta = \mu$, since $\lambda^2 + \mu^2 = 1$. In the latter case, the matrix is

$$\begin{pmatrix} \lambda & \mu \\ \mu & -\lambda \end{pmatrix}$$

which satisfies the equation $x^2 - 1 = 0$, and since $x^2 - 1 = (x + 1)(x - 1)$ is not a prime this case cannot occur. This completes the proof of the theorem.

The last theorem becomes of especial interest when combined with the following result.

(28.4) Theorem. *Let T be an orthogonal transformation on a real vector space V with an inner product; then V is a direct sum of irreducible invariant subspaces $\{W_1, \cdots, W_s\}$, for $s \geq 1$, such that vectors belonging to distinct subspaces W_i and W_j are orthogonal.*

Proof. We prove the theorem by induction on dim V, the result being obvious if dim $V = 1$. Assume the theorem for subspaces of dimension $<$ dim V and let T be an orthogonal transformation on V. Let W_1 be a nonzero invariant subspace of least dimension; then W_1 is an irreducible invariant subspace. Let $W_1^\perp$ be the subspace consisting of all vectors orthogonal to the vectors in W_1. We prove that

$$W = W_1 \oplus W_1^\perp.$$

Clearly, $W_1 \cap W_1^\perp = \{0\}$, since $(w, w) \neq 0$ if $w \neq 0$. Now let $w \in W$ and let $\{w_1, \cdots, w_s\}$ be an orthonormal basis for W_1 where $s = 1$ or 2. Then

$$w = \sum_{i=1}^{s} (w, w_i)w_i + \left(w - \sum_{i=1}^{s} (w, w_i)w_i \right)$$

and since $\sum_1^s (w, w_i)w_i \in W_1$ and $w - \sum_1^s (w, w_i)w_i \in W_1^\perp$ we have $W = W_1 + W_1^\perp$. This fact together with the result that $W_1 \cap W_1^\perp = \{0\}$ implies that $W = W_1 \oplus W_1^\perp$.

Now we prove the key result that $W_1^\perp$ is also an invariant subspace. Let $w' \in W_1^\perp$. Since T is orthogonal, $T(W_1) = W_1$ and $(W_1, w') = (T(W_1), T(w')) = (W_1, T(w')) = 0$. Therefore $T(w')$ is also orthogonal to all the vectors in W_1.

Since $T(W_1^\perp) \subset W_1^\perp$, T is an orthogonal transformation of $W_1^\perp$ and, by the induction hypothesis, $W_1^\perp$ is a direct sum of pairwise orthogonal irreducible invariant subspaces. Since $V = W_1 \oplus W_1^\perp$, the same is true for V, and the theorem is proved.

Combining Theorems (28.3) and (28.4) we obtain the following determination of the form of the matrix of an orthogonal transformation.

(28.5)   Theorem.   *Let T be an orthogonal transformation of a real vector space V with an inner product; then there exists an orthonormal basis for V such that the matrix of T with respect to this basis has the form*

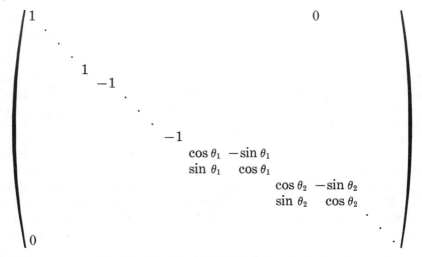

with zeros except in the 1-by-1 or 2-by-2 blocks along the diagonal.

Proof.   The proof is immediate by Theorems (28.3) and (28.4), since we can choose orthonormal bases for the individual subspaces W_i in Theorem (28.4) which, when taken together, will form an orthonormal basis of V.

EXERCISES

1. Prove that, if T is an orthogonal transformation on R_2 such that $D(T) = -1$, there exists an orthonormal basis for R_2 such that the matrix of T with respect to this basis is

$$\begin{pmatrix} -1 & 0 \\ 0 & 1 \end{pmatrix}.$$

2. An orthogonal transformation T of R_3 is called a *rotation* if $D(T) = 1$. Prove that if T is a rotation in R_3 there exists an orthonormal basis of R_3 such that the matrix of T with respect to this basis is

$$\begin{pmatrix} 1 & 0 & 0 \\ 0 & \cos\theta & -\sin\theta \\ 0 & \sin\theta & \cos\theta \end{pmatrix}$$

for some real number θ.

3. Prove that an orthogonal transformation T in R_m has 1 as a characteristic root if $D(T) = 1$ and m is odd. What can you say if m is even?

Note. Exercises 4 to 12 give an important generalization of orthogonal transformations to complex vector spaces. In these exercises, $V = \{u, v, \cdots\}$ denotes a finite-dimensional vector space over the complex field $C = \{a, b, \cdots\}$ and $\bar{a}$ denotes the complex conjugate of $a \in C$.

4. If $a \in C$ is viewed as a vector in R_2, then its length is given by $\sqrt{a\bar{a}}$. Now let C_n be the vector space of n-tuples over C. Then in order to define an inner product on C_n which is related to length in the case of C_1, we define

$$(u, v) = \sum_{i=1}^{n} a_i \bar{b}_i$$

where $u = \langle a_1, \cdots, a_n \rangle$, $v = \langle b_1, \cdots, b_n \rangle$. Prove that (u, v) has the properties:

(1) $(u_1 + u_2, v) = (u_1, v) + (u_2, v)$, $(u, v_1 + v_2) = (u, v_1) + (u, v_2)$; $(u, v) = \overline{(v, u)}$, $(au, v) = a(u, v)$, $(u, av) = \bar{a}(u, v)$, for all $u, v \in V$, $a \in C$.

(2) For all $u \in V$, (u, u) is real and nonnegative. Moreover, $(u, u) = 0$ if and only if $u = 0$. We define the *length* $||u||$ of u by $||u|| = \sqrt{(u, u)}$, $u \in V$.

5. Let V be an arbitrary finite-dimensional vector space over C. A mapping (u, v) which assigns to each pair of vectors $\{u, v\}$ a complex number (u, v) is called a *hermitian scalar product* (after

the French mathematician C. Hermite) if (u, v) has the properties (1) and (2) in Exercise 4. A set of vectors $\{u_1, \cdots, u_s\}$ in V is called an *orthonormal set* if $||u_i|| = 1$ for all i and $(u_i, u_j) = 0$ for $i \neq j$. Prove that every subspace W of V has an orthonormal basis. Let $\{u_1, \cdots, u_s\}$ be an orthonormal basis for W and let $v = \sum a_i u_i$ and $w = \sum b_i u_i$ be arbitrary vectors in W. Prove that $(v, w) = \sum a_i \bar{b}_i$.

6. A linear transformation $U \in L(V, V)$ is called a *unitary transformation* on V if $||U(v)|| = ||v||$ for all v. Prove that $U \in L(V, V)$ is unitary if and only if $(Uv, Uw) = (v, w)$ for all $v, w \in V$. [*Hint:* Suppose $||Uv|| = ||v||$ for all v. Applying this formula to $v + w$ and $v + iw$, show that

$$(Uv, Uw) + (Uw, Uv) = (v, w) + (w, v)$$

and that

$$i(Uw, Uv) - i(Uv, Uw) = i(w, v) - i(v, w).$$

Comparing these formulas, show that $(Uv, Uw) = (v, w)$.]

7. Prove that the unitary transformations on V form a group under multiplication.

8. Let $\{v_1, \cdots, v_n\}$ be an orthonormal basis for V. Prove that the following statements concerning $U \in L(V, V)$ are equivalent.

   (A) U is a unitary transformation.

   (B) $\{U(v_1), \cdots, U(v_n)\}$ is an orthonormal set of vectors.

   (C) If $U(v_i) = \sum_{j=1}^{n} a_{ji} v_j$, then the matrix $\mathbf{A} = (a_{ij})$ has the property that

   $$\mathbf{A} \cdot {}^t\bar{\mathbf{A}} = \mathbf{I}$$

   where the (i, j) entry in ${}^t\bar{\mathbf{A}}$ is $\bar{a}_{ji}$. A matrix $\mathbf{A} \in M_n(C)$ such that $\mathbf{A} \cdot {}^t\bar{\mathbf{A}} = \mathbf{I}$ is called a *unitary matrix*; it is the matrix of a unitary transformation with respect to an orthonormal basis.

9. Let a be a characteristic root of a unitary transformation U. Prove that $a\bar{a} = 1$.

10. Let U be a unitary transformation on V. Prove that there exists an orthonormal basis for V consisting of characteristic vectors of U. [*Hint:* Use induction on the dimension of V. Find a characteristic vector v_1 such that $||v_1|| = 1$. Show that $S(v_1)^\perp = \{w \in V : (w, v_1) = 0\}$ is invariant relative to U, and that $V = S(v_1) \oplus S(v_1)^\perp$. Then apply an induction hypothesis to U acting on $S(v_1)^\perp$.]

11. Prove that if **A** is a unitary matrix there exists a unitary matrix **B** such that $\mathbf{BAB}^{-1}$ is a diagonal matrix whose nonzero entries all have absolute value 1.

12. Show that

$$\mathbf{A} = \begin{pmatrix} 0 & i \\ -i & 0 \end{pmatrix}$$

is a unitary matrix. Find a unitary matrix **B** such that $\mathbf{BAB}^{-1}$ is a diagonal matrix.

29. THE PRINCIPAL-AXIS THEOREM

In a beginning course in analytic geometry the following problem is considered. Let

$$f(x_1, x_2) = ax_1^2 + bx_1x_2 + cx_2^2 + dx_1 + ex_2 + f = 0$$

be an equation of the second degree in x_1 and x_2. The problem is to find a new coordinate system

$$X_1 = (\cos\theta)x_1 + (\sin\theta)x_2 + c_1$$
$$X_2 = (-\sin\theta)x_1 + (\cos\theta)x_2 + c_2$$

obtained by a rotation and a translation from the original one, such that in the new coordinate system the equation becomes either of the following.

(29.1) $\qquad f(X_1, X_2) = AX_1^2 + BX_2^2 + C = 0.$

(29.2) $\qquad f(X_1, X_2) = AX_2^2 - DX_1 = 0.$

The graph of $f(X_1, X_2) = 0$ can then be classified as a circle, ellipse, hyperbola, parabola, etc. It is clear that, if we can first find a rotation of axes

$$X_1 = (\cos\theta)x_1 + (\sin\theta)x_2$$
$$X_2 = (-\sin\theta)x_1 + (\cos\theta)x_2$$

such that the second-degree terms $ax_1^2 + bx_1x_2 + cx_2^2$ become

(29.3) $\qquad\qquad AX_1^2 + BX_2^2,$

then the new equation has the form

$$f(X_1, X_2) = AX_1^2 + BX_2^2 + CX_1 + DX_2 + D$$

and can be put in the form (29.1) or (29.2) by a translation of axes: $X_1' = X_1 + c_1$, $X_2' = X_2 + c_2$.

The problem we shall consider in this section is a generalization of the problem of finding a rotation of axes that will put the second-degree terms of $f(x_1, x_2)$ in the form (29.3).

(29.4) Definition. Let V be an n-dimensional vector space over the real numbers R. A *quadratic form* on V is a function Q which assigns to each vector $a \in V$ a real number $Q(a)$ such that the following conditions are satisfied.

(1) $Q(\alpha a) = \alpha^2 Q(a)$, $\alpha \in R$, $a \in V$.
(2) If we define $B(a, b) = \frac{1}{2}[Q(a + b) - Q(a) - Q(b)]$, then B is a *bilinear function* on V, that is,*

$$B(\alpha a_1 + \beta a_2, b) = \alpha B(a_1, b) + \beta B(a_2, b),$$
$$B(a, \alpha b_1 + \beta b_2) = \alpha B(a, b_1) + \beta B(a, b_2),$$

for all a, $b \in V$ and α, $\beta \in R$.

(29.5) Theorem. *Let Q be a quadratic form on V and let $\{e_1, \cdots, e_n\}$ be a basis of V over R. Define an n-by-n matrix $\mathbf{S} = (\sigma_{ij})$ by setting*

$$\sigma_{ij} = B(e_i, e_j), \qquad 1 \le i, \;\; j \le n,$$

where B is the bilinear function defined in part (2) of Definition (29.4). Then ${}^t\mathbf{S} = \mathbf{S}$, and for all $a = \sum \alpha_i e_i \in V$ we have

$$\textbf{(29.6)} \qquad Q(a) = B(a, a) = \sum_{i,j=1}^{n} \alpha_i \alpha_j \sigma_{ij} = \sum_{i=1}^{n} \alpha_i^2 \sigma_{ii} + 2 \sum_{i<j} \alpha_i \alpha_j \sigma_{ij}.$$

Conversely, if $\mathbf{S} = (\sigma_{ij})$ is an arbitrary n-by-n real matrix such that ${}^t\mathbf{S} = \mathbf{S}$, then (29.6) defines a quadratic form Q such that if we set $B(a, b) = \frac{1}{2}[Q(a + b) - Q(a) - Q(b)]$ then $B(e_i, e_j) = \sigma_{ij}$.

REMARK.   Assuming the truth of the theorem, the function

$$f(x_1, x_2) = ax_1^2 + bx_1x_2 + cx_2^2$$

defines a quadratic form on R_2 such that if $\{x_1, x_2\}$ are the coordinates of a vector x with respect to the basis $\{e_1, e_2\}$ then the matrix of f defined in the theorem is given by

$$\begin{pmatrix} a & \frac{1}{2}b \\ \frac{1}{2}b & c \end{pmatrix}.$$

---

* Bilinear functions are sometimes called *bilinear forms*.

Proof of Theorem (29.5).   The first part of the theorem is immediate from Definition (29.4). For the converse, let $S = {}^tS$ be given and define a function

$$B(a, b) = \sum_{i,j=1}^{n} \alpha_i \beta_j \sigma_{ij}$$

for $a = \sum \alpha_i e_i$, $b = \sum \beta_i e_i$. Then B is a bilinear function on V such that $B(e_i, e_j) = \sigma_{ij}$ and $B(a, b) = B(b, a)$, for $a, b \in V$. It is also clear that if we define

$$Q(a) = B(a, a)$$

then Q is a quadratic form such that $B(a, b) = \frac{1}{2}[Q(a + b) - Q(a) - Q(b)]$, since $B(a, b) = B(b, a)$. This completes the proof.

(29.7)   Definition.   A real n-by-n matrix S is called *symmetric* if ${}^tS = S$. The *matrix* $S = (\sigma_{ij})$ of a *quadratic form* Q with respect to the basis $\{e_1, \cdots, e_n\}$ is defined by

$$\sigma_{ij} = B(e_i, e_j)$$

where

$$B(a, b) = \frac{1}{2}[Q(a + b) - Q(a) - Q(b)]$$

is the bilinear function associated with Q.

(29.8)   Theorem.   *Let Q be a quadratic form on V whose matrix with respect to the basis $\{e_1, \cdots, e_n\}$ is $S = (\sigma_{ij})$. Let $\{f_1, \cdots, f_n\}$ be another basis of V such that*

$$f_i = \sum_{j=1}^{n} \gamma_{ji} e_j, \qquad 1 \leq i \leq n.$$

Then the matrix of Q with respect to the basis $\{f_1, \cdots, f_n\}$ is given by

$$S' = {}^tCSC$$

where $C = (\gamma_{ij})$.

Proof.   Let $S' = (\sigma'_{ij})$. Then

$$\sigma'_{ij} = B(f_i, f_j) = B\left(\sum_{k=1}^{n} \gamma_{ki} e_k, \sum_{l=1}^{n} \gamma_{lj} e_l \right)$$

$$= \sum_{k=1}^{n} \sum_{l=1}^{n} \gamma_{ki} \gamma_{lj} B(e_k, e_l)$$

$$= \sum_{k=1}^{n} \sum_{l=1}^{n} \gamma_{ki} \sigma_{kl} \gamma_{lj},$$

and the theorem is proved.

Now we can state the main theorem of this section.

(29.9)   Principal-Axis Theorem.*   *Let V be a vector space over R with an inner product (a, b) and let $\{e_1, \cdots, e_n\}$ be an orthonormal basis of V. Let Q be a quadratic form on V whose matrix with respect to $\{e_1, \cdots, e_n\}$ is $\mathbf{S} = (\sigma_{ij})$. Then there exists an orthonormal basis $\{f_1, \cdots, f_n\}$ such that the matrix of Q with respect to $f_1, \cdots, f_n$ is*

$$\mathbf{S'} = \begin{pmatrix} \sigma_1 & & & 0 \\ & \sigma_2 & & \\ & & \cdot & \\ & & & \cdot \\ 0 & & & \sigma_n \end{pmatrix}$$

where the σ_i are the characteristic roots of $\mathbf{S}$. If

$$f_i = \sum_{j=1}^{n} \gamma_{ji} e_j, \qquad 1 \leq i \leq n,$$

then $\mathbf{C} = (\gamma_{ij})$ is an orthogonal matrix. If $a \in V$ is expressed in terms of the new basis $\{f_1, \cdots, f_n\}$ by $a = \sum_{i=1}^{n} \alpha_i f_i$, then $Q(a) = \sum_{i=1}^{n} \alpha_i^2 \sigma_i$. The vectors $f_1, \cdots, f_n$ are called the principal axes of Q.

(29.10)   Definition.   A linear transformation T on a real vector space with an inner product (a, b) is called a *symmetric transformation* if

$$(Ta, b) = (a, Tb), \qquad a, b \in V.$$

(29.11)   *Let $\{e_1, \cdots, e_n\}$ be an orthonormal basis of V. A linear transformation $T \in L(V, V)$, whose matrix with respect to $\{e_1, \cdots, e_n\}$ is $\mathbf{S} = (\sigma_{ij})$, is a symmetric transformation if and only if $\mathbf{S}$ is a symmetric matrix.*

The proof is similar to the proof of part (4) of Theorem (15.11) and will be omitted.

(29.12)   Theorem.   *Let T be a symmetric transformation on a real vector space V; then there exists an orthonormal basis of V consisting of characteristic vectors of V.*

---

* For a different proof and an application of this theorem to mechanics, see Synge and Griffith, p. 318 (listed in the Bibliography).

We shall first prove that Theorem (29.12) implies Theorem (29.9) and then we shall prove Theorem (29.12).

Proof that (29.12) *implies* (29.9). In the notation of Theorem (29.9) let Q be a quadratic form on V with the matrix $\mathbf{S}$ with respect to the orthonormal basis $\{e_1, \cdots, e_n\}$. By Theorems (29.8) and (29.5) and the results of Section 15 it is sufficient to construct an *orthogonal* matrix $\mathbf{C}$ such that

$$
{}^t\mathbf{CSC} = \begin{pmatrix} \sigma_1 & & 0 \\ & \ddots & \\ 0 & & \sigma_n \end{pmatrix}
$$

where $\sigma_1, \cdots, \sigma_n$ are the characteristic roots of $\mathbf{S}$. For an *orthogonal* matrix $\mathbf{C}$, ${}^t\mathbf{C} = \mathbf{C}^{-1}$ and therefore it is sufficient to find an orthogonal matrix $\mathbf{C}$ such that

$$
\mathbf{C}^{-1}\mathbf{SC} = \begin{pmatrix} \sigma_1 & & 0 \\ & \ddots & \\ 0 & & \sigma_n \end{pmatrix}.
$$

This is a problem on the linear transformation T whose matrix with respect to $\{e_1, \cdots, e_n\}$ is $\mathbf{S}$. By (29.11), T is a symmetric transformation and from the results of Section 15 the task of finding $\mathbf{C}$ is exactly the problem stated in Theorem (29.12).

Proof of Theorem (29.12). We first prove that V is a direct sum of pairwise orthogonal irreducible invariant subspaces relative to T. The argument is the same as the proof of Theorem (28.4); we have only to check that, if W is invariant relative to T, then $W^\perp$ is invariant relative to T. Let $w' \in W^\perp$ and $w \in W$; then

$$(w, Tw') = (Tw, w') = 0$$

since $Tw \in W$ and $w' \in W^\perp$. We may now conclude that V is the direct sum of pairwise orthogonal irreducible invariant subspaces $\{W_1, \cdots, W_s\}$.

It is now sufficient to prove that for all i, where $1 \le i \le s$, dim $W_i = 1$. Since dim $W_i = 1$ or 2, it is sufficient to prove that a symmetric transformation T on a two-dimensional real vector space W always has a characteristic vector. Let $\{w_1, w_2\}$ be an orthonormal basis for W; then, relative to $\{w_1, w_2\}$, T has a symmetric matrix

$$
\begin{pmatrix} \lambda & \xi \\ \xi & \mu \end{pmatrix}, \qquad \lambda, \mu, \xi \in R.
$$

This matrix satisfies the equation

$$x^2 - (\lambda + \mu)x + (\lambda\mu - \xi^2) = 0.$$

Letting $A = -(\lambda + \mu)$ and $B = \lambda\mu - \xi^2$, we have

$$
\begin{aligned}
A^2 - 4B &= (\lambda + \mu)^2 - 4(\lambda\mu - \xi^2) \\
&= \lambda^2 - 2\lambda\mu + \mu^2 + 4\xi^2 = (\lambda - \mu)^2 + 4\xi^2 \geq 0
\end{aligned}
$$

for all real numbers λ, ξ, μ. Therefore the polynomial $x^2 + Ax + B$ factors into linear factors in $R[x]$, and it follows from Section 24 that W contains a characteristic vector. This completes the proof of the theorem.

EXERCISES

1. Consider the symmetric matrix

$$
\mathbf{X} = \begin{pmatrix} -1 & -3 & 0 \\ -3 & -1 & 0 \\ 0 & 0 & 1 \end{pmatrix}.
$$

a. Find the characteristic roots of $\mathbf{X}$.

b. Define a symmetric transformation T in R_3 whose matrix with respect to the orthonormal basis of unit vectors $\{e_1, e_2, e_3\}$ is $\mathbf{X}$. Find by the methods of Chapter 7 a basis of R_3 consisting of characteristic vectors of T [we know that can be done, by Theorem (29.12)]. Modify this basis to obtain an orthonormal basis $\{f_1, f_2, f_3\}$ of R_3 consisting of characteristic vectors of T. Let

$$f_i = \sum_{j=1}^{3} \mu_{ji} e_j$$

and

$$Tf_i = \alpha_i f_i, \qquad \alpha_i \in R, \quad i = 1, 2, 3.$$

Then $\mathbf{M} = (\mu_{ij})$ is an orthogonal matrix, such that $\mathbf{M}^{-1}\mathbf{X}\mathbf{M}$ is diagonal. Since $\mathbf{M}$ is orthogonal, $\mathbf{M}^{-1} = {}^t\mathbf{M}$, so this computational procedure also can be applied to find the principal axes of a vector space with respect to a quadratic form.

2. Find an orthonormal basis of R_2 which exhibits the principal axes of the quadratic form

$$8x_1^2 + 8x_1x_2 + 2x_2^2.$$

3. A quadratic form Q can be viewed as a function $x \to Q(x_1, \ldots, x_n)$ where $x_1, \ldots, x_n$ are the components of the vector x with respect to some basis of the vector space. The form Q is said to be positive definite if all the characteristic roots of the matrix $\mathbf{S}$ of Q are positive. Show that if $Q(x_1, \ldots, x_n)$ is a positive definite quadratic form with matrix $\mathbf{S}$, then

$$I = \int_0^\infty \cdots \int_0^\infty e^{-Q(x_1, \ldots, x_n)} \, dx_1 \, dx_2 \cdots dx_n = 2^{-n} \sqrt{\frac{\pi^n}{\det \mathbf{S}}}.$$

[*Hint:* First show that if $\lambda > 0$,

$$\int_0^\infty e^{-\lambda x^2} = (\pi/4\lambda)^{1/2}.$$

(See R. C. Buck, *Advanced Calculus*, 2nd ed., McGraw-Hill, 1965; Ch. 3.) Then use the principal-axis theorem to find an orthogonal matrix $\mathbf{C}$ such that the transformation

$$x_i = \sum_{j=1}^n \gamma_{ij} y_j, \qquad \mathbf{C} = (\gamma_{ij}),$$

carries $Q(x_1, \cdots, x_n)$ into $\lambda_1 y_1^2 + \cdots + \lambda_n y_n^2$, where the λ_i are the (positive) characteristic roots of $\mathbf{S}$. Then use the formula for changing the variable in a multiple integral (see R. C. Buck, loc. cit.) to show that

$$I = \int_0^\infty \cdots \int_0^\infty e^{-(\lambda_1 y_1^2 + \cdots + \lambda_n y_n^2)} |J| \, dy_1 \cdots dy_n,$$

where J is the jacobian of the transformation, and is ± 1. The integral can now be done by the one-variable case.]

30. FINITE SYMMETRY GROUPS IN THREE DIMENSIONS*

We begin with some general remarks about orthogonal transformations on an n-dimensional real vector space V with an inner product (u, v). If $S \subset V$, we denote by $S^\perp$ the set of all vectors $v \in V$ such that $(s, v) = 0$ for all $s \in S$. Then $S^\perp$ is always a subspace and, as we have shown in Section 28, if S is a subspace then

$$V = S \oplus S^\perp.$$

---

* This section is optional.

In particular, if x is a nonzero vector, then $(x)^\perp$ is an $(n-1)$-dimensional subspace such that

$$V = S(x) \oplus (x)^\perp.$$

In the language of Section 10, $(x)^\perp$ is a hyperplane passing through the origin. Perhaps the simplest kind of orthogonal transformation on V is a transformation T such that, for some nonzero vector x,

$$Tx = -x$$
$$Tu = u, \qquad u \in (x)^\perp.$$

If H denotes the hyperplane $(x)^\perp$, then T is called a *reflection with respect to H*.* Geometrically, T sends each point of V onto its mirror image with respect to H, leaving the elements of H fixed. The matrix of a reflection T, with respect to a basis containing a basis for the hyperplane left fixed by T and a vector orthogonal to the hyperplane, is given by

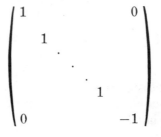

so that we have

$$T^2 = 1, \qquad D(T) = -1$$

for all reflections T. Our first important result is the following theorem, due to E. Cartan and J. Dieudonné, which asserts that every orthogonal transformation is a product of reflections.

(30.1) Theorem. *Every orthogonal transformation on an n-dimensional vector space V with an inner product is a product of at most n reflections.*

Proof.† We use induction on n, the result being clear if $n = 1$, since the only orthogonal transformations on a one-dimensional space are ± 1. Suppose dim $V > 1$ and that the theorem is true for orthogonal transformations on an $(n-1)$-dimensional space. Let T

---

* The question of the uniqueness of a reflection with respect to a given hyperplane is settled in the Exercises.

† A proof of a more general form of the theorem is given by Artin (listed in the Bibliography).

be a given orthogonal transformation on V and let $x \neq 0$ be a vector in V.

CASE 1.   Suppose $Tx = x$; then if $u \in H = (x)^\perp$ we have

$$(Tu, x) = (Tu, Tx) = (u, x) = 0,$$

so that $Tu \in H$, and T defines an orthogonal transformation on the $(n - 1)$-dimensional space H. By the induction hypothesis there exist reflections $T_1, \cdots, T_s$, for $s \leq n - 1$ of H, such that

(30.2) $Tu = T_1 \cdots T_s u, \qquad u \in H.$

Extend each T_i to a linear transformation T_i' on V by defining $T_i' x = x$ and $T_i' u = T_i u$, for $u \in H$, $i = 1, \cdots, s$. We show now that each T_i' is a reflection on V. There exists an $(n - 2)$-dimensional subspace $H_i \subset H = (x)^\perp$ whose elements are left fixed by T_i; then T_i' leaves fixed the vectors in the hyperplane $H_i' = H_i + S(x)$ of V. Moreover, if x_i generates $H_i^\perp$ in H, then $x_i \in (H_i')^\perp$ and $T_i' x_i = T_i x_i = -x_i$. These remarks show that T_i' is a reflection with respect to H_i'. Finally, from the definition of the transformations T_i' and (30.2) it follows that

$$T = T_1' \cdots T_s'.$$

Thus we have shown that an orthogonal transformation which leaves a vector fixed is a product of at most $n - 1$ reflections.

CASE 2.   Suppose $Tx \neq x$; then $u = Tx - x \neq 0$. Let $H = (u)^\perp$ and let U be a reflection with respect to H. We have

$$(Tx + x, Tx - x) = (Tx, Tx) + (x, Tx) - (Tx, x) - (x, x)$$
$$= 0$$

because T is orthogonal and the form is symmetric. Therefore, $Tx + x \in H = (u)^\perp$ where $u = Tx - x$ and we have

$$U(Tx + x) = Tx + x.$$

Since U is a reflection with respect to $H = (Tx - x)^\perp$ we have

$$U(Tx - x) = -(Tx - x).$$

Adding these equations, we obtain

$$2UT(x) = 2x$$

and hence

$$UT(x) = x.$$

By Case 1 there exist $s \leq n - 1$ reflections $T_1, \cdots, T_s$ such that

$$UT = T_1 \cdots T_s.$$

Since $U^2 = 1$ we have

$$T = U(UT) = UT_1 \cdots T_s$$

which is a product of at most n reflections. This completes the proof.

As a corollary, we obtain some geometrical insight into the following result, which was proved in another way in the exercises of Section 28.

(30.3)   Corollary.   *Let T be an orthogonal transformation of a three-dimensional real vector space such that $D(T) = +1$. Then there exists a nonzero vector $v \in V$ such that $Tv = v$.*

Proof. We may assume $T \neq 1$. By Theorem (30.1), T is a product of one, two, or three reflections of determinant -1. It follows that T is a product of exactly two reflections, $T = T_1 T_2$, where T_i is a reflection with respect to a two-dimensional space H_i for $i = 1, 2$. By Theorem (7.17),

$$\dim (H_1 + H_2) + \dim (H_1 \cap H_2) = \dim H_1 + \dim H_2 = 4$$

and since $\dim (H_1 + H_2) \leq 3$ we have $\dim (H_1 \cap H_2) \geq 1$. Let x be a nonzero vector in $H_1 \cap H_2$; then $Tx = x$, and the corollary is proved.

We define a *rotation* in a three-dimensional space as an orthogonal transformation of determinant $+1$. Then the corollary asserts that every rotation in three dimensions is a rotation about an axis, the axis being the line determined by the vector left fixed. This fact is of fundamental importance in mechanics and was proved with the use of an interesting geometrical argument by Euler.* We shall see that it is also the key to the classification of finite symmetry groups in R_3. Our presentation of this material is based on the introductory discussion in Section 14 and the proof of the main theorem is taken from Weyl's book (see the Bibliography). Apart from its geometrical interest, Weyl's argument gives a penetrating introduction to the theory of finite groups.

Let us make the problem precise. By a *finite symmetry group* in three dimensions we mean a finite group of orthogonal transformations in R_3. For simplicity we shall determine the *finite groups of rotations* in R_3 and indicate in the exercises the connection with the

---

* See Synge and Griffith, pp. 279–280 (listed in the Bibliography).

general problem. Let us begin with a list of some examples of finite rotation groups in R_3. By the *order* of a finite group we mean the number of elements in the group. The cyclic group $\mathcal{C}_n$ of order n and the dihedral group $\mathcal{D}_n$ of order $2n$, discussed in Section 14, are the first examples.

For our purposes in this section it is better to think of $\mathcal{D}_n$ as the symmetry group of a regular n-sided polygon. Although the transformation S in $\mathcal{D}_n$ which flips the polygon over along a line of symmetry is a reflection when viewed as a transformation in the plane, S is a rotation when viewed as a transformation in R_3.

The next examples are the symmetry groups of the regular polyhedra in R_3. There are exactly five of these, which are listed in the following table along with the number of vertices V, edges E, and faces F.

	F	E	V
tetrahedron	4	6	4
cube	6	12	8
octahedron	8	12	6
dodecahedron	12	30	20
icosahedron	20	30	12

(For a derivation of this list, based on Euler's formula for polyhedra "without holes," $F - E + V = 2$, see the book by Courant and Robbins and also those by Weyl and by Coxeter, listed in the Bibliography.) The faces are equilateral triangles in the case of the tetrahedron, squares in the case of the cube, equilateral triangles in the case of the octahedron, pentagons in the dodecahedron, and equilateral triangles in the case of the icosahedron; see Figure 8.1.

Apparently, we should obtain five different groups of rotations from these figures, the group in each case being the set of all rotations that carry the figure onto itself. On closer inspection we see that this is not the case. For example, the cube and the octahedron are dual in the sense that, if we take either figure and connect the centers of the faces with line segments, these line segments are the edges of the other; see Figure 8.2. Thus, any rotation carrying the cube onto itself will also be a symmetry of the octahedron, and conversely. Similarly, the dodecahedron and the icosahedron are dual figures. So, from the regular polyhedra we obtain only three additional groups: the group $\mathcal{J}$ of rotations of the tetrahedron, the group $\mathcal{O}$ of rotations of the octahedron, and the group $\mathcal{J}$ of rotations of the icosahedron.

Our main theorem can now be stated.

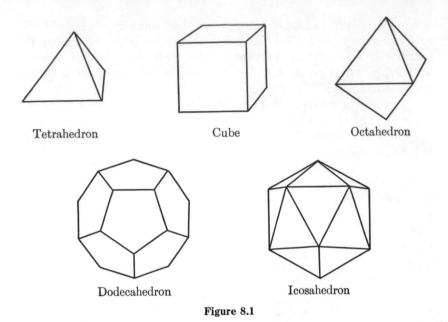

Tetrahedron   Cube   Octahedron

Dodecahedron   Icosahedron

Figure 8.1

(30.4) Theorem. *Let $\mathcal{G}$ be a finite group of rotations in R_3; then $\mathcal{G}$ is isomorphic with one of the groups in the following list:*

$$\mathcal{C}_n, \quad n = 1, 2, \cdots,$$
$$\mathcal{D}_n, \quad n = 1, 2, \cdots,$$
$$\mathcal{T}, \mathcal{O}, \text{ or } \mathcal{I}.$$

Proof. Let S be the unit sphere in R_3 consisting of all points* $x \in R_3$ such that $||x|| = 1$. If $T \in \mathcal{G}$, then $Tx \in S$ for every $x \in S$,

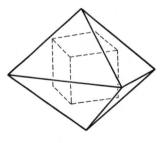

Figure 8.2

---

* We shall speak of the elements in R_3 as points in this discussion.

and T is completely determined by its action on the elements of the sphere S because S contains a basis for R_3. Every $T \in \mathcal{G}$ such that $T \neq 1$ leaves fixed two antipodal points on the sphere, by Corollary (30.3), and no others. These points are called the *poles* of T. Since $\mathcal{G}$ is finite, the set of all poles of all elements T of $\mathcal{G}$ such that $T \neq 1$ is a finite set of points on the sphere S; we proceed to examine this set in great detail.

Let p be a pole on S. The set of all elements T of $\mathcal{G}$ such that p is a pole of T, together with the identity element 1, is clearly a *subgroup* of $\mathcal{G}$, that is, a subset of $\mathcal{G}$ which itself forms a group under the operation defined on $\mathcal{G}$. The order of this subgroup is called the *order of the pole p* and is denoted by v_p.

Next we define two poles p and p' *equivalent* and we write $p \sim p'$ if and only if $p = Tp'$ for some $T \in \mathcal{G}$. The set of all poles equivalent to p is called the *equivalence class* of p. We prove that each pole belongs to one and only one equivalence class. Since $1 \in \mathcal{G}$, $p = 1p$, and so p belongs to the equivalence class of p. Now we have to show that if a pole p belongs to the equivalence classes of p' and p'' these equivalence classes coincide. Let q belong to the equivalence class of p'; then $q \sim p'$, and $q = Tp'$ for some $T \in \mathcal{G}$. Since $p \sim p'$ and $p \sim p''$, we have $p = T'p'$ and $p = T''p''$ for T' and $T'' \in \mathcal{G}$, and hence $p' = (T')^{-1}T''p''$. Then $q = T(T')^{-1}T''p''$ so that $q \sim p''$. We have shown that the equivalence class of p' is contained in the equivalence class of p'', and a similar argument establishes the reverse inclusion. This completes the proof that a pole belongs to one and only one equivalence class.

(30.5)   Lemma.   *Equivalent poles have the same order.*

Proof of Lemma (30.5).   Let $p \sim p'$, let $\mathcal{K}$ be the subgroup of $\mathcal{G}$ consisting of the identity 1 together with the elements which have p as a pole, and let $\mathcal{K}'$ be the corresponding subgroup for p'. Let $p = Tp'$. Then an easy verification shows that the mapping $X \rightarrow TXT^{-1}$ is a one-to-one mapping of $\mathcal{K}'$ onto $\mathcal{K}$, and this establishes the lemma.

(30.6)   Lemma.   *Let p be a pole of order v_p and let n_p be the number of poles equivalent to p; then $v_p n_p = N$ where N is the order of $\mathcal{G}$.*

Proof of Lemma (30.6).   Let $\mathcal{K}$ be the subgroup associated with p and, for $X \in G$, let $X\mathcal{K}$ denote the set of all elements $Y \in \mathcal{G}$ such that $Y = XT$ for some $T \in \mathcal{K}$. We observe first that, for all $X \in \mathcal{G}$, Xp is a pole and that poles Xp and $X'p$ are the same if and only if

$X' \in X\mathcal{K}$. Thus the number of poles equivalent to p is equal to the number of distinct sets of the form $X\mathcal{K}$. The set $X\mathcal{K}$ is called the *left coset of $\mathcal{K}$ containing X*. We prove now that each element of $\mathcal{G}$ belongs to one and only one left coset and that the number of elements in each left coset is v_p. If $X \in \mathcal{G}$, then $X = X \cdot 1 \in X\mathcal{K}$ since $1 \in \mathcal{K}$. Now suppose $X \in X'\mathcal{K} \cap X''\mathcal{K}$; we show that $X'\mathcal{K} = X''\mathcal{K}$. We have, for $Y \in X'\mathcal{K}$, $Y = X'T$ for some $T \in \mathcal{K}$. Moreover, $X \in X'\mathcal{K} \cap X''\mathcal{K}$ implies that $X = X'T' = X''T''$ for T' and $T'' \in \mathcal{K}$. Then $Y = X'T = X(T')^{-1}T = X''T''(T')^{-1}T \in X''\mathcal{K}$. Thus, $X'\mathcal{K} \subset X''\mathcal{K}$ and, similarly, $X''\mathcal{K} \subset X'\mathcal{K}$. Therefore $X'\mathcal{K} = X''\mathcal{K}$ and we have proved that each element of $\mathcal{G}$ belongs to a unique left coset. Now let $X\mathcal{K}$ be a left coset. Then the mapping $T \to XT$ is a one-to-one mapping of $\mathcal{K}$ onto $X\mathcal{K}$ and each left coset contains v_p elements where v_p is the order of $\mathcal{K}$.

We have shown that the number of poles equivalent to p is equal to the number of left cosets of $\mathcal{K}$ in $\mathcal{G}$. From what has been shown, this number is equal to N/v_p, and Lemma (30.6) is proved.

Now we can finish the proof of Theorem (30.4). Consider the set of all pairs (T, p) with $T \in \mathcal{G}$, $T \neq 1$, and p a pole of T. Counting the pairs in two different ways* we obtain

$$2(N - 1) = \sum_p (v_p - 1)$$

and collecting terms on the right-hand side according to the equivalence classes of poles, C, we have

$$2(N - 1) = \sum n_C(v_C - 1)$$

where n_C is the number of poles in an equivalence class C, v_C is the order of a typical pole in C [see Lemma (30.5)], and the sum is taken over the different equivalence classes of poles. Applying (30.6) we obtain

$$2(N - 1) = \sum_C (N - n_C) = \sum_C \left(N - \frac{N}{v_C} \right).$$

Dividing by N we obtain

(30.7) $$2 - \frac{2}{N} = \sum_C \left(1 - \frac{1}{v_C} \right).$$

The left side is >1 and <2; therefore there are at least two classes C

---

* We use first the fact that each $T \neq 1$ is associated with two poles and next that with each pole are associated $(v - 1)$ elements $T \in \mathcal{G}$ such that $T \neq 1$.

and at most three classes. The rest of the argument is an arithmetical study of the equation (30.7).

CASE 1.   There are two classes of poles of order v_1, v_2. Then (30.7) yields

$$\frac{2}{N} = \frac{1}{v_1} + \frac{1}{v_2}, \qquad 2 = \frac{N}{v_1} + \frac{N}{v_2},$$

and we have $N/v_1 = N/v_2 = 1$. This case occurs if and only if $\mathcal{G}$ is cyclic.

CASE 2.   There are three classes of poles of orders v_1, v_2, v_3, where we may assume $v_1 \leq v_2 \leq v_3$. Then (30.7) implies that

$$2 - \frac{2}{N} = \left(1 - \frac{1}{v_1}\right) + \left(1 - \frac{1}{v_2}\right) + \left(1 - \frac{1}{v_3}\right)$$

or

$$1 + \frac{2}{N} = \frac{1}{v_1} + \frac{1}{v_2} + \frac{1}{v_3}.$$

Not all the v_i can be greater than 2; hence $v_1 = 2$ and we have

$$\frac{1}{2} + \frac{2}{N} = \frac{1}{v_2} + \frac{1}{v_3}.$$

Not both v_2 and v_3 can be ≥ 4; hence $v_2 = 2$ or 3.

Case 2a: $v_1 = 2$, $v_2 = 2$. Then $v_3 = N/2$, and in this case $\mathcal{G}$ is the dihedral group.

Case 2b: $v_1 = 2$, $v_2 = 3$. Then we have

$$\frac{1}{v_3} = \frac{1}{6} + \frac{2}{N},$$

and $v_3 = 3$, 4, or 5. For each possibility of v_3 we have:

$v_1 = 2$, $v_2 = 3$, $v_3 = 3$;   then $N = 12$ and $\mathcal{G}$ is the tetrahedral group $\mathcal{T}$.
$v_1 = 2$, $v_2 = 3$, $v_3 = 4$;   then $N = 24$ and $\mathcal{G}$ is the octahedral group $\mathcal{O}$.
$v_1 = 2$, $v_2 = 3$, $v_3 = 5$;   then $N = 60$ and $\mathcal{G}$ is the icosahedral group $\mathcal{I}$.

EXERCISES

1. Let V be a real vector space with an inner product.
   a. Prove that, if T_1 and T_2 are reflections with respect to the same hyperplane H, then $T_1 = T_2$.
   b. Prove that, if T is an orthogonal transformation that leaves all

elements of a hyperplane H fixed, then either $T = 1$ or T is the reflection with respect to H.

c. Let T be the reflection with respect to H and let $x_0 \in H^\perp$. Prove that T is given by the formula

$$T(x) = x - 2 \frac{(x, x_0)}{(x_0, x_0)} x_0, \qquad x \in V.$$

2. Let $\mathcal{G}$ be a finite group of orthogonal transformations and let $\mathcal{H}$ be the rotations contained in $\mathcal{G}$. Prove that $\mathcal{H}$ is a subgroup of $\mathcal{G}$ and that if $\mathcal{H} \neq \mathcal{G}$ then, for any element $X \in \mathcal{G}$ and $X \notin \mathcal{H}$, we have

$$\mathcal{G} = \mathcal{H} \cup X\mathcal{H}, \qquad \mathcal{H} \cap X\mathcal{H} = \varnothing.$$

3. Let $\mathcal{G}$ be an arbitrary finite group of invertible linear transformations on R_3. Prove that there exists an inner product $((x, y))$ on R_3 such that the $T_i \in \mathcal{G}$ are orthogonal transformations with respect to the inner product $((x, y))$. [*Hint:* Let (x, y) be the usual inner product on R_3. Define

$$((x, y)) = \sum_{T_i \in \mathcal{G}} (T_i(x), T_i(y))$$

and prove that $((x, y))$ has the required properties. Note that the same argument can be applied to finite groups of invertible linear transformations in R_n for n arbitrary.]

4. Let $\mathcal{G}$ be the set of linear transformations on C_2 where C is the complex field whose matrices with respect to a basis are

$$\pm \begin{pmatrix} 1 & 0 \\ 0 & 1 \end{pmatrix}, \qquad \pm \begin{pmatrix} 0 & 1 \\ -1 & 0 \end{pmatrix}, \qquad \pm \begin{pmatrix} 0 & i \\ i & 0 \end{pmatrix}, \qquad \pm \begin{pmatrix} i & 0 \\ 0 & -i \end{pmatrix}.$$

Prove that $\mathcal{G}$ forms a finite group and that there exists no basis of C_2 such that the matrices of the elements of $\mathcal{G}$ with respect to the new basis all have real coefficients. (*Hint:* If such a basis did exist, then $\mathcal{G}$ would be isomorphic either with a cyclic group or with a dihedral group, by Exercise 3 and the results of Section 14.)

SOLUTIONS of
SELECTED EXERCISES

In the case of numerical problems where a simple check is available, no answers are supplied. On theoretical problems, comments or hints on one method of solution are given, but not all the details. Of course there are often many valid ways to do a particular problem, and a correct solution may not always agree with the one given below.

SECTION 2

1.(a). $u = a/b$ and $v = c/d$ are the solutions of the equations $bu = a$ and $dv = c$ respectively. Multiply these equations by d and b and add, obtaining

$$bd(u + v) = ad + bc.$$

2.(c). Consider the following cases:
(i) $a \geq 0, b \geq 0$, (ii) $a \geq 0; b < 0; a < 0, b \geq 0; a < 0, b < 0$.
In each case, $|ab|$, and $|a| \, |b|$ can be found from the definition, and compared.

(f). Use (d) to show that

$$-|a| \leq a \leq |a|, \qquad -|b| \leq b \leq |b|.$$

Add these inequalities to obtain

$$-(|a| + |b|) \leq a + b \leq |a| + |b|.$$

The result follows from (d).

3. If $0 \leq \lambda \leq 1$, show that $x = \lambda a + (1 - \lambda)b$ is between a

and b by proving that $x - a \geq 0$ and $b - x \geq 0$. Conversely, if $a < x < b$, show that $\lambda = (b - x)/(b - a)$ is between 0 and 1 and that $x = \lambda a + (1 - \lambda)b$.

4. If $a^2 \leq b^2$, then $b^2 - a^2 = (b + a)(b - a) \geq 0$. Because $b \geq 0$ and $a \geq 0$, $b + a \geq 0$ and it follows that $b - a \geq 0$.

SECTION 3

1.(b). The statement holds for $k = 1$. Assume it holds for $k \geq 1$. Then

$$1 + 3 + 5 + \cdots + (2k - 1) + [2(k + 1) - 1]$$
$$= k^2 + 2(k + 1) - 1 = (k + 1)^2.$$

2. There are $3^3 = 27$ distinct mappings of $\{1, 2, 3\}$ into itself. There are 6 one-to-one mappings. There are 3^n n-tuples $\langle x_1, \cdots, x_n \rangle$ with $x_i \in \{1, 2, 3\}$.

3. $x \to x^n$ is one-to-one when n is odd and is not one-to-one when n is even.

4. For the associative law, we have, for all $x \in X$,

$$[f(gh)](x) = f[(gh)(x)] = f(g[h(x)])$$

while

$$[(fg)h](x) = (fg)[h(x)] = f(g[h(x)]).$$

The elements of F do not satisfy the commutative law. For example, let $X = \{1, 2, 3\}$, and let f be the mapping: $f(1) = 2$, $f(2) = 1$, $f(3) = 3$; and g be the mapping: $g(1) = 1$, $g(2) = 3$, $g(3) = 2$. Show that $fg \neq gf$.

5. Let $x \in X$. Then $x = i(x) = (fg)(x) = f[g(x)]$, and hence f is onto.

6. Suppose $f(x) = f(x')$ for x and $x' \in X$. Then apply h, to obtain $hf(x) = hf(x')$. Since $hf = i$, $x = x'$.

7. The set of all real numbers $x \geq 1$ satisfies conditions (1) and (2) of Definition (3.1). From statement (3) it follows that all natural numbers x satisfy $x \geq 1$. Now suppose there exists a natural number x such that $1 < x < 2$. Let N' be the set of all natural numbers $n \neq x$. Since all natural numbers n are not less than 1, it is clear that there is no natural number y such that $y + 1 = x$, because such a y

would have to be less than 1. Therefore N' satisfies conditions (1) and (2) of Definition (3.1) and is a subset of N, different from N, contradicting the third part of the definition.

10.   Let $E(n)$ satisfy (a) and (b) of (3.3). If $E(n)$ is false for some n, then by the Principle of Well-Ordering there is a least natural number n_0 for which $E(n_0)$ is false. Show that this contradicts either (a) or (b) of (3.3).

SECTION 4

1.(a). $(\alpha + \beta\sqrt{2})(\gamma + \delta\sqrt{2}) = (\alpha\gamma + 2\beta\delta) + (\alpha\delta + \beta\gamma)\sqrt{2}$
$(\alpha \pm \beta\sqrt{2}) \pm (\gamma + \delta\sqrt{2}) = (\alpha \pm \gamma) = (\beta \pm \delta)\sqrt{2}.$

$$(\alpha + \beta\sqrt{2})^{-1} = \frac{\alpha}{\alpha^2 - 2\beta^2} - \frac{\beta}{\alpha^2 - 2\beta^2}\sqrt{2}.$$

(b). $(\alpha + \beta\sqrt{q})(\gamma + \delta\sqrt{q}) = (\alpha\gamma + q\beta\delta) + (\alpha\delta + \beta\gamma)\sqrt{q}$
$(\alpha + \beta\sqrt{q}) \pm (\gamma + \delta\sqrt{q}) = (\alpha \pm \gamma) + (\beta \pm \delta)\sqrt{q}$

$$(\alpha + \beta\sqrt{q})^{-1} = \frac{\alpha}{\alpha^2 - q\beta^2} - \frac{\beta}{\alpha^2 - q\beta^2}\sqrt{q}.$$

Note that $\alpha^2 - q\beta \neq 0$ for all rational numbers α and β not both zero because $\sqrt{q}$ is irrational.

(d). $Z(3)$ and $Z(5)$ are fields. $Z(4)$ and $Z(6)$ are not. In the case of $Z(4)$ and $Z(6)$ there exist elements $\alpha \neq 0$ for which no inverse α^{-1} exists.

In order to verify the associative law for addition in the case of $Z(5)$, for example, without checking all possible cases in a table, we proceed as follows. A number differs from its remainder after division by 5 by a multiple of 5. Then

$$a \oplus b = a + b + 5k; \qquad (a \oplus b) \oplus c = (a \oplus b) + c + 5l.$$

Combining these results, we see that $(a \oplus b) \oplus c$ differs from $(a + b) + c$ by a multiple of 5. Similarly $a \oplus (b \oplus c)$ differs from $a + (b + c)$ by a multiple of 5. Since $(a + b) + c = a + (b + c)$ in the system of integers, we see that $(a \oplus b) \oplus c$ and $a \oplus (b \oplus c)$ differ by a multiple of 5, and hence are equal. A similar argument can be used to prove some of the other field axioms.

SECTION 5

1.(a). $Q = (3, 1, -1)$; (b). $Q = (4, 2, -2)$; (c). $Q = (5, 2, 0)$.

2. $T = (1, 1, 0)$. We have $\overrightarrow{PT} = \langle 0, 2, -1 \rangle$, $\overrightarrow{PQ} = \langle 1, 2, 0 \rangle$, $\overrightarrow{RS} = \langle -1, 0, -1 \rangle$. This problem illustrates vector addition:

$$\overrightarrow{PQ} + \overrightarrow{RS} = \overrightarrow{PQ} + \overrightarrow{QT} = \overrightarrow{PT}.$$

3.(a).   No λ exists such that $\overrightarrow{PS} = \lambda \overrightarrow{PQ}$; (b). $\lambda = -2$; (c). $\lambda = \frac{1}{2}$.

SECTION 6

1.(a). Linearly independent; (b). Linearly dependent, $-3\langle 1, 1 \rangle + \langle 2, 1 \rangle + \langle 1, 2 \rangle = 0$; (c). Linearly independent; (d). Linearly dependent, $\beta\langle 0, 1 \rangle + \alpha\langle 1, 0 \rangle - \langle \alpha, \beta \rangle = 0$; (e). Linearly dependent, $\langle 1, 1, 2 \rangle - \langle 3, 1, 2 \rangle - 2\langle -1, 0, 0 \rangle = 0$; (f). Linearly independent; (g). Linearly dependent.

3.   Let $a = \langle \alpha_1, \alpha_2 \rangle$, $b = \langle \beta_1, \beta_2 \rangle$, $c = \langle \gamma_1, \gamma_2 \rangle$. If $a = b = c = 0$ then the result is clear. Next suppose $\alpha_1 = \beta_1 = \gamma_1 = 0$. Then we may assume $\alpha_2 \neq 0$, for example. Then $\beta_2 a - \alpha_2 b + 0c = 0$. Now suppose $\alpha_1 \neq 0$. Let $b' = b - \beta_1\alpha_1^{-1}a$, $c' = c - \gamma_1\alpha_1^{-1}a$. Then $b' = \langle 0, \beta_2 - \beta_1\alpha_1^{-1}\alpha_2 \rangle$, $c' = \langle 0, \gamma_2 - \gamma_1\alpha_1^{-1}\alpha_2 \rangle$. There exist real numbers ξ, η, not both zero, such that $\xi b' + \eta c' = 0$. Then

$$\xi b + \eta c + (-\xi\beta_1\alpha_1^{-1} - \eta\gamma_1\alpha_1^{-1})a = 0.$$

4.(a). Not a subspace; (b). Subspace; (c). Subspace; (d). Not a subspace; (e). Subspace; (f). This set is a subspace if and only if $B = 0$; (g). Not a subspace.

5.(a). Subspace; (b). Not a subspace; (c). Subspace; (d). Not a subspace; (e). Subspace; (f). Subspace; (g). Subspace; (h). This set is a subspace if and only if g is the zero function: $g(x) = 0$ for all x.

6.   Let $f_1, \cdots, f_n$ be a finite set of polynomial functions. Let x^n be the highest power of x appearing with a nonzero coefficient in any of the polynomials $\{f_i\}$. Then every linear combination of $f_1, \cdots, f_n$ has the form $\alpha_0 + \alpha_1 x + \cdots + \alpha_n x^n$. But there certainly exist polynomials, such as x^{n+1}, which cannot be expressed in this form. To be certain on this point, we observe that upon differentiating $n + 1$

times, all linear combinations of $f_1, \cdots, f_n$ become zero, while there are polynomials whose $n + 1$st derivative is different from zero.

7. Yes. Let S and T be subspaces. Let $a, b \in S \cap T$. Then $a + b \in S$ and $a + b \in T$ so $a + b \in S \cap T$. Similarly, if $a \in S \cap T$ and $\alpha \in F$, $\alpha a \in S \cap T$.

8. No. For example, in R_2, let $S = S(\langle 1, 0 \rangle)$, $T = S(\langle 0, 1 \rangle)$. Then $\langle 1, 1 \rangle = \langle 1, 0 \rangle + \langle 0, 1 \rangle \notin S \cup T$.

SECTION 7

1. and 2.(a). Linearly dependent (check your relation of linear dependence in this and subsequent problems). Basis: $\langle -1, 1 \rangle$, $\langle 0, 3 \rangle$; (b). Linearly dependent, basis $\langle 2, 1 \rangle$, $\langle 0, 2 \rangle$; (c). Linearly dependent, basis $\langle 1, 3, 4 \rangle$, $\langle 0, 4, 5 \rangle$; (d). Linearly dependent, basis $\langle 1, 0, 0 \rangle$, $\langle 0, 1, 0 \rangle$, $\langle 0, 0, 1 \rangle$; (e). Linearly dependent; (f). Linearly independent.

3. If df/dt is identically zero, then f is a constant, and $f = cf_0$, where f_0 is the function everywhere equal to 1. The dimension of the subspace consisting of all f whose second derivative is zero is two.

4. $Q(\sqrt{2})$ is a two-dimensional vector space over Q, with a basis consisting of $\{1, \sqrt{2}\}$.

5. It does not. The subspace spanned by $\langle 1, 3, 4 \rangle$, $\langle 4, 0, 1 \rangle$, and $\langle 3, 1, 2 \rangle$ has a basis $\langle 1, 3, 4 \rangle$, $\langle 0, 4, 5 \rangle$ (by Problems 1 and 2.c). An arbitrary linear combination of these vectors has the form $\langle \alpha, 3\alpha + 4\beta, 4\alpha + 5\beta \rangle$. If $\langle 1, 1, 1 \rangle$ is one of these linear combinations, then $\alpha = 1$, $3 + 4\beta = 1$, $\beta = -\frac{1}{2}$, and $4\alpha + 5\beta = 4 - \frac{5}{2} \neq 1$.

6. It does. A basis for the subspace, in echelon form, is $\langle 1, -1, 1, 0 \rangle$, $\langle 0, 2, 1, -1 \rangle$, $\langle 0, 0, -\frac{7}{2}, -\frac{1}{2} \rangle$. A typical element in the subspace is $\langle \alpha, -\alpha + 2\beta, \alpha + \beta - \frac{7}{2}\gamma, -\beta - \frac{1}{2}\gamma \rangle$. Comparing with $\langle 2, 0, -4, -2 \rangle$, we obtain $\alpha = 2$, $\beta = 1$, $\gamma = 2$.

7. Let $\{t_1, \cdots, t_m\}$ be a basis for T, and let $S \subset T$. Then every set of $m + 1$ vectors in S is linearly dependent, by Theorem 7.6. Let $\{s_1, \cdots, s_k\}$ be a set of linearly independent vectors in S such that every set of $k + 1$ vectors is linearly dependent. By Lemma 6.8, every vector in S is a linear combination of $\{s_1, \cdots, s_k\}$. Therefore $\{s_1, \cdots, s_k\}$ is a basis for S, and $\dim S \leq \dim T$. Finally, let $\dim S = \dim T$ and $S \subset T$. Let $\{s_1, \cdots, s_m\}$ be a basis for S. Then by

Theorem 7.6, $\{s_1, \cdots, s_m, t\}$ is linearly dependent for all $t \in T$, since dim $T = m$. By Lemma 6.8 again, $t \in S$ and $S = T$.

8. Suppose $\alpha_1 a_1 + \cdots + \alpha_m a_m = \alpha_1' a_1 + \cdots + \alpha_m' a_m$. Then $(\alpha_1 - \alpha_1')a_1 + \cdots + (\alpha_m - \alpha_m')a_m = 0$. By the linear independence of $a_1, \cdots, a_m$, we have $\alpha_1 = \alpha_1', \cdots, \alpha_m = \alpha_m'$.

9. There are 4 vectors in V, 3 one-dimensional subspaces, and 3 different bases.

10. dim $(S + T) \leq 3$. Therefore dim $(S \cap T) = $ dim $S +$ dim $T -$ dim $(S + T) \geq 1$, by Theorem 7.17.

11. dim $S = $ dim $T = 3$, dim $(S + T) = 4$, dim $(S \cap T) = 2$.

SECTION 8

1.(a). Solvable; (b). Solvable; (c). Solvable; (d). Solvable; (e). Solvable; (f). Not solvable; (g). Not solvable.

2. There is a solution if and only if $\alpha \neq 1$.

3. It is sufficient to prove that the column vectors of an m-by-n matrix, with $n > m$, are linearly dependent. The column vectors belong to R_m, and since there are n of them, they are linearly dependent by Theorem 7.6.

4. This result is also a consequence of Theorem 7.6.

SECTION 9

1. The dimension of the solution space is 2. Let c_1, c_2, c_3, c_4 be the column vectors. Then $c_1 + 3c_2 - 4c_3 = 0$ and $c_1 + c_2 - 2c_4 = 0$. Therefore a basis for the solution space is $\langle 1, 3, -4, 0 \rangle$ and $\langle 1, 1, 0, -2 \rangle$.

2. The dimensions of the solution spaces are as follows. The actual solutions should be checked:

(a) zero   (b) one   (c) two   (d) one
(e) two   (f) one   (g) zero

3. By Theorem 8.9, every solution has the form $x_0 + x$ where x_0 is the solution of the nonhomogeneous system and x is a solution of the homogeneous system. The dimension of the solution space of

the homogeneous system is two, and the actual solutions found may be checked by substitution.

4. A, B, and C must satisfy the equations

$$3A + B + C = 0,$$
$$-A \quad\quad + C = 0$$

or

$$A \begin{pmatrix} 3 \\ -1 \end{pmatrix} + B \begin{pmatrix} 1 \\ 0 \end{pmatrix} + C \begin{pmatrix} 1 \\ 1 \end{pmatrix} = 0.$$

The solution space of the system has dimension one, so that any two nontrivial solutions are multiples of each other.

5.   We have to find a nontrivial solution to the system

$$A \begin{pmatrix} \alpha \\ \gamma \end{pmatrix} + B \begin{pmatrix} \beta \\ \delta \end{pmatrix} + C \begin{pmatrix} 1 \\ 1 \end{pmatrix} = 0.$$

The rank of the matrix is at most two, so there certainly exists a nonzero solution. To show that two such solutions are proportional, we have to show that the rank is two. If the rank is one, then $\alpha = \gamma$ and $\beta = \delta$, and the points are not distinct, contrary to assumption.

SECTION 10

3.   The result is immediate from Theorem 10.6.

4.   Since L is one-dimensional, $L = p + V$ where V is the directing space, and $p \in L$. By (10.2) $q - p \in V$, and since dim $V = 1$, V consists of all scalar multiples of $q - p$.

5.   This result follows from the definition of hyperplane in Problem 3, and Theorem 10.6.

6.   In the case of the first problem, for example, the solution involves finding two distinct solutions of the system $x_1 + 2x_2 - x_3 = -1$, $2x_1 + x_2 + 4x_3 = 2$. This is done by the methods of the previous sections.

7.   The line through p and q consists of all vectors $p + \lambda(q - p)$, by Problem 4. By (10.2), $q - p$ belongs to the directing space of V, and hence $p + \lambda(q - p) \in V$ for all λ.

9.   Dim $(S_1 + S_2) = 4$, dim $(S_1 \cap S_2) = $ dim $S_1 + $ dim $S_2 - $ dim $(S_1 + S_2) = 2$.

10.   By Problem 4, a typical point on the line has the form $x = p + \lambda(q - p)$, where $p = \langle 1, -1, 0 \rangle$ and $q = \langle -2, 1, 1 \rangle$. Substitute the coordinates of x in the equation of the plane and solve for λ.

SECTION 11

1.   The mappings in (c), (d), (e) are linear transformations; the others are not.

3. $2T$: $y_1 = 6x_1 + 2x_2$
$$y_2 = 2x_1 - 2x_2$$
$T - U$: $y_1 = -4x_1$
$$y_2 = -x_2$$
T^2: $y_1 = 10x_1 - 4x_2$
$$y_2 = -4x_1 + 2x_2$$

To find the system for TU, we let U: $\langle x_1, x_2 \rangle \to \langle y_1, y_2 \rangle$ where $y_1 = x_1 + x_2$, $y_2 = x_1$; T: $\langle y_1, y_2 \rangle \to \langle z_1, z_2 \rangle$ where $z_1 = -3y_1 + y_2$, $z_2 = y_1 - y_2$. Then TU: $\langle x_1, x_2 \rangle \to \langle z_1, z_2 \rangle$, where $z_1 = -2x_1 - 3x_2$, $z_2 = x_2$.
   $TU \neq UT$.

4. $(DM)f(x) = D[xf(x)] = xf'(x) + f(x)$.
$MD\, f(x) = (Mf')(x) = xf'(x)$. $DM \neq MD$.

5.   From $0 + 0 = 0$, we obtain $T(0) + T(0) = T(0)$, hence $T(0) = 0$. From $v + (-v) = 0$, we obtain $T(v) + T(-v) = T(0) = 0$, hence $T(-v) = -T(v)$.

7.   Let $T \in L(V, V)$ be invertible. Then we have to prove that T is one-to-one and onto. Let T^{-1} be the inverse of T. Suppose $T(v_1) = T(v_2)$. Applying T^{-1}, we obtain $v_1 = v_2$, and T is one-to-one. Now let $v \in V$. Since $TT^{-1} = 1$, we have $v = T[T^{-1}(v)]$ and T is onto. (See Problems 5 and 6 in Section 3.)

8. T is an isomorphism, while U and TU are not isomorphisms.

9.   First suppose the system has only the trivial solution, and suppose the transformation sends both $x = \langle x_1, \cdots, x_n \rangle$ and $x' = \langle x_1', \cdots, x_n' \rangle$ onto the same vector. Then $\langle x_1 - x_1', \cdots, x_n - x_n' \rangle$ is a solution of the homogeneous system, and is zero. Therefore $x = x'$ and the transformation is one-to-one. Conversely, if the homogeneous system has a nontrivial solution x, then the transformation maps both x and zero onto the same vector, and is not one-to-one.

10. The transformations in (a) and (c) are one-to-one; the others are not.

15. D maps the constant polynomials into zero, so that D is not one-to-one. I maps no polynomial onto a constant polynomial $\neq 0$, so that I is not onto. The equation $DI = 1$ implies that D is onto and that I is one-to-one.

SECTION 12

1.
$$\begin{pmatrix} -1 & 2 \\ -1 & 0 \end{pmatrix} \begin{pmatrix} 1 & 1 \\ 0 & 1 \end{pmatrix} = \begin{pmatrix} -1 & 1 \\ -1 & -1 \end{pmatrix}$$

$$\begin{pmatrix} -1 & 2 & 3 \\ 1 & 1 & 1 \end{pmatrix} \begin{pmatrix} 1 & 1 \\ 1 & 0 \\ 2 & -1 \end{pmatrix} = \begin{pmatrix} 7 & -4 \\ 4 & 0 \end{pmatrix}$$

$$\begin{pmatrix} 0 & 1 \\ 0 & 0 \end{pmatrix} \begin{pmatrix} 0 & 1 \\ 0 & 0 \end{pmatrix} = \begin{pmatrix} 0 & 0 \\ 0 & 0 \end{pmatrix},$$

$$\begin{pmatrix} 1 & 0 & 0 \\ 0 & -1 & 0 \\ 0 & 0 & 2 \end{pmatrix} \begin{pmatrix} 1 & 1 & 0 \\ -1 & 2 & 1 \\ 1 & 1 & 3 \end{pmatrix} = \begin{pmatrix} 1 & 1 & 0 \\ 1 & -2 & -1 \\ 2 & 2 & 6 \end{pmatrix}$$

2. Let $S: F_n \to F_m$ be defined by the equations $y_i = \sum_{j=1}^{n} \alpha_{ij} x_j$, $i = 1, \cdots, m$, and T by the equations $y_i = \sum_{i=1}^{n} \beta_{ij} x_j$. Then $S + T$ maps $x = \langle x_1, \cdots, x_n \rangle$ onto $S(x) + T(x)$, and hence is defined by the system of equations $y_i = \sum_{j=1}^{n} (\alpha_{ij} + \beta_{ij}) x_j$, whose matrix is $\mathbf{A} + \mathbf{B}$.

3. Let $\mathbf{A} = (\alpha_{ij})$ be an m-by-n matrix, $\mathbf{B} = (\beta_{ij})$ an n-by-p matrix, and $\mathbf{C} = (\gamma_{ij})$ a p-by-q matrix. Then the (i, j) entry of $(\mathbf{A}\mathbf{B})\mathbf{C}$ is $\sum_{s=1}^{p} \left(\sum_{r=1}^{n} \alpha_{ir} \beta_{rs} \right) \gamma_{sj}$. The (i, j) entry of $\mathbf{A}(\mathbf{B}\mathbf{C})$ is $\sum_{t=1}^{n} \alpha_{it} \left(\sum_{u=1}^{p} \beta_{tu} \gamma_{uj} \right)$, and it is not difficult to show that these expressions are equal.

4. (a). Has a unique solution; (b). Has a one-dimensional solution space; (c). The solutions are of the form $x_0 + x$, where x_0 is one solution of the nonhomogeneous equation, and x is an arbitrary

vector in the two-dimensional solution space of the homogeneous system.

5.   Multiplying $\mathbf{DA}$ is equivalent to multiplying the ith row of $\mathbf{A}$ by δ_i, while multiplying on the right multiplies the ith column by δ_i.

6.   If $\mathbf{A} = (\alpha_{ij})$ commutes with all the diagonal matrices $\mathbf{D}$, then by Problem 5, we have $\delta_i\alpha_{ij} = \alpha_{ij}\delta_j$ for all δ_i and δ_j in F. If $i \neq j$, it follows that $\alpha_{ij} = 0$.

7.   These results were proved for linear transformations in Section 11; the same arguments can be used here.

8.   Every linear transformation on the space of column vectors has the form $\mathbf{x} \rightarrow \mathbf{B} \cdot \mathbf{x}$ for some n-by-n matrix $\mathbf{B}$. The linear transformation $\mathbf{x} \rightarrow \mathbf{A} \cdot \mathbf{x}$ is invertible if and only if there exists a matrix $\mathbf{B}$ such that $\mathbf{B}(\mathbf{A} \cdot \mathbf{x}) = \mathbf{A}(\mathbf{B} \cdot \mathbf{x}) = \mathbf{x}$ for all $\mathbf{x}$. By the associative law (Problem 3), these equations are equivalent to $(\mathbf{BA})\mathbf{x} = (\mathbf{AB})\mathbf{x} = \mathbf{x}$ for all $\mathbf{x}$. Then show that for an n-by-n matrix $\mathbf{C}$, $\mathbf{Cx} = \mathbf{x}$ for all $\mathbf{x}$ is equivalent to $\mathbf{C} = \mathbf{I}$. Thus the equations simply mean that the matrix $\mathbf{A}$ is invertible.

If $\mathbf{A}$ is invertible, then $\mathbf{x} = \mathbf{A}^{-1}\mathbf{b}$ is a solution of the equation $\mathbf{Ax} = \mathbf{b}$ because $\mathbf{A}(\mathbf{A}^{-1}\mathbf{b}) = (\mathbf{AA}^{-1})\mathbf{b} = \mathbf{Ib} = \mathbf{b}$ by the associative law. If $\mathbf{x}'$ is another solution, then $\mathbf{Ax} = \mathbf{Ax}'$, and multiplying by $\mathbf{A}^{-1}$, we obtain $\mathbf{A}^{-1}(\mathbf{Ax}) = \mathbf{A}^{-1}(\mathbf{Ax})$. It follows that $\mathbf{x} = \mathbf{x}'$.

10. From the proof of Theorem 7.22, there exist elementary operations of types (1), (2) which reduce the rows of $\mathbf{A}$ to echelon form. The number of nonzero rows is the dimension of the vector space generated by the rows of $\mathbf{A}$, which is the rank of $\mathbf{A}$ by Theorem 9.7. Now suppose $\mathbf{A}$ is invertible. Then $\mathbf{A} \cdot \mathbf{x} = \mathbf{0}$ implies $\mathbf{x} = \mathbf{0}$, so the dimension of the solution space of the homogeneous system of equations with coefficient matrix $\mathbf{A}$ is zero. By Corollary 9.3, $\mathbf{A}$ has rank n. Therefore the matrix whose rows are in echelon form, which we obtained in the first part of the argument, will have the form

$$\begin{pmatrix} \alpha_{11} & \alpha_{12} & \cdots & \alpha_{1n} \\ 0 & \alpha_{22} & \cdots & \alpha_{2n} \\ \cdots\cdots\cdots\cdots\cdots\cdots \\ 0 & 0 & 0 & 0 & \alpha_{nn} \end{pmatrix},$$

with $\alpha_{11}, \cdots, \alpha_{nn}$ all different from zero. Applying elementary operations of type 3, we may assume that $\alpha_{11}, \cdots, \alpha_{nn}$ are all equal to one. Then by adding a suitable multiple of the second row to the first we can make $\alpha_{12} = 0$, without changing α_{11}. Similarly we can add multiples of the third row to the first and second to make $\alpha_{13} = \alpha_{23} = 0$, without affecting α_{11} or α_{22}. Continuing in this way, we reduce **A** to the identity matrix.

SECTION 13

1. The matrices with respect to the basis $\{u_1, u_2\}$ are

$$S = \begin{pmatrix} 1 & 1 \\ -1 & 0 \end{pmatrix}, \qquad T = \begin{pmatrix} 0 & 1 \\ 1 & 0 \end{pmatrix}, \qquad U = \begin{pmatrix} 2 & 0 \\ 0 & -2 \end{pmatrix}.$$

With respect to the new basis $\{w_1, w_2\}$ the matrix of S is

$$S' = \begin{pmatrix} \dfrac{5}{4} & \dfrac{3}{4} \\[2mm] -\dfrac{7}{4} & -\dfrac{1}{4} \end{pmatrix} = XSX^{-1}, \qquad \text{where } X = \begin{pmatrix} \dfrac{1}{4} & -\dfrac{1}{4} \\[2mm] \dfrac{1}{4} & \dfrac{3}{4} \end{pmatrix}$$

$$\left[X = \begin{pmatrix} 3 & 1 \\ -1 & 1 \end{pmatrix}^{-1} \right].$$

2.

	a	b	c	d
S	rank 1, nullity 1	not invertible	$u_1 + u_2$	$u_1 + u_2$
T	rank 2, nullity 0	invertible	—	—
U	rank 3, nullity 0	invertible	—	—

3.

$$D = \begin{pmatrix} 0 & 1 & 0 & & & 0 \\ 0 & 0 & 2 & & & \\ \vdots & & \ddots & \ddots & & \vdots \\ \vdots & & & \ddots & \ddots & \\ \vdots & & & & \ddots & k-1 \\ 0 & & & & & 0 \end{pmatrix}, \qquad \begin{array}{l} \text{rank} = k - 1, \\ \text{nullity} = 1. \end{array}$$

4. Yes. The vectors x, y, and z are linearly independent and can be extended to a basis $\{x, y, z, w\}$ of the vector space by Theorem 7.15. There exists a linear transformation such that $T(x) = e_1$, $T(y) = 0$, $T(z) = 0$ by Theorem 13.1.

5. No. We have $x_1 - y_1 + z_1 = 0$, and if U is a linear transformation, then $U(x_1) - U(y_1) + U(z_1) = 0$.

7. The matrix of UT is the product of the matrices of U and T.

8. The rank of T is the dimension of $T(V)$. A basis for $T(V)$

can be selected from among the vectors $T(v_i)$, $i = 1, \cdots, n$. Since $T(v_i) = \sum_j \alpha_{ji} w_j$, a subset of the vectors $\{T(v_i)\}$ forms a basis for $T(V)$ if and only if the corresponding columns of the matrix $\mathbf{A}$ of $\mathbf{T}$ form a basis for the column space of $\mathbf{A}$. Therefore dim $T(V) = $ rank $(\mathbf{A})$.

9. The transformation S in Problem 2 is an example of this phenomenon.

10. If $TS = 0$ for $S \neq 0$, then $v_1 = S(v) \neq 0$ for some $v \in V$, and $Tv_1 = 0$. Conversely, let $T(v_1) = 0$, for some nonzero vector v_1. There exists a basis $\{v_1, v_2, \cdots, v_n\}$ of V starting with v_1. Define S on this basis by setting $S(v_1) = v_1$, $S(v_2) = \cdots = S(v_n) = 0$. Then $S \neq 0$ and $TS = 0$.

11. Let $ST = 1$. Let $\{v_1, \cdots, v_n\}$ be a basis for V. Since $ST = 1$, it follows that $\{Tv_1, \cdots, Tv_n\}$ is also a basis of V. On each of these basis elements, $TS(Tv_i) = Tv_i$, so that TS agrees with the identity transformation on a basis. Therefore $TS = 1$.

13. This result follows from the fact that similar matrices can be viewed as matrices of a single linear transformation with respect to different bases, and that their characteristic roots are the characteristic roots of the linear transformation. A direct proof can be made as follows. Let $\mathbf{A} = \mathbf{S}^{-1}\mathbf{B}\mathbf{S}$ for some invertible $\mathbf{S}$. If $\mathbf{x} \neq 0$ and $\mathbf{A}\mathbf{x} = \alpha\mathbf{x}$, then $\mathbf{B}(\mathbf{S}\mathbf{x}) = \alpha(\mathbf{S}\mathbf{x})$ and $\mathbf{S}\mathbf{x} \neq 0$.

15. Suppose for some invertible $\mathbf{S}$

$$\mathbf{S}^{-1}\mathbf{A}\mathbf{S} = \begin{pmatrix} \delta_1 & & 0 \\ & \ddots & \\ 0 & & \delta_n \end{pmatrix}.$$

Show that $(\mathbf{S}^{-1}\mathbf{A}\mathbf{S})^m = \mathbf{S}^{-1}\mathbf{A}^m\mathbf{S}$ for all positive integers m. Then it follows that $\delta_i^m = 0$ for each i and m such that $\mathbf{A}^m = 0$. Then all δ_i are zero, and hence $\mathbf{A} = 0$.

SECTION 14

1.(e). Two vectors are perpendicular if and only if the cosine of the angle between them is zero. From the law of cosines, we have

$$\|b - a\|^2 = \|a\|^2 + \|b\|^2 - 2\|a\| \|b\| \cos \theta.$$

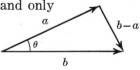

Since
$$\|b - a\|^2 = (b - a, b - a) = \|a\|^2 + \|b\|^2 - 2(a, b),$$
we have
$$\cos \theta = \frac{(a, b)}{\|a\| \, \|b\|}.$$
Therefore $a \perp b$ if and only if $(a, b) = 0$.

(f). $\|a + b\| = \|a - b\|$ if and only if $(a + b, a + b) = (a - b, a - b)$. This statement holds if and only if $(a, b) = 0$.

2.(a).   If x belongs to both $p + S$ and $q + S$, then $x = p + s_1 = q + s_2$, with s_1 and $s_2 \in S$. It follows that $p \in q + S$ and $q \in p + S$, and hence that $p + S = q + S$.

(b).   The set $L = p + S$ of all vectors of the form $\{p + \lambda(q - p)\}$ is easily shown to be a line containing p and q. Let $L' = p + S'$ be any line containing p and q. Then $q - p \in S'$ and since S and S' are one-dimensional $S = S'$. Since the lines L and L' intersect and have the same one-dimensional subspace, $L = L'$ by (a).

(c). p, q, r are collinear if they belong to the same line $L = p + S$. In that case $q - p \in S$ and $q - r \in S$ and since S is one-dimensional, $S(q - p) = S(q - r)$. Conversely, if $S(q - p) = S(q - r)$, the lines determined by the points p and q, and q and r have the same one-dimensional spaces. Hence they coincide by (a).

(d).   Let $L = p + S$ and $L' = p' + S'$ be the given lines. From parts (a) and (b) we may assume $S \neq S'$. Since dim S = dim $S' = 1$, $S \cap S' = 0$. If x_1 and x_2 belong to $L \cap L'$, then $x_1 - x_2 \in S \cap S'$, hence $x_1 = x_2$. In order to show that $L \cap L'$ is not empty, let $S = S(s)$, $S' = S(s')$; then we have to find λ and λ' such that $p + \lambda s = p' + \lambda's'$, and this is true since any 3 vectors in R_2 are linearly dependent.

3. $\lambda = \dfrac{-(p - r, q - p)}{\|q - p\|^2}$. The perpendicular distance is

$$\|u - r\| = \left\| p - r - (p - r, q - p) \frac{q - p}{\|q - p\|^2} \right\|.$$

SECTION 15

1.(a). $\dfrac{1}{\sqrt{3}} \langle 1, 1, 1, 0 \rangle, \dfrac{1}{\sqrt{51}} \langle 5, -1, -4, -3 \rangle.$

2. 1, $\sqrt{12}\,(x - \tfrac{1}{2})$, $a(x^2 - x + \tfrac{1}{6})$.

3.(a). $(v, w) = \sum\limits_{i,j} \xi_i \eta_j (u_i, u_j) = \sum \xi_i \eta_j \gamma_{ji}$.

   (b).   Let $v = \sum\limits_{i=1}^{n} \xi_i u_i$. Then $(v, u_k) = \sum\limits_{i=1}^{n} \xi_i (u_i, u_k) = \xi_k$.

4.   Let $Tv_1 = \xi_1 v_1$, $Tv_2 = \xi_2 v_2$. Then $\|Tv_i\| = \|v_i\|$ implies ξ_1 and ξ_2 are ± 1. We also have $(v_1, v_2) = \xi_1 \xi_2 (v_1, v_2)$, and since $\xi_1 \neq \xi_2$, $\xi_1 \xi_2 = -1$.

7.   Let $\{v_1, \cdots, v_n\}$ be an orthonormal basis of V, and let

$$w_1 = \alpha_{11} v_1 + \cdots + \alpha_{1n} v_n$$

$$\cdot$$
$$\cdot$$
$$\cdot$$

$$w_d = \alpha_{d1} v_1 + \cdots + \alpha_{dn} v_n$$

be a basis for W. A vector $x = x_1 v_1 + \cdots + x_n v_n$ belongs to $W^\perp$ if and only if $(x, w_1) = \cdots = (x, w_d) = 0$. Thus $x_1, \cdots, x_n$ have to be solutions of the homogeneous system

$$\alpha_{11} x_1 + \cdots + \alpha_{1n} x_n = 0$$

$$\cdot$$
$$\cdot$$
$$\cdot$$

$$\alpha_{d1} x_1 + \cdots + \alpha_{dn} x_n = 0.$$

The result is now immediate from Corollary 9.3.

8.   It can be shown that there exist orthonormal bases $\{v_i\}$ and $\{w_i\}$ of V such that $\{v_1, \cdots, v_d\}$ is a basis for W_1, and $\{w_1, \cdots, w_d\}$ is a basis for W_2. By Theorem 15.11, there exists an orthogonal transformation T such that $Tv_i = w_i$ for each i. Then $T(W_1) = W_2$.

9.(a).   By Exercise 7, dim $S(n)^\perp = 2$. It is sufficient to prove that the set P of all p such that $(p, n) = \alpha$ is the set of solutions of a linear equation. Let $\{v_1, v_2, v_3\}$ be an orthonormal basis for R_3, and let $n = \alpha_1 v_1 + \alpha_2 v_2 + \alpha_3 v_3$. Then $x = x_1 v_1 + x_2 v_2 + x_3 v_3$ satisfies $(p, n) = \alpha$ if and only if $\alpha_1 x_1 + \alpha_2 x_2 + \alpha_3 x_3 = \alpha$. This shows that the set of all p such that $(p, n) = \alpha$ is a plane. Using the results of Section 10, we can assert that $P = p_0 + S(n)^\perp$, where p_0 is a fixed solution of $(p, n) = \alpha$.

   (b).   Normal vector: $\langle 3, -1, 1 \rangle$.

   (c). $x_1 - x_2 + x_3 = -2$, or $(n, p) = -2$.

   (d).   The plane with normal vector n, passing through p is the set of all vectors x such that $(x, n) = (p, n)$, or $(x - p, n) = 0$.

(f).   The normal vector n must be perpendicular to $\langle 2, 0, -1 \rangle$ $- \langle 1, 1, 1 \rangle$ and to $\langle 2, 0, -1 \rangle - \langle 0, 0, 1 \rangle$ by (d). Then use the method of part (e).

(g).   Following the hint, we write the second equation in the form $p_0 - p = \lambda n + (u - p)$. Taking the inner product with n yields $0 = \lambda(n, n) + (u - p, n)$.

(h).   We have $u = \langle 1, 1, 2 \rangle$, $p = \langle 0, 0, 1 \rangle$, $n = \langle 1, 1, -1 \rangle$. Then $3\lambda = (u - p, n) = 1$, $\lambda = \frac{1}{3}$. Then the distance is $\|p_0 - u\| = \frac{1}{3}\|n\|$.

SECTION 16

1.   Using the definition and Theorem 16.6, we have $D(\langle \xi, \eta \rangle, \langle \lambda, \mu \rangle) = D(\langle \xi, 0 \rangle, \langle \lambda, 0 \rangle) + D(\langle \xi, 0 \rangle, \langle 0, \mu \rangle) + D(\langle 0, \eta \rangle, \langle \lambda, 0 \rangle) + D(\langle 0, \eta \rangle, \langle 0, \mu \rangle) = \xi\mu - \eta\lambda$. $D(\langle \xi, 0 \rangle, \langle \lambda, 0 \rangle) = 0$ because the vectors involved are linearly dependent. $D(\langle \xi, 0 \rangle, \langle 0, \mu \rangle) = \xi\mu D(e_1, e_2)$, while $D(\langle 0, \eta \rangle, \langle \lambda, 0 \rangle) = -D(\langle \lambda, 0 \rangle, \langle 0, \eta \rangle) = -\lambda\eta$. The rest of the problem is done by solving the equations, and comparing the results with the formula for $D(a_1, a_2)$.

3.(a).   The operations required to put a set of vectors $\{a_1, \cdots, a_n\}$ in echelon form are (a) interchanging two vectors and (b) replacing a vector a_i by $a_i + \lambda a_j$, $i \neq j$. By Theorem 16.6, these operations change $D(a_1, \cdots, a_n)$ by a factor of ± 1. Thus if $\{a_1, \cdots, a_n\}$ are linearly independent, $D(a_1, \cdots, a_n) = \pm D(b_1, \cdots, b_n)$ where $b_1, \cdots, b_n$ are in echelon form. If the sign is -1, then $D(u_1, \cdots, a_n) = D(-b_1, b_2, \cdots, b_n)$, and $-b_1, b_2, \cdots, b_n$ are also in echelon form.

(b).   If $b_1, \cdots, b_n$ are in echelon form, say $b_1 = \langle \beta_1, \beta_{12}, \cdots, \beta_{1n} \rangle$, $b_2 = \langle 0, \beta_2, \beta_{23}, \cdots, \beta_{2n} \rangle$, etc., then $\beta_1, \beta_2, \cdots$ are all different from zero. By replacing b_1 by $b_1 + \lambda b_2$ for a suitable choice of λ we can make $b_1' = \langle \beta_1, 0, \beta_{13}', \cdots, \beta_{1n}' \rangle$. Adding multiples of b_3 to b_1 and b_2 we can make $\beta_{13}' = \beta_{23} = 0$. Continuing in this way, we do not change the value of $D(b_1, \cdots, b_n)$, and have $D(b_1, \cdots, b_n) = D(\beta_1 e_1, \cdots, \beta_n e_n)$. Thus $D(b_1, \cdots, b_n) = \beta_1 \cdots \beta_n$.

4.(b). $D(a_1, a_2, a_3) = -2$.

5.   All that has to be proved is that

$$D^*(a_1, \cdots, a_n) = D^*(a_1, \cdots, a_i + a_j, \cdots, a_j, \cdots, a_n)$$

and this is immediate from assumptions (3) and (4) about D^*.

SECTION 18

3. Let T be an orthogonal transformation. If $\mathbf{A}$ is the matrix of T with respect to an orthonormal basis, then $\mathbf{A}^t\mathbf{A} = \mathbf{I}$, and since $D(\mathbf{A}) = D(^t\mathbf{A})$ we have $D(\mathbf{A})^2 = 1$.

4. α is a characteristic root of T if and only if the null space of $T - \alpha 1$ is different from zero. This occurs if and only if $T - \alpha 1$ is not one-to-one. This statement is equivalent to $D(T - \alpha 1) = 0$, by Theorem 18.8.

5. In order to prove that $\sigma\tau$ is a permutation, it must be proved that $\sigma\tau$ is one-to-one and onto.

(a). The definition of T_σ is possible by Theorem 13.1. We have $T_\sigma T_\tau v_i = T_\sigma v_{\tau(i)} = v_\sigma(_{\tau(i)}) = v_{\sigma\tau(i)} = T_{\sigma\tau}(v_i)$, so $T_{\sigma\tau} = T_\sigma T_\tau$.

(b). The matrix of T_ρ is

$$\begin{pmatrix} 0 & 1 & 0 & 0 \\ 1 & 0 & 0 & 0 \\ 0 & 0 & 0 & 1 \\ 0 & 0 & 1 & 0 \end{pmatrix}.$$

(c). $\epsilon(\sigma) = \pm 1$ because the columns of the matrix of T_σ with respect to the basis $v_1, \cdots, v_n$ are a rearrangement of the columns of the identity matrix. The statement $\epsilon(\sigma\tau) = \epsilon(\sigma)\epsilon(\tau)$ is simply the multiplication theorem.

(d). Let $X = \{1, 2, \cdots, n\}$ and assume by induction that every permutation of $\{1, 2, \cdots, n - 1\}$ is a product of transpositions. If $\sigma(n) = n$, then σ can be regarded as a permutation of $\{1, 2, \cdots, n - 1\}$, and is a product of transpositions. Suppose $\sigma(n) = i \neq n$. Then $[(in)\sigma](n) = (in)[\sigma(n)] = (in)(i) = n$. By the induction hypothesis $(in)\sigma$ is a product of transpositions. Since $(in)[(in)\sigma] = \sigma$, we see that σ is also a product of transpositions.

SECTION 19

4. Expanding the determinant along the first row, we see that it has the form $Ax_1 + Bx_2 + C$. Substituting (α, β) or (γ, δ) for (x_1, x_2) makes two rows of the determinant equal, and hence the equation $Ax_1 + Bx_2 + C = 0$ is satisfied by the points (α, β) and (γ, δ).

6.   The image of the square is the parallelogram $\{\lambda T(e_1) + \mu T(e_2)\colon 0 \le \lambda,\ \mu \le 1\}$. The area of the parallelogram is $|D(T(e_1), T(e_2))|$, where $T(e_1)$ and $T(e_2)$ are the columns of the matrix of T with respect to the basis $\{e_1,\ e_2\}$ of R_2.

7.   Since

$$\begin{vmatrix} \alpha_1 & \alpha_2 & 1 \\ \beta_1 & \beta_2 & 1 \\ \gamma_1 & \gamma_2 & 1 \end{vmatrix} = \begin{vmatrix} \alpha_1 & \alpha_2 & 1 \\ \beta_1 - \alpha_1 & \beta_2 - \alpha_2 & 0 \\ \gamma_1 - \alpha_1 & \gamma_2 - \alpha_2 & 0 \end{vmatrix},$$

the determinant is

$$\begin{vmatrix} \beta_1 - \alpha_1 & \beta_2 - \alpha_2 \\ \gamma_1 - \alpha_1 & \gamma_2 - \alpha_2 \end{vmatrix},$$

which is the area of the parallelogram with edges $\langle \beta_1,\ \beta_2 \rangle - \langle \alpha_1,\ \alpha_2 \rangle$, $\langle \gamma_1,\ \gamma_2 \rangle - \langle \alpha_1,\ \alpha_2 \rangle$. The area of the triangle is one-half the area of this parallelogram.

SECTION 20

1. $Q = \frac{2}{3}x - \frac{1}{9},\ R = -\frac{1}{9}x^2 - x - \frac{2}{3}$.

2.   Let $\alpha_1,\ \cdots,\ \alpha_k$ be distinct zeros of f. Then $f = (x - \alpha_1)g_1$. Since $\alpha_2 \ne \alpha_1$, $x - \alpha_2$ is a prime polynomial which divides f but not $x - \alpha_1$. Therefore $x - \alpha_2$ divides g_1 and $f = (x - \alpha_1)(x - \alpha_2)g_2$. Continuing in this way, $f = (x - \alpha_1) \cdots (x - \alpha_k)g$, and hence $\deg f \ge k$.

4.   If the degree of f is two or three, any nontrivial factorization will involve a linear factor, and hence a zero of f. The result is false if $\deg f > 3$. For example, $f = (x^2 + 1)^2$ has no zeros in R, but is not a prime in $R[x]$.

5.   Suppose m/n satisfies the equation. Multiplying the resulting equation by n^r we obtain

$$a_0 m^r + a_1 m^{r-1} n + \cdots + a_r n^r = 0.$$

Then n divides $a_0 m^r$, and since n does not divide m^r, $n \mid a_0$. Similarly $m \mid a_r$.

7.   In $Q[x]$, the prime factors are: (a). $(2x + 1)(x^2 - x + 1)$; (c). $(x^2 + 1)(x^4 - x^2 + 1)$.

In $R[x]$, the prime factors are: (a). $(2x + 1)(x^2 - x + 1)$; (c). $(x^2 + 1)(x^2 + \sqrt{3}\,x + 1)(x^2 - \sqrt{3}\,x + 1)$.

8.   In Z or $F[x]$, an element a is determined up to a unit factor by giving, for each prime p, the exponent to which p appears in the prime factorization of a. Thus if a and b are given, and if $d \mid a$ and $d \mid b$, a prime p must appear in d at most as many times as it appears in a or b. It follows that $(a, b) = p^{u_1}, \cdots, p_r^{u_r}$. A similar argument establishes the formula for the least common multiple. The relation between $(a, b)[a, b]$ and ab follows from the fact that for any pair of nonnegative integers m and n, min $\{m, n\}$ + max $\{m, n\}$ = $m + n$.

9.   The process must terminate, otherwise we have an infinite decreasing sequence of nonnegative integers, contrary to the Principle of Well-Ordering (3.2). Now suppose $r_{i_0} \neq 0$ and $r_{i_0} + 1 = 0$. From the way the r_i's are defined, $r_{i_0} \mid r_{i_0}$ and r_{i_0-1}. From the preceding equation we see that $r_{i_0} \mid r_{i_0-2}$. Continuing in this way we obtain $r_{i_0} \mid a$ and $r_{i_0} \mid b$. On the other hand, starting from the top, if $d \mid a$ and $d \mid b$, then $d \mid r_0$. From the next equation we get $d \mid r_1$. Continuing we obtain eventually $d \mid r_{i_0}$. Thus $r_{i_0} = (a, b)$.

10.(a). $2x + 1$.

SECTION 21

1. $-10 + 10i$, $\frac{1}{13}(3 - 2i)$, $\frac{1}{5}(3 + 4i)$.

2. $\cos 3\theta = (\cos \theta)^3 - 3 \cos \theta(\sin \theta)^2$, obtained by taking the real part of both sides in the formula $(\cos \theta + i \sin \theta)^3 = \cos 3\theta + i \sin 3\theta$.

3. $\lambda(\cos \theta_k + i \sin \theta_k)$ where λ is a real fifth root of 2 and $\theta_k = \dfrac{2\pi k}{5}$, $k = 0, 1, 2, 3, 4$.

5.   The one-to-one mapping that produces the isomorphism is
$$\alpha + i\beta \rightarrow \begin{pmatrix} \alpha & -\beta \\ \beta & \alpha \end{pmatrix}.$$

SECTION 22

2.   Let $\{v_1, \cdots, v_m\}$ be a basis for V and $\{w_1, \cdots, w_n\}$ a basis for W. For each pair (i, j), let E_{ij} be the linear transformation such

that $E_{ij}v_j = w_i$, and $E_{ij}v_k = 0$ if $k \neq j$. Then the mn linear transformations $\{E_{ij}\}$ form a basis for $L(V, W)$.

4. Suppose T is invertible, and let $m(x) = x^r + \cdots + \alpha_1 x + \alpha_0$ be the minimal polynomial. Suppose $\alpha_0 = 0$. Then $m(x) = xm_1(x)$. Moreover, $m_1(T) \neq 0$ since $m(x)$ is the minimal polynomial. Then $m(T) = Tm_1(T) = 0$, contradicting the fact that T is invertible.

Conversely, suppose $\alpha_0 \neq 0$. Then $m(x) = m_1(x) \cdot x + \alpha_0$ for some polynomial $m_1(x)$, and $m_1(T)T = -\alpha_0 1$. Then $-\alpha_0^{-1}m_1(T) = T^{-1}$.

5. $x^2 - x - 2$, $x^3 - 1$, $x^2 + x - 1$, x^3.

6.(a). For each v_i, $f(T)v_i = (T - \xi_1) \cdots (T - \xi_n)v_i = 0$ since the factors $T - \xi_k$ commute, and $(T - \xi_i)v_i = 0$.

(b). Let $m(x) = \Pi(x - \xi_j)$, where the ξ_j are the distinct characteristic roots of T. By the argument of part (a), $m(T) = 0$. Then the minimal polynomial of T divides $m(x)$. It is enough to show that if $m'(x) = \Pi_{\xi_j \neq \xi_k}(x - \xi_j)$, then $m'(T) \neq 0$. We have

$$m'(T)x_k = \prod_{\xi_j \neq \xi_n} (\xi_k - \xi_j)x_k \neq 0,$$

and the result is proved.

SECTION 23

2. The minimal polynomial of $\begin{pmatrix} 1 & -2 \\ 1 & -1 \end{pmatrix}$ is $x^2 + 1$, which can be factored into distinct linear factors in $C[x]$ but not in $R[x]$.

3. Since $d(x) \mid f(x)$, $n[d(T)] \subset n[f(T)]$. Conversely, let $f(T)v = 0$. Since $d(x) = a(x)m(x) + b(x)f(x)$ for some polynomials $a(x)$ and $b(x)$, we have

$$d(T)v = a(T)m(T)v + b(T)f(T)v = 0,$$

since $f(T)v = 0$ and since $m(x)$ is the minimal polynomial. Thus $n[f(T)] \subset n[d(T)]$ and the result is established.

SECTION 25

1.(a). $(x + 2)^2$.
   (b). $(x + 2)^2$.

(c). -2 (appearing twice in the characteristic and minimal polynomials).

(d).   No. Because the minimal polynomial is not a product of distinct linear factors.

(e).   Let $v = x_1 v_1 + x_2 v_2$ be a vector with unknown coefficients such that $(T + 2)v = 0$. Using the definition of T, this leads to a system of homogeneous equations with the nontrivial solution, $(1, -1)$. Then $v_1 - v_2$ is a characteristic vector for T.

(f).   A basis which puts the matrix of T in triangular form is $w_1 = v_1 - v_2$, $w_2 = v_2$. Then $\mathbf{SB} = \mathbf{AS}$ where

$$\mathbf{B} = \begin{pmatrix} -2 & 1 \\ 0 & -2 \end{pmatrix}, \qquad \mathbf{S} = \begin{pmatrix} 1 & 0 \\ -1 & 1 \end{pmatrix}.$$

3.   The minimal polynomial of T is $x^2 + \alpha\beta$, where $\alpha\beta > 0$. The minimal polynomial is not a product of distinct linear factors in $R[x]$, and the answer to the question is no.

4.   Use the triangular form theorem.

5.   The minimal polynomial of T divides $x^2 - x$, and therefore has distinct linear factors in $C[x]$. There does exist a basis of V consisting of characteristic vectors.

6.   The minimal polynomial divides $x^r - 1$ which has distinct linear factors in $C[x]$, namely $x - (\cos \theta_k + i \sin \theta_k)$, $k = 0, \cdots, r - 1$, where $\theta_k = \dfrac{2\pi k}{r}$.

7. V has a basis consisting of characteristic vectors of T if and only if $\lambda \neq 0$.

SECTION 27

1.   Let $T^* f_i = \sum {}_j \beta_{ji} f_j$. Evaluating both sides at v_k, we have

$$f_i(Tv_k) = \beta_{ki},$$

and

$$f_i(Tv_k) = \alpha_{ik}.$$

4.   It is clear that $W \subset (W^\perp)^\perp$. Then show that W and $(W^\perp)^\perp$ have the same dimension.

SECTION 28

5.   In order to prove that every subspace of V has an orthonormal basis, imitate the Gram-Schmidt process discussed in Chapter 4.

11. This result is immediate from Problems 8 and 10.

SYMBOLS
(Including Greek Letters)

Lower-case Greek Letters Used in This Book

α	alpha
β	beta
γ	gamma
δ	delta
ϵ	epsilon
ζ	zeta
η	eta
θ	theta
λ	lambda
μ	mu
ν	nu
ξ	xi (ksi)
π	pi
ρ	rho
σ	sigma
τ	tau
φ	phi
ψ	psi
ω	omega

Partial List of Symbols Used

R	field of real numbers
$a \in A$	set membership

$A \subset B$	set inclusion
$f: A \to B$	function (or mapping) from A into B
$\langle \alpha_1, \cdots, \alpha_n \rangle$	vector with components $\{\alpha_1, \cdots, \alpha_n\}$.
$\sum x_i$	summation
$\Pi\, u_i$	product
$S(v_1, \cdots, v_n)$	vector space generated (or spanned) by $\{v_1, \cdots, v_n\}$.
$C[R]$	continuous real valued functions on R
$P[R]$	polynomial functions on R
$L(V, W)$	linear transformations from V into W
$\mathbf{A},\, \mathbf{a}$	matrices (write by hand $\tilde{A}$, a)
$^t\mathbf{A}$	transpose of a matrix A
$\|\alpha\|$	absolute value
(u, v)	inner product
$\|u\|$	length of a vector u
$D(u_1, \cdots, u_n),\, D(\mathbf{A}),$ det $\mathbf{A},\, D(T)$	determinant of a set of vectors, of a matrix, of a linear transformation
$F[x]$	polynomials with coefficients in a field F
$\bar{z}$	conjugate of a complex number z
$V_1 \oplus V_2$	direct sum of vector spaces
$f(T)$	polynomial in a linear transformation T
$n[f(T)]$	null space of $f(T)$
$S^\perp$	set of vectors orthogonal to the vectors in S
e^A	exponential of a matrix $\mathbf{A}$

BIBLIOGRAPHY

Albert, A. A. (ed.), *Studies in Mathematics*, Vol. II: *Studies in Modern Algebra* (Buffalo: Mathematical Association of America, 1963).

Artin, E., *Geometric Algebra* (New York: Interscience, 1957).

Birkhoff, G., and S. MacLane, *Survey of Modern Algebra*, rev. ed. (New York: Macmillan, 1953).

Bourbaki, N., *Algèbre*, Chapitre 2, "Algèbre linéaire," 3rd ed. (Paris: Hermann, Actualités Scientifiques et Industrielles, no. 1144).

Coddington, E., and N. Levinson, *Theory of Ordinary Differential Equations* (New York: McGraw-Hill, 1955).

Coxeter, H. S. M., *Regular Polytopes* (London: Methuen, 1948).

Coxeter, H. S. M., *Introduction to Geometry* (New York: Wiley, 1962).

Courant, R., and H. Robbins, *What Is Mathematics?* (New York: Oxford University Press, 1941).

Gruenberg, K., and A. Weir, *Linear Geometry* (Princeton: Van Nostrand, 1967).

Halmos, P. R., *Finite Dimensional Vector Spaces*, 2nd ed. (Princeton: Van Nostrand, 1958).

Jacobson, N., *Lectures in Abstract Algebra*, Vol. II: *Linear Algebra* (Princeton: Van Nostrand, 1953).

Landau, E., *Foundations of Analysis*, English translation (New York: Chelsea, 1951).

Lang, S., *Algebra* (Reading, Mass.: Addison-Wesley, 1965).

MacLane, S., and G. Birkhoff, *Algebra* (New York: Macmillan, 1967).

Polya, G., *How to Solve It* (Princeton: Princeton University Press, 1945).

Schreier, O., and E. Sperner, *Modern Algebra and Matrix Theory*, English translation (New York: Chelsea, 1952).

Synge, J. L., and B. A. Griffith, *Principles of Mechanics* (New York: McGraw-Hill, 1949).

Van der Waerden, B. L., *Modern Algebra*, Vols. I and II: English translation (New York: Ungar, 1949 and 1950).

Weyl, H., *Symmetry* (Princeton: Princeton University Press, 1952).

INDEX

Absolute value, 8, 156
Algebraically closed field, 158
Area, 115
Associative law, 4, 16, 67, 78
   generalized, 24
Axioms, for a determinant function, 116
   for a field, 4, 19
   for a group, 70
   for a ring, 68
   for a vector space, 20
   for a volume function, 137

Basis, 37
   change of, 85
   dual, 191
Bilinear function, 105, 206

Cauchy-Schwarz inequality, 106
Cayley-Hamilton theorem, 176
Change of basis, 85
Characteristic polynomial, 175
Characteristic root (eigenvalue, proper
   value), 89, 131, 167, 175
Characteristic vector (eigenvector,
   proper vector), 90, 167
Collinear, 104
Commutative law, 4, 16, 79
Completeness axiom, 8
Complex number, 155
   conjugate of, 157
   De Moivre's theorem, 158
   polar representation of, 157
   roots of unity, 158
Components of a vector, 21

Coordinates, 22
Cramer's Rule, 136

Determinant, complete expansion of,
   126, 133
   computation of, 120
   definition of, 116
   existence of, 122
   Hadamard's inequality, 133
   minor, 137
   of a linear transformation, 130
   of linearly independent vectors, 120
   of a matrix, 104, 127
   of a product of matrices, 129
   row and column expansions, 134
   of the transpose of a matrix, 127
   uniqueness of, 121
   van der Monde, 140
   as a volume function, 138
Dimension, 37, 53
Direct sum, 167
Directed line segment, 22
Directing space, 58
Distributive law, 4, 68
Division process (for polynomials), 145
Dual space, 191

Echelon form, 40, 80, 120
Equations, linear, *see* System of linear
   equations
   polynomial, 147
   vector differential, 185
Exponents, 13

Factor theorem, 148
Field, algebraically closed, 158
  of complex numbers, 156, 160
  definition of, 19
  examples of, 19, 161
  ordered, 4
  quotient, 153
  of rational functions, 153
Function (mapping), 10
  bilinear, 105, 206
  domain of, 10
  linear, 191
  one-to-one, 10
  onto, 10
  polynomial, 23, 147

Gram-Schmidt orthogonalization proc-
    ess, 108
Greatest common divisor, 148, 154
  existence of, 149, 154
Group, coset, 218
  cyclic, 99, 215, 220
  definition of, 70
  dihedral, 99, 215, 220
  finite rotation groups in R_3, 214, 216
  subgroup, 217
  symmetry groups, 97, 102

Hadamard's inequality, 133
Hermitian scalar product, 203
Homogeneous system of equations, 46,
    52
  nontrivial solution of, 46
  solution space of, 50
Hyperplane, 62, 140, 212

Identity matrix, 79
Identity transformation (notation: i or
    1), 16, 68
Induction, 12
Induction hypothesis, 13
Inequality, Cauchy-Schwarz, 106
  Hadamard, 133
  triangle, 107
Inner product, 55, 105
Integers, 15
  unique factorization of, 151
Invariant subspace, 167
  irreducible, 199
Invertible linear transformation, 69,
    165
Invertible matrix, 79
Isomorphism, of fields, 143, 160

of groups, 102, 161
of rings of linear transformations and
    matrices, 85
of vector spaces, 72

Jordan normal form, 196

Least upper bound, 8
Line, 57, 103
  parallel lines, 104
Linear combination, 29
Linear dependence, 26
  determinant of linearly dependent
    vectors, 117
  relation of, 26
  test for, 42
Linear function, 191
Linear independence, 26
Linear manifold, 58
  dimension of, 58
  directing space of, 58
  equations of, 60
Linear transformation, characteristic
    polynomial of, 175
  definition of, 64
  diagonable, 170, 180
  distance-preserving, 99
  examples of, 65
  inverse of, 69
  invertible (nonsingular), 69, 89, 165
  matrix of, 82
  minimal polynomial of, 164, 175
  nilpotent, 173, 180, 192
  null space of, 88
  one-to-one, 89, 130
  orthogonal, 109, 131, 202, 212, 220
  product of, 66
  rank of, 88, 93
  reflection, 101, 212
  rotation, 101, 203
  sum, 66
  symmetric, 208
  transpose of, 192, 196
  unitary, 204

Mapping, see Function
Mathematical induction, 12
Matrix, addition of, 74, 84
  augmented, 48
  characteristic polynomial of, 175
  column rank of, 55
  column subspace of, 46
  column vectors of, 45

definition of, 45
determinantal rank of, 137
diagonal, 78, 91, 93, 170, 205
elementary, 79
exponential of, 184
function, 183
identity, 79
invertible, 79, 135
Jordan normal form of, 196
of a linear transformation, 82, 196
minimal polynomial of, 165
orthogonal, 110, 188
product, 76, 84
of a quadratic form, 207
rank of, 48, 55, 129
row rank of, 54
row subspace of, 46
row vectors of, 45
similarity of, 87, 93
symmetric, 207
transpose of, 109, 127, 196
unitary, 204
Multiplication of matrices, 76

Natural numbers, 11
well-ordering principle, 12
Nilpotent linear transformation, 173, 180, 192
Nonhomogeneous system, 46, 47
Cramer's rule, 136
Nonsingular linear transformation, 69

n-tuple, 14

Ordered pair, 15
Orthogonal transformation, 109, 113, 202
Orthogonal vectors, 107
Orthonormal set, 107, 204

Parallelogram law, 22
Permutations, 131
even, odd, 132
product of, 132
signature of, 132
Plane in R_n, 58, 112
Point, 22
Polynomial, characteristic, 175
definition of, 142
degree of, 144
derivative of, 65
minimal, 164

prime (irreducible), 148
unique factorization, 150
zero of, 147
Polynomial ring $F[x]$, 143
Prime, 148, 159
in $R[x]$, 159
Prime polynomial (irreducible polynomial), 148, 159
Principal-axis theorem, 208

Quadratic form, 206, 211
matrix of, 207

Rank, 48, 129
row, column, 55
of a linear transformation, 88
Rational number, 15
Real number, 4
Remainder theorem, 148
Replacement theorem, 34
Ring, 68
commutative, 69, 143
polynomial, 143
Root, characteristic, 89
of a polynomial equation, 147
of unity, 158

Sequence, 15
Set, element of, 9
empty set $\varnothing$, 9
equality of, 9
finite, infinite, 14
intersection of, 10
subset, 9
union of, 10
Solution, dimension of solution space, 53
nontrivial, 46
of a polynomial equation, 147
of a system of equations, 46
of a vector differential equation, 185
Square root, 16
Subfield, 15
Subspace, 30
basis, 41
column, 46
cyclic, 190
dimension of, 53
direct sum of, 167
finitely generated, 32
generators of, 32
intersection of, 33, 39, 62
invariant, 167

irreducible invariant, 199
of R_2, 33
row, 46
spanned by vectors, 31
sum of (notation: $S + T$), 39
union of, 33, 39
Subtraction, 6
of vectors, 21
Symmetry, 94
System of linear equations, 45, 65, 77
coefficient matrix of, 45
Cramer's rule, 136
homogeneous, 46
nonhomogeneous, 46
solution of, 46
solution vector, 46
unknowns, 45

Triangle inequality, 107
Triangular form theorem, 172

Unique factorization, 150, 151
Unit, 148

Unit vectors, 36
Unitary transformation, 204

van der Monde determinant, 140
Vector, 20
algebraic properties of, 24, 25
characteristic, 90, 167
column, 45
components of, 21
interpretation of, 22
length of, 99, 105, 156, 203
product of a vector by a scalar, 20
row, 45
sum of, 20
Vector space, 20
basis of, 37
dimension of, 37
examples of, 21, 23, 24
Volume function, 137

Well-ordering principle, 12

NOTES

NOTES

NOTES

NOTES

NOTES

NOTES

NOTES

NOTES